1	The Cathedral or Colledge Church	15	Castle Gate
2	St. Peters Church	16	Colledge Gate
3	St. Andrews Church	17	Sudbury Gate
4	St. Martins Church	18	St. Martins Gate
5	St. Nicholas Church	19	Fore Gate
6	St. Clements Church	20	Friers Gate
7	St. Albans Church	21	Frog Gate
8	St. Helens Church	22	High Streete
9	St. Swithins Church	23	Friers Streete
10	St. Iohns	24	Pitch Croft
11	Alls. Church	25	Bridge over Severn
12	The Fort Royall	26	The Water house
13	Castle hill	27	The Key
14	Bishops Palace		

the way to London

HANLEY CASTLE

The Original Bridge at Upton-on-Severn

HANLEY CASTLE

AN EPISODE OF

THE CIVIL WARS

AND

THE BATTLE OF WORCESTER

W.S. SYMONDS

Cappella Archive
Book on Demand Limited Editions

First Edition: W. North, Tewkesbury, 1883.
Revised Edition: Cappella Archive, Malvern 1999.

This copy was printed on demand : August 2002

British Library Cataloguing-in-Publication Data
A catalogue record for this book is
available from the British Library

ISBN 0-9525308-9-9

Cappella Archive
Foley Terrace Great Malvern England

*Typeset in a Cappella realization of a Baskerville of 1769 and
printed on Five Seasons paper from John Purcell of London.*

The Author's Preface to the First Edition

IN THE PREFACE of the new and illustrated edition of *Malvern Chase*, I have alluded to the success of an attempt to interest the inhabitants of the neighbourhood in which I have resided nearly forty years, in local history and traditions which had become, like the Dodo, well nigh extinct. *Hanley Castle* has been written with a like motive.

PENDOCK RECTORY 1883.

Editor's Preface

THIS BOOK is a companion volume to *Malvern Chase* which recounts the events in the Wars of the Roses leading up to the Battle of Tewkesbury. In *Hanley Castle*, William Symonds provides an equally vivid account of the English Civil War between 1635 and 1651 at a time when political and religious divisions were so strong that brother fought brother, and sons were in conflict with fathers. Castles were razed, homes burnt, and families expelled; land was seized and books and furniture sold. Art, sculpture, churches, and shrines were destroyed by religious zealots, and the Prayer Book was banned. Most dispiriting of all, men and women were tortured, burnt, or massacred in retribution for similar atrocities.

The text is almost identical with that of the original edition of 1883, but I have divided some extremely long paragraphs into shorter units and removed the quotation marks which surrounded the names of plants and animals. I have taken away some exclamation marks of no particular emphasis and speech marks have been discarded where reported speech is actually written. There are one or two occasions where a sequence of clauses or phrases has been moved into a more logical order and, in deference to current usage, 'Scotch' has been replaced by Scottish or Scots.

DAVID BYRAM-WIGFIELD
GREAT MALVERN

Contents

Agag – the Battle of Dunbar – the King's Court among the Scottish
Puritans – Scottish Lassies and the Committee of Ministers – Flight of Charles
II from Sermons – Change in Scottish Politics – New Year's Day 1651 and the
Coronation – crossing the Border – the Fisherman again – Worcester the
Rendezvous for Loyal Cavaliers.

Illustrations

End Papers from the map of Worcester engraved by Burnford.

Introduction

THANK GOD for Worcestershire parsons, especially the historians. Mandell Creighton's monumental *History of the Papacy* was finished in 1885 shortly before he became a canon of Worcester Cathedral. At exactly the same time over at Pendock, the Reverend William Symonds was completing this wonderfully romantic *tour de force* of the English Civil War.

I love best the final chapter as it builds up into a crescendo of loyalty for the forlorn Charles II on the murderous battlefield at Worcester. Even at its most fanciful, the narration is gripping. There is the description of the steadfast old Worcestershire families of 'country gentlemen and cavaliers' as they rally to the royal cause on Pitchcroft before the battle. Then the disastrous failure of a crucial night attack on Cromwell's camp at Perry Wood, because of the revelations of Gise, the tailor and Parliamentary spy; 'hanged the day following as a just reward for his treachery'.

By a skilful aberration in the plot, the author enables himself to include the ancient legend of Cromwell's compact with the devil in order to secure a victory; 'the tall horseman was clad from head to foot in armour, but the steel was hissing hot'.

But the reader should not be alarmed. The bulk of this book is not only honestly chronicled but also based on careful and loving research. Should you want a more balanced view, you can always dip into Malcolm Atkins' *Worcestershire in the Civil War*, which is an excellent modern study. Otherwise why not linger over William Symonds and his romantic evocation of the Worcestershire past?

JEFF CARPENTER
formerly Mayor of the City of Worcester

Chapter One

THE SMALL town of Upton-on-Severn is situated on the river Severn between Tewkesbury and Worcester. The Romans appear to have chosen it as a site for one of their martial camps, and Roman coins and relics have been found in the field that tradition has marked out as the Camp.[1] In after years the Roman station became a Saxon 'ton', or village, and there is the Saxon's Lode across the Severn to this day. Uptonbury is now Buryfield.

The Saxons loved to create pastures round their villages, and to clear the forest glades of the hazel and the yellow gorse, while nothing attracted them more than a brook which would turn a mill, and whose waters cherished the silver trout and the lissom eel. Just such a place was situated a little more than a mile to the westward of Upton, and in early Saxon times a grange and a mill were erected by the banks of a brook flowing from the Malvern hills, and broad leys were made in the forest for pastures at Hanley, for such the place was called.

With its pleasant surroundings, on the borders of a great forest which stretched from Worcester to Gloucester, Hanley became the resort of the wealthier Saxon eorls. The hunting quarters were famous, and there was a good supply of fish from the Severn – the salmon and shad, the lamprey and lampern – all loved by eorls and ecclesiastics, while the wild woods ever furnished herbs for pottling, such as mints and pepper worts, or for surgery, as bloodworts.

Later on, at 'his manor of Hanley', there lived Brictric Meawe, a gallant Saxon, who was Lord of the Manor of Gloucester, and attached to the Court of Edward the Confessor. This Earl had the misfortune to attract the affections of Matilda, daughter of the Earl of Flanders, to which he did not respond, a slight she determined to revenge if only she had the opportunity. In after years the opportunity arose. Matilda became the wife of William the Conqueror, and on his conquest of England she caused the unhappy Brictric to be seized at Hanley and imprisoned at Winchester, where he died miserably.

In after times, when Henry the Third was king, the Saxon grange was converted by the de Clares into a Castle, and this became the residence of the Red Earl, Gilbert de Clare, and his wife the Princess Joan, daughter of Edward the First. This great king frequently visited Worcester, and we may be sure enjoyed hunting in that Malvern Chase which he granted to his son-in-law. Here also lived the last of the de Clares, who died in the prime of youth, fighting for Edward the Second on the fatal field of Bannockburn.

After this, Hanley Castle became a favourite residence of the Beauchamps. Here Isabel Despencer, herself of royal blood, presented her first husband, Richard Beauchamp, with a daughter in 1415, when Henry the Fifth was king. At Hanley Castle she married her second husband, that famous Earl of Warwick who took the standard of Owen Glendower on Shrewsbury field, and who was afterwards guardian of Henry the Sixth and Regent of France. He lies beneath his grand monument at Warwick; she lies by the chapel built to the memory of her first husband in the ancient Abbey of Tewkesbury.

At Hanley Castle died their son, who was made Duke of Warwick by Henry the Sixth, and here lived for years his sister Anne, who married Richard Neville the 'King-maker, the great commanding Warwick, the setter up and plucker down of kings'. Henry the Seventh appropriated the property of the Beauchamps, and in the days of James the First the Castle of Hanley belonged to the Crown, but was well-nigh deserted and neglected. From its situation it could be easily destroyed by cannon, and even the great Keep must have succumbed in a short time to artillery acting from the broad leys which commanded the castle from the eastward.

Nevertheless it was a place the hunter still loved to visit, and King James often declared that he would himself hunt a stag from his castle of Hanley in Malvern Chase. He never came, however, and it was rented from the Crown by my father, Miles Forester, who loved the locality on account of its connection with my mother's ancestors; for its sylvan beauty, its great moat filled with fishes, its keep in which we lived, the shattered turrets which formed the angles, and the connecting galleries now overgrown with ivy and polypody, tower cress, and pennywort.

My father was a younger son of those Foresters who for centuries had settled on the wolds of Shropshire and from whom was descended the famous Robin Hood. He was a well-educated gentleman, had more than a smattering of Greek, could translate easily Virgil and Horace, and was well read in the works of Chaucer, Holinshed, Churchyard, Bacon, and above all in the plays of Master Shakspeare. He was acquainted with Ben Jonson when he was poet laureate, and attended his funeral in Westminster Abbey. He was a Churchman and a royalist to the backbone.

My mother was related to the Earls of Westmoreland and a descendant of that Isabel Despencer who was the great, great grand-daughter of Edward the Third, so she was proud of Hanley Keep, which she declared to have been unjustly appropriated by Henry the Seventh. She was ever ready to discourse upon the daring deeds of Crecy or of Agincourt, or to summon in imagination the forms of knights, who had long since been dust, to the grass-grown tilt-yard in which I played, and where she would expatiate upon the changes that had passed over her kith and kin.

The characters of both my father and mother were more suited to the age of chivalry than to the Court of the pedantic Scottish king, James Stewart, who was ever frightened at the sight of swords and guns, or steel armour, and whose sole idea in granting the honour of knighthood was to obtain the fees that had to be paid for it. Badger-baiting, cock-fighting, and coney hunting had little charm for my father, who ever enjoyed manly exercises, while he detested the winebibbing and drunkenness, which too often converted the gentlemen, and even the ladies of King James' Court, into maundering buffoons and tipsy queans.

On the accession of Charles the First, a considerable change for the better took place at Court, and lords and ladies, knights and gentlemen became more modest, or at least more quiet in their demeanour. The new King was reported to be zealous for religion and a supporter of the Church party, to which both my father and mother belonged.

I was born at Hanley Castle in the year 1622, and was soon after baptized at the parish church as Richard Plantagenet Forester – Richard in memory of the great Coeur-de-Lion, and Plantagenet at the request of my mother, in remembrance of that blood which is supposed to circulate in our veins.

Young as I was when she died, I have a distinct remembrance of my mother's earnest face, and of frequent embraces by her loving arms. I can see, as I pen these words, a vision of a mother's smile which has often come back to me in dreams and waking moments, and has remained with me through a long life. I remember, also, my sister Isabella appearing as a new-born babe, but, alas, it was an ominous appearance, for her birth was the cause of our mother's death and our father's life-long sorrow. She was christened Isabella Despencer but, the week after, our mother was consigned to the tomb, and my father found himself a widower with two small children demanding his care and attention.

After my mother was laid in the grave in the parish church of Hanley, hard by the Castle, my father summoned his only sister, Mistress Tabitha Forester, a maiden lady of forty, to aid him in managing his household and his children. 'Sister Tab' was ever kind, although not beautiful to look upon, and had an income of her own and a house of considerable dimensions in Old Street in Upton, with steps of stone up to the door, which had a knocker. She was very intimate with the Rector, and was wellknown to every child as one who always had her pockets – and they were large ones – filled with apples.

She was proud of her family and their crest of a bugle-horn, which they bore in memory of their forest homes and huntings in the days of King Canute. She had been even known to dispute with my mother as to the antiquity of the Foresters being greater than that of the Despencers. She was continually asked to be gossip, or godmother, to various babes, and on such occasions wore her 'silk calimanco gown', as she wrote, soon after the event: 'Ould Mrs Barclay and myself were gossips, God bless hitt, Amen'. At Easter she wore a double cobweb lawn and a muff. In winter she was dressed 'in a woollen gown, liver coloured, and made up with a stomacher'.[2] She was charitable, as we learn from her Diary, which is now, fortunately for these Memoirs, in my possession. Aunt Tabitha was acquainted with those good Royalists, Sir Henry Slingsby, Colonel Manley, and Mr Symonds, the antiquary, who all kept diaries, and thus in the year of our Lord 1628, I find the following entry:

> '1628, Ap. 1. Rachel calfed – a bull calf – bad Rachel.' 'A pound of shugger to send Mrs Eaten', and 'a yeard and a half of scarlet baize to make her a waistcoate and four yards of red galloon to bind him'. 'Miles went to Lunnon'. 'Mem. this yeere, viz. 23 August, 1628, George Duke of Buckingham was killed at Porchmouth by one John ffelton a leiftennant, and the terme before I saw a phesie of his death by the numerall letters in his name.'[3]

Thus one of my earliest reminiscences was the summoning of my father to London to give evidence respecting the disforesting of Malvern

Chase, and the prayers put up by our household for his safe return. Also the distich, which the common people at Upton bandied from mouth to mouth respecting Dr Lambe, the Duke of Buckingham's physician, who had been tried at Worcester for sorcery:

> *Let Charles and George do what they can,*
> *The Duke shall die like Dr Lambe.*

I can also recall the commotion caused by the disforesting of Malvern Chase in 1632, and the riots and misdemeanours which arose in consequence. Aunt Tabitha says:

'No more rent oats and rent hens the Lord be thankit, no more shutting up pooching prisners in our Banbury Chamber at Hanley Castle, no mare hanging at Rydde Green.'

A Forest was royal property, and therefore differed from a Chase, which could be held by a subject. Thus Malvern Chase was a royal forest until it was granted to Gilbert de Clare, Earl of Gloucester, by Edward I. Then when Henry VII took possession of all the Beauchamp and Warwick property, the Chase went to the Crown until the year 1630, when King Charles I granted one-third of the Chase of Malvern to some of his adherents. Then came the decree for disafforestation, which was most strenuously opposed by several self-elected 'proprietors', who had squatted on the waste, and now advanced their claims to be whole and sole proprietors of the cribbed lands.

The King wished to sell the Chase to replenish his well-nigh exhausted funds, while those who had squatted within the boundaries and enjoyed the privilege of commoning were right furious at the proposed enclosures. It ended by King Charles selling one-third and allowing the remainder to go for the benefit of the parishes included in the Chase itself. Some of the squatters then became Royalists.

In the days of the de Clares and the Beauchamps, Malvern Chase was the home of the wild boar, the stag, the hare and the coney, while many birds and squirrels found shelter in the great trees and masses of foliage, which stretched away for miles. Here and there was a great turf glade and a forest pool surrounded by dells of greenery, but this was now all at an end, for down came the forest trees, and farms and peasants' houses were erected on the haunts of the deer and the wild boar. Great commons and long downs succeeded to dense bush, and the partridge and hare took the place of the stag and hind. Where our forefathers hunted the wild boar we laid springes for partridges, and the coney burrowed in the haunts of the badger.

Hanley Church stood upon the Ley above the Castle. There had been a Saxon edifice of wood upon the same site, then a Norman building of stone, and after that the de Clares built the present church in the days when Edward I and II were kings. The old Rector was a minister who had been exemplary in life, and faithful in duty, and was actually staggered when, in after years, he was told by some of his neighbours that loyalty was a crime against his country. Poor old man, he lived long enough to find the use of his loved Prayer-Book made penal, and the highest of our Church festivals abolished. But my earlier years passed happily before these things came upon us.

My father was a lover and observer of nature, and a roamer in the woods, or among the Malvern hills, in search of the stag, which still frequented certain haunts where was once the Chase. Like Izaac Walton he knew the craft of the angler, and would sometimes take me to the silver Wye or sparkling Teme. We had hounds which would hunt a roebuck and a fox, or track a deer; and as Longdon Marshes were still a sure find for a heron, we kept a good cast of Stackpole falcons.

But my love of woodcraft and hillside roaming was not allowed to interfere with my education, and daily I proceeded to Upton-on-Severn and pursued a course of study under my father's friend, a learned scholar known as Master Kelly. He had the reputation of being the wisest man in all our neighbourhood, as Madam Penelope Lechmere had the credit of being the wisest woman. He was a grandson of the spiritualist, John Kelly, who in the days of Queen Elizabeth was the associate of the still more famous Dr Dee, once Rector of Upton, and report said that some of his ancestor's mysterious powers had been transmitted to our friend.

At all events many feared him. He was a somewhat weird-looking man, but strong and sturdy, and he lived at a lone house by the Severn, known as the Waterside, and one strange habit was to pace the great Severn meadow, the Hamme, for hours together on a star-light night, when he was supposed to be casting horoscopes by the aid of the planets, and communing with those spiritual powers which.control the destiny of men. Circumstances had thrown Kelly much into the company of my father, who could appreciate the deep lore of the scholar, while he enjoyed his exquisite performances on the fife and flageolet. His old, gabled, timbered house contained some queer things which had descended to him from his ancestor, the Magician, and some collected by himself during years of travel. A stuffed crocodile from the Nile grinned fearfully from a ledge above the door of the apartment he usually occupied. Stone beetles and bottled asps were there, and a dried toad from the Indies that might have died of small-pox, so covered was it with great pustules.

A mariner's compass of the date of the fourteenth century – one of the first ever used – lay by the side of a wheel clock of the eleventh century and a Spanish chart of Arabic numeration of the same date; while a parchment of arithmetic of the date of 1253 when the modern system was first introduced into England, hung against the door. There was ring money of the ancient Britons, silver Edwards and gold Richards, and a tract of Pelagius, the monk of Bangor, lay inside a pamphlet just issued by Archbishop Laud. A tiger's head occupied the centre of the mantel-piece, flanked by two human skulls, and at one end of the room a curtain concealed a recess containing the perfect skeleton of a man.

The usual dress of Master Kelly was somewhat antiquated, and partook more of the fashion of Queen Elizabeth than of the days of King Charles, but his long scholar's gown was made of the best materials. As warlike times drew on, he often changed the scholar's garb for that of a Cavalier, but at home he ever wore the gown and a velvet skull cap. That he was a philosopher and man of science may be gathered from Aunt Tabitha's diary:

'1634 the 8 Novr. Mem. This winter in the end of Janry did fall the greatest snowe that was seen in the memory of man, and it was soe extreme colde & violent & tempestuous, that divers going home from mrket and elsewhere, weere smothered & starved to death. And in August following a greate quantitie of the same snowe and ice did remayne at Brockington quarre, & divers went purposely to see it, & yet it was a most extreme hott summer.[4] Mem. The Earl of Worcester came to Handley Castle. He spends his leesure hrs in philosophicall persuits, & I beleeve came to see Master Kelly's fizzing & spitting machine that he keeps soe secret & makes such a fuss about.'

Often and often John Kelly accompanied me to our Castle of Hanley, if such it could be called, when more than two-thirds were ruined towers and shattered chambers. As I grew older I was often permitted to be present with my Aunt Tabitha when he and my father held long and earnest conferences respecting the troubles which now began to mani-fest themselves throughout the whole kingdom. It was evident that King Charles was now surrounded by a number of rebellious subjects. Indeed, Sister Tab's Diary contains the following note:

'Mem. This was the wettest summer that ever was known, & in the midst of harvest not one dry day in a fortnight, & wee had [8] floods betweene Midsummer & Micls.' 5 Mem. Pym & Hampden, Strode & Prynne, traitors all, & worst is Prynne. How I should like to dress them all downe with Roman stingeing nettles.'

Chapter Two

IN OUR young days our father was on good terms with our neighbours, and the neighbours with one another. Squire Bromley of Hamme Court, and Mr Lechmere of Severn End, were both lovers of the chase and visitors from time to time at Hanley Castle, and although after supper they would hold long arguments with my father and our rector respecting predestination, election, and reprobation, they always parted friends. Dick Bromley would come across the Longdon Heath to fish in our moat, or hunt for birds' nests in the woodlands, and Mary, the only daughter, was a dear friend of Isabel's, and they would wander together in search of the early primroses and the first sweet violets.

Mary and I too were great friends, for it once happened that she overreached herself in trying to pick a yellow water-flag and fell into the moat, and all I saw was a pale, frightened little face sinking below the water. I jumped in without a moments reflection and seized Polly, as we called her, by the hair. As I was only ten years old and could not swim, we should both have been drowned had not my father heard Isabel's screams and pulled us out together, dripping like drowned rats.

It was about this time in 1632 that our neighbours were first set together by the ears respecting religious matters. My father and Aunt Tabitha, with our rector at Hanley, Mr Dowdeswell of Bushley Park, and others, supported the views of the new Archbishop Laud, in giving more imposing ceremonials to the national worship of the Church of England, and approved of surplices, painted glass, and beautiful church architecture. But this was not the feeling of Mr Bromley, Mr Ligon, or Mr Lechmere, who regarded these attempts with anger as tending to the restoration of Popery, against which there was absolute horror and detestation, owing to the reaction caused by the reign of 'Bloody Mary'; the bishop's work of 'Bonner the Butcher', who was a Hanley man; and the massacre of the Huguenots.

Then a great disturbance took place in the country because the Court and Archbishop Laud, and the High Church party forbade the printing of the favourite book of the Puritans, viz., the Book of Martyrs, by Mr Fore; but this was nothing to the storm which arose in 1637, when Mr William Prynne, a barrister, the Rev Henry Burton, a London parson, and Dr John Bastwick, a physician, were set on three pillories and had

their ears cut off, and their cheeks stamped with hot branding irons
with SL for *seditious libeller* in the sight of a great crowd. Mr Prynne had
been tortured before in 1632, by having his ears cut off and sewn on
again, and now made a speech defying the Star Chamber, the Archbishop, and Rome at the back of them, as having by these practices
controverted the law of England; while Bastwick's wife received his ears
in her lap and kissed him, and Burton was carried into a house fainting.

It was through this action of the Star Chamber and the Government
that such men as Mr Bromley, Mr Lechmere, and Mr Ligon became
Puritans. They were driven to it by 'conscientious views', they said. But
my father, Mr Childe of Pull Court, Sir Giles Nanfan of Birtsmorton
Court, Mr Gower of Coomb hill,[1] and Mr Richard Dowdeswell of
Bushley Park, although they disapproved of the mutilation of the
prisoners, thought they deserved imprisonment and punishment, and
great divisions arose.

When they met, my father contended that Archbishop Laud was a
conscientious prelate. Mr Bromley declared that the blackest crimes
recorded in history were committed by wrong-headed conscientious
people, and instanced Queen Mary and Bishops Bonner and Gardiner
as examples. My father argued for the divine right of bishops to the
government of the Church, and the divine right of kings; Mr Bromley
maintained that Laud was an example against belief in this infallibility,
and asked my father what he thought of the exercise of the divine right
by the estimable King John, or the fascinating Henry VIII. Mr Lechmere, too, who was a lawyer, declared that the treatment of Prynne
and Bastwick was against all law, and that the imprisonment of Sir John
Eliot was altogether tyrannical and most illegal.

But despite the unfriendly feelings now manifested by the heads of
the families, Madams Bromley and Lechmere would visit Aunt Tabitha,
and hold counsels on the subject of conserves and rheumatism, Welsh
flannels and ointments for the poor. Mary Bromley, too, continued a
constant visitor to Hanley Castle as my sister's loved companion; but
Dick, her brother, was sent to a school at Geneva, where Mr Bromley
wished him to imbibe the spirit and teaching of Calvinism, and I lost
sight of him for years.

The disputes concerning religious matters became every day more
serious. King Charles and Archbishop Laud determined to impose the
Common Prayer Book upon the people of Scotland by force of arms,

while the Covenanters held that Episcopacy was incompatible with the existence of liberal institutions and the true worship of God, so Scotland resolved to have no bishop. During the whole of the year 1639, my father was absent in Scotland engaged on commissions for the King.

In 1640 after all kinds of unhappy disagreements with his Scottish subjects and many quarrels with the English Puritans, Charles determined upon making Sir Thomas Wentworth, now Earl of Strafford, his principal minister. Strafford was a man who embodied the spirit of rule by force. His idea was to 'vindicate the monarchy from the conditions and restraints of subjects, and to uphold the divine right of kings', and he succeeded in persuading the King and the Council that this was the only way to rule in England, to make our country as powerful in Europe as France had become under Richelieu. 'Thorough' was Wentworth's watchword, and this meant crush out, with a strong hand, the freedom of will of all subjects.

The King summoned a Parliament soon after my father's return from Scotland, and he was returned as member for Chiltern. But long before this Long Parliament met, political and religious animosities had become very decided in all our counties and towns. The King and his Council strove with might and main to extend the Anglican Church over England and Scotland, while, on the other hand, thousands of resolute Puritans and Presbyterians found the liturgy of the Church of England very distasteful. And this was not all; the Puritans accused Archbishop Laud not only of apeing the Roman ceremonies, but of 'rank cruelty'. He put to the torture of the rack, John Archer, a mere youth who had joined some rioters, and this after the judges, in the case of Felton, had decided against the use of torture.[2]

Mary Bromley was spending a few days with us when we received the news of my father's election. She said nothing, but I could see that something clashed with her feelings, and I knew that she was somewhat imbued with the puritanism and dissent of her father. After the custom of all royalist gentlemen I had indulged in the habit of using occasional oaths, but I never swore in the presence of Mary without seeing her dark eyes flash with indignation, or perhaps moistened by a tear, so that I became somewhat chary of the big Cavalier curses.

It was a happy time, these young days of ours, long ago. We three would ride off on the summer mornings and explore the still wooded recesses of Malvern Chase, round Welland and Castlemorton. Glorious trees still cast their shade about the Gullet Pass, the Holly Bush, and the Ragged Stone, and there were legends which Mary knew right well, and tales of gallant hounds, hawks and tercels, foresters bold, and weird shadows which crept over the vale.

Mary was two years my junior; she was tall, with large dark eyes, and hair like a raven's wing, but she had a softness and gentleness of expression, inherited from her father, who tried hard to imitate the stern fanaticism of the Puritanic school, but never succeeded. Isabel, my only and darling sister, was a fair-haired lassie, with ways and manners like a cooing turtle-dove, and a fashion of her own of alluring a man's heart out of his very bosom whether he would or no. Mary loved books and historic and legendary lore, but Isabel from her childhood cared not for study, and Sister Tab found it no easy matter to induce her to learn to read and write. She had a voice like a mavis, and was never tired of trolling Cavalier ditties, or playing the Welsh harp in accompaniment to her ballads.

The time was rapidly approaching when the bitter quarrelling which arose upon religious questions and political matters was to affect the quiet neighbourhood of Upton-on-Severn. I have mentioned the torturing of Messrs Prynne and Bastwick, then, later on, Mr John Lilburne was whipped at the cart's tail and put in the pillory for uttering bold speeches against the bishops; and still later, Archbishop Laud and Wentworth proposed to flog Mr Hampden, a member of Parliament and a very popular country gentleman.

My father altogether disapproved of these harsh measures, nevertheless he thought that rebellious persons deserved punishment, perhaps fines or imprisonment; but the first act of the new Parliament, of which he was now a member, was to pass a resolution to justify such writings as those of Prynne, and to enter judgments fixing enormous damages for the punishments he and others had undergone. In short, my father soon found that the King's party in the House of Commons was in a fearful minority, and his vote was but as a single drop in a troubled sea.

It happened that early in the year of our Lord 1641 I was going to Master Kelly's respecting some propositions in Euclid which puzzled me, when, at the Cross at Upton, I found a crowd of people gathered together around Mr Cocktail, a dissenting minister, who was holding forth, in a very excited manner, upon the necessity of carrying out justice upon high-born delinquents, and endeavouring to prove by texts from Scripture 'that heaven would be greatly delighted and gratified by a bloody sacrifice'.[3]

As I listened to this discourse I remarked that it produced considerable effect upon the rabble, and they cheered and shouted long and loud for 'justice against the traitor Strafford'. Startled at such manifestations against this great minister of the King, I reached Master Kelly's in no small ferment of temper, and asked him what it all meant?

I remember now the expression of Master Kelly's countenance as I gave him, to the best of my power, a sketch of the preacher's discourse. He remained silent for some minutes with a look of utter concentration, as if he were gazing into space and trying to gather some idea of the future from the infinitude beyond the stars.

At last he said, "The Commons of England want the heads of Laud and Strafford." He then turned to me and said, "I always told your father, Richard, that Wentworth, now Earl of Strafford, would be the ruin of himself and his King. Who but he and Laud, and their accursed Star Chamber, could have persuaded a naturally tender-hearted monarch to sanction the bodily torture of Prynne, Lilburne, and Archer, and the prosecution of Mr Hampden and numerous others? Let Strafford die! God grant we may yet save the King!"

Then calmly turning over his papers he replied to my questions on mathematical subjects, and invited me to a bout of fencing on the Hamme meadow near his dwelling.

Among his other accomplishments Master Kelly was a perfect swords- man, whether with the cut and slash of the broadsword, or the tierce of the rapier. My father had the credit of being one of the first swordsmen in England, but I have heard him say that he could not hold his own against Master Kelly for five minutes. Under such tuition it was impossible not to learn much of the art of attack and defence, and the "Good, right good," or "Try again," from the lips of my instructor, gave me confidence, as I tried pass after pass and rally after rally, when he attacked and sent my foil flying in the air. In the same broad meadow, too, I learnt the management of the basket-hilted sword on horseback, charging rows of nettles and tall marsh mallows as they grew by the side of the great ditches, So that, in time, I was no mean horseman and swordsman also.

Meetings similar to the one I witnessed at the Cross at Upton, were inflaming the minds of the populace in all parts of England, and the consequences soon became apparent. I well remember on a bright May morning the sweet peacefulness of the scene, as the lark was carolling above our old Castle of Hanley, and the nightingale singing in the bushes by the brook. As if in bitter contrast, the news was brought to us that Wentworth, Earl of Strafford, had been taken from his prison in the Tower of London, to the scaffold on Tower Hill, and, as the executioner held up his severed head, one hundred thousand men, women, and children, shouted "God save the King" and went away to testify their joy in the evening, by lighting bonfires in the streets.

Not many weeks had passed away after Upton had learnt the news of the execution of Strafford, a quarrel arose between my aunt and Mistress Cocktail. That personage called at Hanley Castle and proceeded to say that the execution of the Earl was a righteous act, and the higher a man's rank, the greater his crime. It was in vain my aunt tried to change the subject of discourse; in vain she asked the price of soap and butter, or praised the Welsh honey, or offered a wonderful receipt for pickling beef. Mistress Cocktail persisted in holding forth upon the celebrated Remonstrance of the State of the Kingdom, presented by the House of Commons to King Charles, and indulging in treasonable remarks which made my aunt's hair to stand on end and likewise her temper. I was not present at this clashing of tongues, but it made a great impression upon my sister Isabel, who gave me an account of it as she sat by my side while I was fishing from the moat bank, and from what I could gather, our aunt was not worsted in the fray.

It was the gradual estrangement of Mr and Mistress Bromley that principally affected us in these our young days, for this included Sweet Mary, and the tears flowed down Isabel's cheeks as she talked of old friends growing cold. We seldom saw Mary now, save when, by some chance, we crossed each other's path, and then she ever stopped me to ask after Isabel, and good, kind Mistress Tab. Young as I was, her generous greeting lightened my heart, while her gentle smile came to me again and again as sunshine to my day dreams. Mary and Isabel were bonny lassies both; and so thought our groom Sampson, who never saw them together that he did not cease his horse strapping and say, "By gom, there goas two tidy wenches however."[4]

Now and then I met Squire Bromley, the *Custos Rotulorum*, and he would give me a kindly nod, but not once, I remarked, did he stop to inquire after my father. I heard of him addressing public meetings on the tyranny of the Star Chamber and the falling away from right-eousness of the Established Church. Accustomed as I had been to listen to the most loyal sentiments, I winced at hearing such anecdotes of our former friend, while I wondered if Mary had contracted these extreme opinions from her parents, and was about to become a puritanic Roundhead in petticoats, and cut off her black curls.

My father's letters from London were cautiously written, but we could see that storms were gathering, and no one knew when or where they would burst. Prynne and his fellow martyrs, as they were called, had been escorted through London in triumph amidst the shouts of thousands who strewed laurels in their paths. The Puritan pulpits were resonant with the downfall of the Established Church, and an Army Plot was said to have been discovered, by which the fallen Strafford had urged the King to make an attack on the Parliament.

The country was full of rumours and fears; all the barbers declared that the House of Commons had been undermined; and the Upton barber, who lived near Upton Bridge in the little, low wooden house with over-hanging gables, had received private intelligence that Lords and Commons had been blown to atoms by tons of gunpowder which had been placed under them. Such reports roused the people for the time, and the barber did a good stroke of hair-cutting, shaving, and talking, till the news came that the gunpowder catastrophe was a hoax.

But this year of 1641 was not to pass away without a terrible catas-trophe to electrify the hearts of the people. Both Houses of Parliament, Lords and Commons, had sworn to defend the Protestant religion to the death! What, then, was the horror of all the people of England, when they learned that the Confederate Catholics of Ireland had massacred sixty thousand Protestants in the course of a few days.

Sworn depositions told how women and children were driven forth to perish by famine in the woods, or how husbands had been tortured in the presence of their wives, and their children's brains dashed out before their faces. Some were burned on set purpose, others drowned for sport or pastime, and if they swam were kept from landing with poles, or shot, or murdered in the water; many were buried alive, and some set into the earth breast high and there left to famish.[5]

This villany was consummated in the month of October, and early in November my father brought the news to Hanley Castle, and sent me to summon Master Kelly to a conference, to which I was admitted. Kelly declared that this awful Irish catastrophe was the result of Strafford's policy. "But what said the King?" he asked, in that clear ringing voice which almost startled the listener when he put some home question and waited for the reply. "What said the King when the news reached him ? Did he speak of punishment for the murder of his Protestant subjects!"

My father hesitated, a rare thing for him; he looked at me, he looked at Kelly, he played with his sword and shuffled on his chair, when, at last, he replied, "His gracious Majesty takes it very coolly, and said when the news reached him, 'This ill news of Ireland may hinder some of these follies in England'."[6]

In silence Kelly arose, and left us to pace up and down the grass-grown courtyard. When we joined him, he said with great vehemence, "I have served the King's father and himself for well-nigh thirty years, and I will not distrust him now; but if he tampers with these Irish murderers and 'takes it coolly' as you say, the next Remonstrance will speak in tones of thunder."

For the remainder of this year my father remained at Hanley Castle, and we were occupied in home pursuits and the sports of the field. He was delighted at the progress I had made in my studies, and with my prowess as a horseman and a swordsman. He did not conceal from me that he believed we were on the eve of civil war, when men like himself would rally round the King, while in all parts of England thousands would support the Parliament. It came to pass as he predicted; the Roundheads and Cavaliers, as the two parties were denominated, quarrelled more and more on the question of Church Establishment and the expulsion of the Bishops from the House of Lords; then came the arrest of the five members, and among them Pym and Hampden, with the episode of the invasion of the House of Commons by King Charles himself, in search of the accused members.

In truth, the new year of 1642 broke upon us most unhappily. Fears and jealousies reigned throughout the land, and our festivities were clouded by the absence of friends we once loved, who were now estranged by suspicion and distrust. Isabel inquired "Why every body was going awry?" My aunt wept; my father was silent; and the servants were gloomy and suspicious.

Chapter Three

WITH THE elements of discord increasing around and my father much from home, it was fortunate for me that I found a friend in Sir Giles Nanfan, a royalist gentleman of good family. He resided at Birtsmorton Court, an ancient manor house under the southern Malvern hills, built principally of wood from Malvern Chase, with stone basement, stone noggings, and great hanging roofs and gables. It is surrounded with a moat, and a strong portcullis hangs from the battlemented gateway.

Birtsmorton Court had been in its day the refuge of Owen Glendower and Sir John Oldcastle, and passed, in the time of Henry VII, into the possession of an old Cornish family, the Nanfans, who intermarried with the Birts or Brutes. The grandfather of Sir Giles was Governor of Calais in the time of Henry VII, and with him once lived as chaplain, the celebrated Cardinal Wolsey, the minister and one of the many victims of the tyranny of Henry VIII.

Sir Giles was a gentleman of the old school, who preferred the somewhat antiquated dress of the time of Elizabeth to the padded doublets and stiff jackets of the days of King James. Neither would he wear the steeple-crowned hat, or the piccadil, or neck band, but ever appeared in a well-starched ruff, with the Surrey cap and plume and the Sidney beard.

He would neither have his beard trimmed 'like a spade or a bodkin, or a penthouse on his upper lip, or an alley on his chin, or a low curl on his head like a bull, or dangling locks like a spaniel, with moustaches sharp at the ends like shoemaker's awls, or hanging down to his mouth like goat's flakes'.[1]

The family of Sir Giles consisted of the ever hospitable Dame Nanfan, a lady many years younger than himself, but as true as steel to her revered husband, their son, Squire Giles, a youth of my own age, and their daughter Bridget. Dame Nanfan was an English lady who esteemed it a pleasure to make her husband's guests welcome; she never gave herself the hoity-toity airs some are in the habit of doing, and think that dignity which their acquaintance deem impudence.

Dame Nanfan was not too proud to see that the beds were well aired, or to superintend the preparation of confections and preserves, or the concoction of a Christmas pudding. The poor loved to meet her in the village, for she was ever ready to sympathize with distress, and when relief was possible it was always forthcoming at the Court.

Giles the younger, my friend and companion, was more thorough as a royalist than myself. Both he and his father were strong advocates of the divine right of kings, but I had my doubts whether there was any divinity in persecution, torture and cruelty, even if administered under the superintendence of an archbishop.

Bridget Nanfan was a lively lassie, a year younger than her brother, full of fun, but over-fond of a practical joke. She was rather handsome than beautiful, a fine rider and good tennis player, but she disliked books, and her education was completed when she could read the Bible, and say the Lord's Prayer and Ten Commandments. The nick-name her brother gave her was 'The Dragoon', and I sometimes wished she had been a little more feminine in her tastes and amusements. Still Bridget was universally beloved in her own neighbourhood, for she was ever ready to preside at the village games, which as yet had not been banished from those parishes in which Sir Giles Nanfan had property.

Time was when Bridget tucked up her kirtle and ran a good race with the fleetest, and the wassail bowl, which was carried from door to door on New Year's eve, was prepared with her own hands, while she was always ready for the May-day dance on the Berrow green by the Duke of York. Alas for the Berrow May-pole! The Puritans found out some resemblance in village games and gambols to the idolatry of the golden calf, so by a decree of the Long Parliament,[2] every May-pole in England and Wales has been taken down and burned.

Although the deer had become scarce from the slaughter which ensued in the disforesting of Malvern Chase, a few stags were still to be found in the glens of the Holly-bush, the Ragged Stone, and Chase End hills, or away at Colin Park and Corsewood Hill, where portions of the wild forest still remained; and many a gallop with hound and horn have I had in the happy days of youth, side by side with Bridget and her brother, among the woodlands in the vale, or sometimes crossing the Malverns, among the green hills of Colwall, Eastnor and Wall Hills, beyond Ledbury. Little did I think then of the contrast between these peaceful scenes and the sorrowful ones I was afterwards doomed to witness in the same country.

The good old sport of hawking was still in vogue with Sir Giles Nanfan. He had a pair of gerfalcons which were given him by King

James, grey with age, but tended as carefully as if in their prime. A portrait of 'King Jamie', in his hawking costume, hung in the great hall, of which the most prominent feature was his Majesty's breeches. But the time was past when 'every gentleman kept a sparrow hawk, and every priest a bobby',[3] and it was a diversion for young gentlewomen to 'man sparrow hawks and merlins'. Giles and I used to kill wild-fowl on the water with our birding guns, and shoot hares sitting, with tolerable success.

Sir Giles had well-tamed hawks with hoods; and bells and jesses, and from time to time we accompanied him to the Longdon or Eldersfield marshes, as yet a sure find for the heron. His constant companion on such occasions was Squire Bartlett, of Hill End, Castlemorton, a well-known elderly gentleman, a good royalist like ourselves, who kept a Fool,[4] and was in the possession of a cock eagle stone,[5] a curious and venerable relic, said to have once belonged to the famous Dr Dee, an astrologer, alchemist, and magician of great repute.[6]

Jack Hafod, the Castlemorton Fool, was more celebrated for his antics than his wit, and may be said to be the last of the fools in this country. 'As big an oaf as Jack Hafod', was a saying in the neighbourhood, but Jack was not such a fool as he looked. Faithful as a dog to the interests of his old master, he never forgot a kindness or forgave an injury, and the unlucky wight who offended him was sure to find sooner or later that Jack was never oblivious of an insult. In consequence of this and of the respect felt for Mr Bartlett, Hafod was treated with a certain amount of deference, and a shake of his shaggy head was enough to set the village boys on the scamper.

It happened in the year 1642, when all the country was talking of the King's attempt to arrest Mr Hampden and other members of the House of Commons, that a party was assembled at Birtsmorton Court for hawking in Longdon marshes, and Mr Bartlett arrived, attended as usual by Jack Hafod. Jack was suffering from sore eyes, and Mr Bartlett begged from Dame Nanfan a bottle of eye water bottled on Holy Thursday.[7] But the dame's store was exhausted, and it was suggested that water from the well of St Waum would answer the same purpose, so Jack was sent across the Swineyard Pass to fetch a bottle for himself instead of carrying his master's hawks.

The hawking party had assembled in the old panelled dining room, with its armorial shields and coats, and among the guests was Mr

Gaston, a gentleman who lived in retirement at an old timbered dwelling opposite Severn End, the residence of Mr Lechmere. Report said that Mr Gaston was a Jesuit in disguise. Then this was contradicted, and he was said to have joined the Church of England, and to have sent his only son to Oxford, where he had been ordained an Anglican clergyman. Again he was believed by some to be tampering with Puritanism, and had been seen listening to the discourses of Mr Baxter.

He was a tall, spare man, with long and thin legs, an elongated face, flat forehead and prominent brows. His nose was arched and high, and his lips thin and compressed. His eyes were sunken, and glittered like black diamonds. He had the credit of being a wonderful trapper of wild animals in the woodlands, or of killing a hare upon her form, but never joined in the hard riding of the chase, or the sport of the birding gun. Springes, bird lime, and netting by night, were the delight of Mr Gaston.

Here, too, were the Messrs Yates, brothers from Bromesberrow, fine, young, manly gentlemen both, but who differed very materially in their political and religious opinions. The elder, Honeywood Yates, at that time the Squire of the parish, was a royalist and Churchman, a dashing Cavalier, and a man of high spirit and courage.

The other, John Yates, was a tall, dignified gentleman, but reserved, and with none of the dash of his elder brother. He had a somewhat haughty expression, and a glance of the eye told that John Yates had a temper too. Sir Giles and Mr Bartlett had gone to the mews to select the peregrines for the day's sport, and we younger ones were left in the dining room. The conversation, unhappily, turned upon the burning questions of the day. Honeywood Yates, Giles and myself, were generally agreed, and settled the affairs of the nation very much to our own satisfaction. John Yates sat for some time looking moody and discontented but silent.

We touched upon the State Church, and Honeywood discoursed upon the blessing it ought to be to the nation at large. He declared, too, that "the King's office, like that of the Church, was sacred even if the occupant of the throne were profane; that the King and State had a right to select a belief for its people, and men and women had no right to choose for themselves. Private views of religion were disloyal to the Church and State, and the Dissent and Puritanism of the present times should be met by penal laws and severity."

For a long time John Yates sat listening, but with angry brow and flashing eye, At last he arose and said, "State Church indeed! Pray tell me if you call those blessings which the State Church showered upon the people when that tyrant Henry VIII and his ministers sent first Protestants and then Catholics to the fire, the torture, and the block, for the love of Mother Church! Was the State Church a blessing in Queen Mary's time, when you had your Gardiner and Bonner, holy priests, presiding over the fires of Smithfield, Oxford, and Gloucester! What say you to the State Church of Philip of Spain, with its Inquisition and ecclesiastical torturers! Or that of France, when its Jesuits, priests too, urged on the royal family to butcher their Protestant subjects in thousands! Out with your State Church say I! It has been the curse of England before, and will become so again, if left to Charles and Laud as an engine to crush the liberties of Englishmen. Even now Laud has revived the abomination of torture, against the law of the land!"

With this he left the room, and did not join the hawking party; but his brother declared he was a good fellow at heart, and would soon get over his tantrums.[8]

We had returned from our sport in the marshes and finished dinner, when Jack Hafod put his shaggy head in at the door, mumbling and shaking his countenance as if he had something important to communicate. He had evidently visited the little tavern at the Wind's Point, as well as the Well of St Waum, and was 'market peart'.

Still two things were evident, one that he wanted some 'fittle', and, secondly, that something unusual was going on at the summit of the Herefordshire Beacon, where he declared, "A nation lot of people, more nor twenty, was a driving in postises like anythink."

As it was only two o'clock in the afternoon, I proposed to ride to the Beacon, when Giles Nanfan offered to accompany me, and challenged his sister Bridget to mount her palfrey also. We therefore left Sir Giles and Mr Bartlett to enjoy their tobacco and sack, and discuss the plays of Shakespeare, and started, a merry trio, for the Wind's Point.

There were few finer riders in our country than the fair sylph who despised the narrow, muddy lanes, and led us over high hedges and enclosures at a rattling pace. Crossing the lane at Birt's Street, we galloped up the hill towards the old Saxon Mill of Castlemorton, and down the slope on the opposite side as if hunting a stag. Bridget then led over some very broken ground, across the mill brook, into the

Malvern trackway near the small hostel of the Robin Hood.

As we rode over the great overgrown fence into the lane, Giles had just joined us, and was expostulating with Bridget for her madcap racing pace, when a gentleman attended by a soldier-servant rode up and enquired the way to Birtsmorton Court. Giles informed him who he was, when the stranger replied that he was the Earl of Cockayne, and the bearer of an important letter from Sir William Russell, of Strensham, now at Worcester, to Sir Giles Nanfan. He said he had lost his way in the winding lanes, and that his horses, his servant and himself were weary and hungry. Under the circumstances Giles thought it right to accompany my Lord to Birtsmorton, as his father might wish to send return despatches without delay.

Bridget and I were thus left to pursue our ride to the Wind's Point alone, and leaving our horses at the little inn, we questioned the landlord, who informed us that the Roundheads had employed labourers to erect a great beacon ladder upon the site of the huge bonfires that had blazed upon the Herefordshire Beacon in olden times. They had sent quantities of 'piche and rozen, tallowe, towe and hurds, to be burnt in a large iron potte'[9] at the summit of the scaffolding. We were informed that it was done by the orders of Mr Bromley of Hamme Court, and other gentlemen, as Mr William Stallard, and Mr Higgins of Eastnor, who were known to be disaffected towards the King.

We now ascended the hill, and found great posts erected with fire pan and combustibles ready for lighting; a shepherd's boy was set to watch it, but from him we could learn nothing save that 'every one else was gaed away', and he was 'well nigh famelled'. Bridget now proposed that we should descend the hill to the well of St Waum, and take a drink of the water, so good for the healing of broken hearts, sore eyes and rheumatism. I laughed at the idea, as we were both strong and healthy, but down the hill we went for the sake of St Waum's spell and Bridget's fancy.

The spring, for well there is none, bubbles forth from a green quaking turf near a narrow inlet of the hills at the corner of the forest which formerly covered a great part of the country between Hereford and the Malverns. Even now it is closely hidden by thickets of eglantine, hawthorn and hazel, and the path was so fully overgrown with trailing plants that we had to charge boldly to get through at all. Bridget's hair was caught by an envious rose briar, and fell in glorious tresses round her neck and shoulders. I, too, lost my riding cap in the struggle to extricate her from the thick bushes. Thus we looked a wild young couple, as, hand in hand, we emerged from the thicket and stood on the little green by the spring, face to face with Mary Bromley and her father.

Our surprise was mutual and somewhat awkward, for Mr Bromley had, on several occasions, shown a decided wish to avoid meeting me, or any of my family, and I was confused, not at meeting Mr Bromley, but at this unexpected rencontre with Mary. Mr Bromley had adopted the steeple-crowned hat, which had become fashionable with Round-heads and dissenters. In times gone by he would have doffed it to Bridget; now he contented himself with a grave salute, but Mary, blushing, came forward with a quiet greeting, while I attempted to take off my cap, in acknowledgment of her courtesy, forgetting that I had lost it in the thicket.

Bridget did not recognize them, for Sir Giles Nanfan had forbidden his family to exchange visits with 'shuffling republicans', as he termed them, nevertheless she made a low curtsey to the Bromleys and cast a comical look at me. I set to work drinking water enough to cure all the plagues in Egypt until Bridget requested me to fill the horn which she had carried at her saddle bow. With a glance over the brim of the cup in my direction, she gravely wished us all "Good health and the healing of St Waum". At this Squire Bromley forgot his Puritan manners, and lifting the steeple hat from his brows made a profound salutation, like a gentleman and a Cavalier.

He now beckoned his daughter to follow him beyond the environ-ment of scrub and bush which surrounded the well, while I busied myself in tearing aside briar and prickly gorse to make a path for Mary. They had left their horses at the Cave of Glendower, or Hermit's Cave, on the hill above, and saluted me gravely as they commenced the ascent. I observed that Mary never once looked back to wave her hand and say goodbye, as in days of old; when Bridget said, "Now, Master Richard, find your hat and let us begone to our horses, unless you wish to give your hand to that gipsy damsel up the mountain."

While on our road back she more than once rallied me on my absence of mind, and advised me to drink more of the water of St Waum, and not look so 'moithered'. On our arrival at Birtsmorton Court we found the Earl of Cockayne engaged with Mr Bartlett and Sir

Giles upon a flask of Canary, and Giles had started for Worcester. A letter from my aunt awaited me, requesting me to return home without delay.

I found my father had arrived at Hanley Castle, bringing the important tidings that the King had determined upon war against his rebellious Parliament, had called forth Commissions of Array, inviting all men to raise for him and the royal cause money and horses and arms, on the security of his forests and parks. On the other side, the Parliament protested against these measures of his Majesty as 'against all law and national liberty'. Sir John Pakington, Sir William Russell, my father, and other decided Royalists were expelled from the House of Commons, and Lord Essex was named Commander of the Parliamentary army of twenty thousand foot and four thousand horse.

The Royalists evinced great reluctance to take up arms, still hoping that the struggle might be averted, but my father was one of the few who foresaw the necessity of immediate action, and after making strenuous efforts to raise recruits, he joined the party of his King at Nottingham, leaving to Sir William Russell of Strensham, Sir John Pakington, Mr Hornyold,[10] Mr Dowdeswell and others, the work of appealing to their countrymen for the defence of their King.

Before his departure he impressed upon me that I was now old enough to take part in the troubles he felt sure were coming upon us, and bid me apply to Kelly for advice, and lose no opportunity of collecting arms and gunpowder, and storing them in the underground passages of Hanley Castle. He advised me to watch the Puritans round Upton-on-Severn, and to send him word of any attempt on their part to take up arms. He warned me respecting one Captain Bound, lived at Seller's Orchard; and who had already espoused the cause of the rebels.

Captain Bound had been a soldier of fortune and fought in the Bohemian wars; he had acquired some money, men said by plunder, and bought a pretty, timbered house, surrounded by orchards and covered with roses and ivy, near to Upton Rectory. He was married to a lady younger than himself, whom he ruled with all the rigour of an eastern despot. To all appearance, he was a man of forty years of age; he was tall and gaunt, with remarkable eyes of different sizes; the large eye squinted, and you could not tell if he was looking at you, until you caught the expression of the little one, which was cruel and pig-like in its aspect. He was noted for his stealthy pursuit of the deer in the remaining woodlands, and from this acquired the soubriquet of the Bloodhound.

He was a great rider and kept two horses, one a large white shambling beast called the Ghost, the other a raking black mare which rejoiced in the title of Hell Cat; a name acquired from the serious damage she had inflicted with her heels and teeth upon more than one of her unhappy grooms. When Captain Bound found that negotiations between the King and Parliament had been really broken off, he declared war against his own rector, Mr Woodforde, a gentle inoffensive man, who loved his Church and his King.

In Queen Elizabeth's time, the altar had been changed into a communion table, and was moved from the east end of the churches to the middle of the nave, but Archbishop Laud obtained a royal injunction to remove all the tables back to their old position in the chancels and secure them from profanation by a rail. This had given great offence to Captain Bound, Mr Cocktail, and other Upton Puritans, so now they insisted that Mr Woodforde should again remove the table, and accused him of calling it an altar, wearing 'a Popish rag, or surplice', and bowing at the name of Christ. MrWoodford naturally declined to obey the orders of Captain Bound and his associates, so a public meeting was called at Upton.

I determined to attend this meeting, and found a large assemblage of the lower orders, with Captain Bound presiding. When this gentleman lived the life of a soldier, among the German legions, he had contracted the habit of swearing fearfully, every other word was an oath; but since he had joined the Puritans, he followed their custom of adapting the language of Scripture to all passing events. He began his speech by exhorting the people to resist all 'prelacy, oppression and malignancy', and 'to cleanse the house of Baal', by which he meant the Church, and 'to turn out all the prophets of Baal', by which he intended to indicate all the clergy, and Mr Woodforde in particular.

After speechifying for some time he became confused, and as I stood near him, I distinctly heard him mutter the word 'damnation'. Then there was considerable maundering, and he went off upon another subject, an exhortation to levy war funds and material for the Parliament, and Moses Brick, Obadiah Cotterill, and Joshua Sniggles were told to 'gird their swords upon their thighs', and to ride forth as the 'chosen champions of the Most High'. Here was more maundering, another blasphemous oath, not heard by the people below, and another call to 'gird up the loins of their resolution and be steadfast to the mark of their high calling'; while the Bricks, the Cotterills, and Sniggles shouted vociferously, but I could stand it no longer, so came forward and said, "Captain Bound, this is rank treason!"

It is not easy to describe the gallant Captain's wrath and indignation at being thus interrupted by a beardless youth. He glared at me with his big eye for a moment, then, shouting at the top of his voice, "Out with the malignant spy! Out with this spawn of a Papist!" He seized me by the collar, and endeavoured to throw me over the side of the platform among the people. But he reckoned beyond his power, for I knew the Cornish hug, and gave him such a grip round his throat as well nigh strangled him. I should, nevertheless, very soon have come to grief, for Bound had with him the sympathy of the audience, but John Kelly strode across the platform, seized us both by the collars of our coats, and separated us as if we were two pieces of paper.

There was no one amidst that rabble audience who did not hold John Kelly in awe, not even Captain Bound, so the 'chosen champions of the Most High' began one by one to return to their own homes. Bound excused himself by abusing me, when Kelly interrupted his speech by saying, "Come with me, Richard Forester," turned on his heel and left the meeting.

It was not only Kelly's strength of arm that kept men in awe, he had the credit of possessing more than common knowledge. Men said that the skulls of the dead in his closet shone with a fiery glare at night, and that he had the power of throwing men and women into a trance by the magic of his eye. Reports were rife that he had a strange glass hidden among his treasures which revealed faces that had long been dust, and whispers were heard from voices which had long been silent. It was certain that on one occasion Bound emerged from the 'den', his teeth chattering and his hair on end, while Mr Gaston had been seen to rush down Dun's Lane leaving his hat behind him; his eyes glaring like hot coals, and his complexion ghastly to look upon.

Chapter Four

WHEN WE reached the Waterside and the well-known room with the crocodile, the skulls, and the old clock, where I had solved many a problem of Euclid and bungled over many a fractious sum of arithmetic, Master Kelly gravely inquired how old I was, to which I replied, "Just twenty."

"Then," said he, "you ought to know better than to lose your head and your temper and forget yourself, as you have done at this meeting of Puritans and revolutionists! What possible good could come of your shouting treason among a crowd of people, every one of whom differed from you in the interpretation of the term, and thinks he has as much right as you have to express his opinion upon the great political questions which are soon about to convulse this unhappy country!"

I angrily muttered something about "fools, rebels and knaves", when Kelly reminded me that Mr Bromley and Mr Ligon were neither fools or knaves, but sober, high-minded gentlemen, and if they became rebels against the Crown, it would not be without strong reasons; maybe the cruelties and tortures inflicted during the ministry of Strafford and Laud and the abominable Star Chamber.

"Besides," he said, "if you read the terms of the proclamation for calling the meeting, you will find that it intended to propose measures for the 'defence of the King'. God grant that the King may see his mistake in time, and may not tamper with those Irish rebels who murdered their Protestant fellow subjects."

On my asking him if he proposed that I should desert the cause of my royal master and my father and all his friends, he replied, "By no means, lad; I admire both your courage and your constancy, but I would have you keep silence lest you get your head broken beyond repair, which you will assuredly do, if you bark and bay as you did to-day. Fight for your King, if you will, but leave tirades of abuse, and mingling texts of Scripture with injurious epithets, to such as Bound and his followers."

I was not pleased at thus being lectured, but I held my tongue with an inward determination to bring Captain Bound to book some day. I then wished Kelly good-bye in somewhat high dudgeon, but he called me back and said, "Let us not part in anger, Richard, my dear pupil," and he held out his hand and shook mine heartily. My heart was in my mouth in a moment, and I was well-nigh embracing one to whom I owed a deep debt of gratitude, when he bade me sit down once more and again resumed his discourse. He spoke to me as if I were his son, and told how he thought times of great danger were drawing near, how the members of the same household would quarrel and differ on the questions of the times, how ruin would overtake whole families now prosperous, and how thousands now living would be numbered with the dead.

"God only knows," he continued, "where you or I may be this time next year, or what may happen to those who now think themselves the most powerful in the land." He then proceeded to show me some contrivances in his little domicile which, he said, might on some occasion stand in good stead to those who knew them, and for the first time in my life I looked into the secrets of the Waterside.

Kelly first took down the crocodile, and opening a slit in its belly, produced a pair of pistolets of fine workmanship, with the apparatus for loading and firing. These he showed me how to use and bid me appropriate them, if at any time I had need of them. The old clock was lined in its interior with small bags containing gold pieces, hidden in a wonderful manner by the machinery of works and wheels.

Behind the suspended skeleton was the door of a closet containing various phials and bottles, and in the floor of this closet was a trap door and some steps leading to a little cove which opened out on the river and contained the wherry in which Kelly frequently rowed, sometimes ascending as far as Worcester.

"We may not," he said, "be always able to pass over the bridge, and a boat may then be useful. In taking these precautions against a sudden emergency, you may judge how convinced I am of impending strife, and should I lose my life or liberty, I wish you and your father to know where all I possess may be found."

On my road back to Hanley Castle I encountered Mr Woodforde, who was very sorrowful at the bickerings and strife which had increased year after year in his once united parish. Mr Woodforde loved the Church of England, but he had none of the theological bitterness which characterized too many of the English clergy at this period, and he had a tolerance for those who differed from him, which, unhappily, they did not always show towards him.

He had a conviction that religion had to do with a man's conduct towards others, rather than with surplices and Geneva gowns, the position of altars, incense, and spangles, and he would, if permitted, have poured balm on the deep wounds of English religious opinion. He had none of that misguided zeal which develops into persecution. He had his own opinions on matters of doctrine and the authority of the Church, but he had no belief that peace and union would be promoted by cropping the ears of his adversaries, or putting his opponent the Nonconformist minister in the stocks. He had been present at the meeting when I had shouted 'Treason', and he now met me with a kindly smile, but shaking his head while he proffered his hand.

He accompanied me to Hanley Castle, and remained to supper. Sister Tab was delighted to see him, and to inquire after many an old acquaintance, who, alas, was a friend to her and him no longer. Isabel had a great reverence for the Upton pastor, and rejoiced to see him at our board as in days of yore. Mr Woodforde had none of the gloomy forebodings of Kelly, but looked forward to the King regaining his popularity, and declared that any insurrection would be promptly quelled by the Royalists, the Puritans would succumb, and all would be right again.

Soon after this my father returned home, and brought the news that many Worcestershire gentlemen had determined to support the King with all the men they could collect, while I was delighted to learn that I was considered old enough to draw the sword in his Majesty's cause.

We learnt also that the Earl of Essex had been appointed Captain General of the Parliamentary army; that some Lords and many gentlemen of the House of Commons had entered the Commons' service, among whom were Mr Oliver Cromwell, member for Cambridge, and a relative of Squire Bromley; Mr John Hampden, the great speaker, a cousin of Mr Cromwell; Mr Denzil Hollis, and Lord Grey of Groby. Mr Hampden raised a regiment amongst his tenants and servants, friends and neighbours. They were clad in green uniforms, with his own motto *vestigula nulla retrorsum* on their standard.

My father was to hold a Colonel's command under Prince Rupert, and I was selected to act as his aide-de-camp and equerry. Thus the month of July 1642 found us actively employed in making warlike preparations, and I was continually exercised in carrying letters and despatches to and fro among the various Royalist gentlemen who held command in the King's army.

In September Prince Rupert arrived at Nottingham, where the King had set up his standard, and he began to scour the country in every direction. My father was now acting as Secretary to the King, so it was left to Giles Nanfan, Mr Dowdeswell and myself, to persuade all we could in our own neighbourhood to join the Royal forces.

On a lovely evening, early in September, instead of netting coveys of partridges, I was riding back from Worcester and had passed Prior's Court and Pixham Ferry, crossed the Old Hills, and reached the turn to Madresfield, when I saw Mary Bromley, seated on her roan cob, awaiting the return of her father, who it seems had ridden up to see Mr Ligon at Madresfield Court. We had not met since the little adventure at Waum's Well.

I doffed my riding cap and Mary made a polite acknowledgment of my greeting. She gave a quick nervous glance at my soldier's dress, while she gathered the coif round her lovely face and busily arranged her riding gear. I could not avoid asking why she was changed, and if we were to be old friends no longer; why she ever looked grave if she passed me by, and never smiled, as she was wont in days of yore, when we roamed together among our forest glens. The colour mounted to her cheeks, but 'ere she could reply our interview was interrupted.

A squadron of mounted Cavaliers rode rapidly down the hill from Worcester. The officer in front, although quite young, was evidently accustomed to command. His bearing was stern and high, his voice loud and commanding. He wore the long hair of the fashionable Cavalier, and spoke with a foreign accent; he had restless, sharp eyes, a long Roman nose, and thin lips which seldom smiled.

He inquired the distance to Hanley Castle in a peremptory tone, and I curtly replied. Taking no notice of my offended demeanour, save by a curl of his lip, he was about to ride on, when one of his attendants said something I did not hear. The officer now condescended for the first time to look me in the face, when he exclaimed, "Gadzooks, so you are the son of my friend, Miles Forester, a welcome meeting! I am Prince Rupert, King Charles' nephew, and at your father's bidding am about to crave your hospitality, it may be for a night or two."

I now made my profound salutations to the distinguished youth, who was soon to prove so gallant a Cavalier but so rash a general, while I assured him that all we had at Hanley Castle was at the service of the King's nephew. At this moment Mr Bromley rode up to join his daughter. He was surprised at finding her surrounded by a gaily dressed corps of Cavalier officers, and judging from Prince Rupert's demeanour that he was a person of consideration, he touched the steeple-crowned hat and bowed. The Prince acknowledged the salute and said to me in an undertone, "One of your Brownists or Anabaptists, I suppose, from his hat and cloak!"

To this I replied by introducing Mr Bromley as my father's friend and neighbour, and Miss Bromley as his daughter, on which the Prince addressed Mary in the courteous manner both he and his brother, Prince Maurice, ever assumed towards women. Nor did he leave her side until we reached the turn to Hanley Castle.

I was thus left to converse with Sir John Pakington, and now and then to address a few words to Mr Bromley, who quietly remarked, "It was kindly meant, Mr Richard Forester, to tell that proud Prince I am a friend of your father's, but it is hardly true! Times have changed since Miles Forester and I clasped each other's hands, drank to the same toast, or attended the same place of worship. The next place he and I, or you and I, may meet, may be some battle-field, where we shall be seeking to shed each other's blood. You are even now wearing the royal uniform, which tells me that you are prepared to fight against the cause which I deem the cause of God, and the liberties of the people of England. We can hardly be friends."

I muttered something about old times and old associations, but it was time for us to separate, and while Sir John Pakington conducted the rest of the troop to Upton for the night, I led the Prince down the roadway to our moated Castle, but not before Sir John had told him of the position and standing of Mr Bromley. He spoke privately to Prince Rupert who said, "We will see about him to-morrow, at his own dwelling; be with me in the early morn."

I now bethought me that the nearest way for Mr Bromley to reach Hamme Court, would be to pass our mill and take the route by Cutthroat Lane, for such is the dreary name of an ancient trackway which leads to Mr Bromley's dwelling on the banks of the Severn. When we reached our outer moat, the Prince reined in his horse, and surveyed in astonishment the grand pile of half ruinous buildings which was once the loved home of the daughter of the great Edward, and the birth-place of the King-maker's wife. The Keep in which we lived was now glowing in the setting sun, and Rupert shaded his eyes as he gazed in admiration, and said "Gadzooks, but you are well lodged, Mr Forester."

"Brumfat, Brumfat, that is his name, is it!" said the Prince, as Mary and her father disappeared round the turn beyond the mill; "I think I have that name on my tablets, with that of Nicholas Slashmere and Monsieur Sliggon, all rebels we must visit to-morrow; but I will show you my tablets and you shall tell me who are loyal in these parts and who are not."

Happily for my aunt's preparations in respect to supper and bed for our distinguished guest, Prince Rupert insisted upon surveying every nook and corner of our old Castle even before he divested himself of his cumbrous military attire. He challenged Isabel to accompany him, and attended by his celebrated poodle dog, Boye, they wandered from tower to keep, and from keep to dungeon. Meanwhile Aunt Tabitha brought forth our forks and provided a fair supper of partridges, capons, cold sucking pig, and dried salmon; and I broached a keg of red wine of Burgundy, which my father kept for high days and holidays.

No longer at the head of his troops, Prince Rupert laid aside his haughty bearing and imperious manner, and delighted Aunt Tabitha by complimenting her upon her forks, telling how his royal grand-mother, Mary Queen of Scots, eat her *quelque choses* with her fingers. No sooner had the Prince alluded to made dishes, than our aunt cross-questioned him upon the diet of the Germans. She had read Fynes Moyrson's *Itinerary*,[1] and much did she want to know about the 'sour cabbages which they call craut, and the drink which they call swoope.'

She asked, too, most particularly about the wormwood wine served before partaking of the little lampreys – which they call nine augur, as having nine eyes – served with white vinegar, and offered to give his Royal Highness the receipt for our own Severn lamperns stewed in cider. Then she went for her own wine of elderberries, and which, when the Prince quaffed it, I perceived that he feared to drink. Observing the virginals in the room he entreated Isabel to sing a ballad, and setting aside Boye, who insisted upon being fondled, she sang without affectation and delay the new ditty:

> *Oh why was England merrie called, I pray you tell me why,*
> *Because Old England merrie was, in merrie times gone by;*
> *She knew no dearth of honest mirth to cheer both son and sire,*
> *But kept it up o'er wassail cup around the Christmas fire.*

The cuckoo's song, the woods among, sounds sweetly as of old,
As bright and warm the sunbeams shine, so why should hearts grow cold!

As she sung the last refrain the Prince clapped his hands, and tears filled Aunt Tabitha's eyes as she thought of friendships now broken, and hearts gone astray.

No sooner had the ladies retired than the Prince drew forth two papers from his doublet and handed them to me to read. One was the King's Proclamation calling upon all his subjects between the ages of sixteen and sixty to repair to the setting up of his standard at Nottingham. The other was a list of disaffected persons in the neighbourhood of Worcester, and I recognized the names of Bromley, Lechmere, Ligon, Bound, and others living within a short distance of Hanley Castle.

The Prince declared that if these disaffected gentlemen could not be compelled to take up arms for the cause of the King, they could and should be compelled to contribute towards the expenses of his army. I ventured to remark that Mr Bromley, notwithstanding his differing in religious matters from us of the Church of England, was royal to the King, and blamed only the ministers who misled him; but I soon perceived the haughty and impatient temper of Rupert by the "Pish! Pish!" with which he met my remarks, as he strode up and down the room, and, calling the white poodle dog which accompanied him, declared that he was more faithful than half the gentlemen of England.

I felt vexed, lest my father should hear of these expostulations and might deem I had committed a breach of hospitality, if not of loyalty, but I knew I had told the truth, and that many who were loyal to their heart's core were disgusted at the deeds of his Majesty's advisers. But the Prince was kind-hearted, notwithstanding his impetuosity, and seeing I was annoyed said, "I shall think none the worse of you, Forester, for standing up for an old friend, Puritan and Roundhead though he be," and I was proceeding to usher him to his bedchamber, when in walked John Kelly.

Chapter Five

I HAD NOT seen Kelly for some weeks, but his appearance did not surprise me, as his custom was to drop in on all occasions when it suited him. No matter when he came, he was ever welcome at Hanley Castle! To my aunt he was respectful and obliging, while Isabel was never tired of listening to his discourse on the wonders he had seen in his travels. To me he was as a father in kindness and a brother in affection.

I was not, however, prepared to find him acquainted with Prince Rupert, who started as he entered the room and said, "Why what brings you here, Master Kelly! A week since I saw you at Oxford, three days ago you were at Nottingham, and now you turn up in this weird old Castle. You are like Will Shakspeare's Ariel."

Kelly smiled as he replied, "I hardly think, your Royal Highness, that my movements are more rapid than your own; but I came here to-night to inform you that Sir John Pakington left the troops you have quartered at Upton-on-Severn under the command of your German Captain, von Prig, and went to Croome. No sooner had he gone than the troops set out to Severn End to make 'requisitions', as they are pleased to call them. Mr Lechmere being in London, they much alarmed Mrs Penelope Lechmere, and not only robbed her hen-roost, but carried off a whole sheep, and a large bundle of religious tracts, which that lady sets especial store by, and which Captain von Prig declared to be treasonable correspondence. To-morrow the German has announced his intention of visiting Mr Bromley at Hamme Court."

I could have wished that Prince Rupert had shown a little more indignation at the thieving propensities of his soldiers, but he merely laughed heartily at Kelly's account of their raid upon Severn End, and it was this want of discipline, this tacit permission to plunder, which soon gained for him the soubriquet of Prince Robber. But Kelly protested in a most decided manner against such unsoldierlike conduct, prophesying that terrible retribution would befall the Royalists if it were persisted in.

The Prince declared himself ready for bed, and I conducted him to his sleeping apartment. While I was assisting him to undress he said, "Call me early, Forester, and we will ride over to this Mr Brumfat ourselves." Kelly's expostulations had not therefore been quite thrown away.

After a hasty breakfast, the Prince mounted his horse and I conducted him at the gallop to the residence of Mr Bromley. The property had come to this family by a marriage with Miss Bourne, an heiress, and one of them had been Chancellor to Queen Elizabeth. The Chancellor's son had fallen into disgrace through supporting the unfortunate Earl of Essex, who lost his head eventually. The house was an old building of forest days, but with Elizabethan additions of chimneys and windows. It was surrounded by fine oaks and elms, and took its name from the broad Severn meadows which lay between the mansion and the river.

The old hall, though somewhat low, was hung around with the fluted armour of Henry the Seventh's time, and with helmets and breastplates of far more ancient date. Among them were some modern birding guns, side by side with the obsolete cross-bow, and swords and shields of all ages. The Chancellor had collected sundry reminiscences of his great Mistress. In a glass case were two of her gowns, and some stockings of silk presented to his lady. Also two wigs, one of black hair and the other of red, with a fan of peacocks' feathers which she presented to the Chancellor after she had danced with him 'so high and disposedly', as recorded:

> *Full oft within the spacious walls,*
> *When he had fifty winters o'er him,*
> *My grave Lord Keeper led the brawls,*
> *The seals and maces danced before him.*

On our arrival we found several scared servants holding troopers' horses, and other steeds were tied to trees and railings. The house was filled with soldiers, and a scene presented itself which I shall not easily forget. Captain von Prig, when he found Mr Bromley sternly refused to give up his arms, proceeded, after the fashion of the foreign soldiers of the times, to use personal violence.

Regardless of the screams of Mrs Bromley and Mary, whom he had locked up in the pantry, he seized the *custos rotulorum* and tied him fast, arms and legs, in a chair Queen Elizabeth sat in when she visited the city of Worcester. One of the soldiers then put her Majesty's red wig upon his head; this did not suit his dark complexion and sombre aspect, so that it was almost impossible to help laughing at the gloomy face of the Squire in that head gear.

But it was no laughing matter with Prince Rupert! He strode across the hall with a shout which startled those who heard it, as it has done since on many a battle field. Seizing the unlucky von Prig by the throat, he dragged him to the door and hurled him down the steps to the pavement below. Hamme Court was soon clear of the troopers, who mounted their horses as quickly as they could. In the mean time I had cut the cord which bound Mr Bromley, and released the ladies from their prison.

Mr Bromley met the excuses and apologies of Prince Rupert with extraordinary self–possession. He neither stormed or swore, but simply said he trusted no more of his Majesty's subjects would be subjected to similar treatment. Alas! he little thought of what would so soon befall hundreds of his fellow subjects! Madam Bromley did not take it so coolly. She had been made a prisoner in her own house, and shut up in her own pantry; one of the Germans had appropriated some of the treasures that had belonged to her ancestors, and some had carried off the contents of the larder. The blood of the Ligons was up and she could not be pacified by Prince Rupert's apologies.

Giles Nanfan here rode up with despatches from Worcester, which contained a communication respecting Mr Bromley himself. The Prince looked grave as he read, and said, "I fear, Sir, I must take you prisoner to Worcester; you appear to have compromised yourself by attending public meetings at Upton, at which the speakers counselled actual dis-loyalty to my uncle the King. Your son also, it seems, has lately arrived in England and taken service with the army of that traitor Lord Essex."

I now came forward and stated that I had attended these gatherings at Upton, that Mr Bromley was not present during the delivery of Captain Bound's treasonable and disloyal speech, and that he ever mentioned the King's name with all honour and respect.

The Prince listened without taking his eyes off the despatch or replying to me, but said to Mr Bromley, "After what has passed, Sir, and the rough usage you have received, so contrary to my wishes, I shall be satisfied with your parole that you will not for one year assist the Parliament's Militia by arms or money, or by attending public meetings for raising such arms or money. By that time we shall have settled with the rebels, who I am glad to think you would not willingly join against my dear uncle the King."

Mr Bromley pledged his word to the extent demanded upon which the Prince gave him his hand and bowed profoundly to the curtseys of

Mrs Bromley and Mary. The trumpet sounded to horse, and as we rode down the narrow lane towards Upton, the Prince said to me in a low tone, "Essex is marching upon Worcester." I started, for although we expected each day to hear some such tidings, the announcement that war, real war, would soon be in our own country and around our own homes, was not to be heard without a thrill. There was no time for moralising, for Rupert pressed his horse to the gallop, nor drew in rein till we arrived in Upton, where Mr Lingham was talking to John Kelly. When Prince Rupert told Kelly of the news he had received in his despatches, he said, "Just before you arrived, Bound galloped over the bridge on Hell Cat; he has been watching your movements, and is gone to give the information to Lord Essex."

The Prince, having ordered refreshment for his troopers at the tavern known as the White Lion, proceeded with Giles Nanfan and myself to inspect Upton Bridge and Church.

Upton Church was then an Edwardian structure, built of sandstone from the red rocks of Stourport, with a tower and tapering spire. It stands, so say the learned, upon the site of a Roman temple, where an image of Diana once rose above the Severn's stream. And here, in ages long after, the Saxons raised an edifice of wood in times when a rude Christianity followed upon the death of Penda, the last of the Saxon heathen kings. Then came the Normans, with their church of stone, the round arch, and semicircular eastern apse; and as time rolled on, this too passed away, and the de Clares and Despensers built the present structure, with its double chancel, its monuments to knights and Crusaders, and its windows of stained glass, alas now broken and defaced by civil war.

On this occasion we looked at the church with soldiers' eyes. How many troopers would it hold, and what kind of defence could be made from it! The message of peace was forgotten as we paced the nave, and talked of piercing the walls for cannon and converting the windows into loop-holes for musketry.

Nor was the bridge close by less an object of our attention. Several bridges have been built at Upton. Old Leland mentions a bridge of wood in the days of Henry VIII, and that was probably erected in the days of the de Clares. The present bridge was reared early in 1600, and with its high arches, massive buttresses, and retreating angles is considered a fine structure.

It now seems monstrous that we looked upon it with the eyes of destructionists, and thought how its foundations might best be blown up by gunpowder. True this was only to be done as a necessity, but Prince Rupert asserted that I and the Upton Royalists must look to this. "Spare not," said he, "a single stone, if the downfall will serve his Majesty." He then asked if we had store of gunpowder at Hanley Castle, if we needed it, but there was merely a supply for our birding pieces.

A fortnight had now passed since King Charles hoisted his standard at Nottingham, and Prince Rupert had ridden far and wide to collect arms and money and recruit soldiers, yet he knew nothing of the movements of the Parliamentary army, nothing of their numbers, or to what place Lord Essex had advanced. Report said that Essex was at Evesham, and his cavalry might ride into Upton at any moment!

"Forester," said the Prince, "you know the country, and I shall depend upon you and your friend, young Nanfan, to aid us in finding that crop-eared Essex with his rebel host, so keep a sharp look out, and spare not the spur. You will report to us at Wick or Worcester."

The trumpet sounded, and in a few moments the whole troop were clattering and jingling along the road by Poole House on the road to Powick.

Giles and I were in high spirits at being thus sent on important service, but his horse was tired, and it was necessary that I should give him a remount; so taking our leave of Kelly, with a promise to send the earliest information we could obtain, we trotted off for Hanley and our Keep. Nanfan was loud in his praises of the Prince, whose dash and energy he declared was in great contrast to his brother, Prince Maurice. He described the army of King Charles at Nottingham as being in a state of chaos from want of a proper organization. Desertions were continual, owing to the want of a proper commissariat. The troops had to feed themselves how and where they could, and even when money was plentiful there was no one to pay the soldiers. This state of things my father was trying to reduce into something like order, and consequently was more occupied with his pen than his sword.

We found all in a state of commotion at Hanley Castle. Mary Bromley had ridden over in haste to entreat Aunt Tabitha to go to Hamme Court and prescribe for Madam Bromley. The events of the morning had so overset the nerves of that lady that she had been seized with a fit of the screamings, and the noise she made was fearful. Aunt Tabitha was famous for her pharmacies, and the chirurgeon at Upton was held in light repute in comparison. In consequence of this, Sampson, the groom, was searching for toads to boil up in elderberry wine, and Isabel in the garden gathering camomile blossoms; Aunt Tabitha was pre-paring to accompany Mary, and every maidservant was engaged on stewings and concoctions.

Mary looked anxious and careworn, but she received me with some-what of the old kindness, thanking me for my interference on her father's part with Prince Rupert. There was little time for interchange of greeting; my aunt was soon placed on the pillion behind Mary and on her lap a basket full of remedies, the unlucky toads among the number. A hasty refreshment, a hurried talk between Giles and Isabel, and a kiss from myself, and we were again in the saddle, on our road to Pershore.

As we approached Defford waste, a wild district of thicket and gorse, we heard the ring of a horse's hoofs behind us. Splashing through the mud at a hand gallop came a rider mounted on Captain Bound's great white horse, the Ghost. He wore a smock, the usual dress of hinds and small farmers, and to our astonishment we found it was John Kelly.

We were so accustomed to see him in his scholar's gown that it was difficult to recognize him in such a disguise, and on our expressing our surprise he said that Captain Bound was continually offering to lend him a horse, a dog, or a birding piece, so he had taken advantage of his liberality and borrowed the Ghost from Mrs Bound, to ride after her husband.

Mrs Bound seemed greatly puzzled, but lent him the horse, and Kelly was on his way to try and prevent any mischief on which the Ghost's master may be engaged. We laughed heartily and criticised the animal, who seemed powerful and capable of long endurance, notwithstanding his rakish appearance.

We passed by the great woodlands of Croome Ferry, lately the domain of the famed Lord Keeper Coventry,[1] and reached the town of Pershore, once so celebrated for its Abbey, by roads so detestable that the disheartened driver of sheep or cattle often said, 'Pershore, God help me'. One would have thought that the rib of St Edburga, daughter of King Edward the Elder, which was purchased at the cost of a hundred pounds sterling,[2] and transported from Winchester, might have had more influence upon highways leading to so sacred a shrine.

Kelly advised us to go to a small ale-house in Lich Street, so called because the dead were carried along it for interment, as the host was well affected to the Royalists, and it was less frequented than the larger inns. The stabling attached to the Cat and Cauliflower was a shed built on the site of the Chapel of St Edburga, but we managed to halter up our horses and supply them with fodder. Having attended to our beasts we proceeded to question the host, who was supplying a group of country folks with horns of Pershore perry:

> *Pershore perry, with a toast,*
> *Is the drink we all like most,*

being a favourite distich with Pershore rhymesters. We could gain no reliable information here concerning the march of Lord Essex, though one man had heard that his scouts had been seen at Evesham; another declared that he slept the night before at Broadway; a third had dreamt that he had set Worcester on fire and slaughtered all the inhabitants; a fourth told a story of a cock and a bottle; and a fifth of a cock and a bull.

The landlord puffed at his tobacco pipe and said nothing, but giving a sly wink at Kelly, these two adjourned to see that the Ghost was well fed and cared for. They seemed to Giles and myself to be absent a long time, but we called for more perry and treated all the company. On their return Kelly proposed that we should take a walk in the town, when he informed us that he would leave us to reconnoitre at Pershore, and would himself ride on to Evesham.

Accordingly away he went, and Giles and I explored the town. There were no defences to the place, not even a wall, but the Avon was so wide and deep as to be impassable to horse or foot, and the narrow bridge was the only one between Evesham and Tewkesbury. A hill rises above the bridge, and down this we saw the Ghost coming at the gallop. Kelly reined up for a moment to tell us that Colonel Fiennes was in Evesham with the advanced guard of Essex. Fiennes had been sent to waylay Sir John Byron, who was escorting a large sum of money from Oxford to Worcester. "Fiennes is sent to cut off Byron," said Kelly, "and the Prince must cut off Fiennes; I will not draw bridle again until I have seen him at Powick."

He then told us that Captain Bound had rushed out of the Crown Inn at Evesham in a state of intense excitement at seeing him on his well-known horse. "They were not texts of Scripture he uttered," said Kelly, "as he ran after me, without his hat, vociferating down the street. But here he comes!" and Bound appeared on the hill above the bridge, just in time to see Kelly crossing it at a pace which gave little hope of Hell Cat overtaking him. Bound took no notice of us as he passed, but his eyes glared, and his teeth were set fast as he drove the spurs into the black mare, who was evidently exhausted with previous exertions.

Mounting our steeds, we returned to Upton and, without delaying there, joined Prince Rupert's forces at Powick. Kelly had arrived before us, and the same evening sent back the Ghost to Seller's Orchard, with a grateful message to Captain and Mrs Bound.

Prince Rupert had wisely selected Powick as head quarters for his own brigade. The church tower commands an extensive prospect of the vales of the Severn and the Teme, and between Powick and Worcester is a great plain favourable for the drilling of cavalry, on which bodies of horse were performing their evolutions under the leadership of Worcestershire Cavaliers.

Prince Rupert had ridden into Worcester, and Kelly found him and his brother Prince Maurice amusing themselves with shooting at maukins representing the Parliamentary generals, surrounded by a number of soldiers and citizens.[3] On receiving the intelligence of the movements of Colonel Fiennes, he entered into a conference with Sir William Russell and other royalist gentlemen, all of whom were ignorant of the position of the Parliamentary forces and had no idea of the near approach of Essex.

The next day we heard that Lord Essex had broken up his camp and was marching slowly upon Worcester. Tidings also arrived that King Charles had left Nottingham, and was marching upon Shrewsbury. It was now necessary for the country gentlemen to declare themselves either for the King or the Parliament, and among others Sir Walter Blount[4] joined the King's forces. Mr John Hornyold[5] of Blackmore Park under the Malvern Hills, was a zealous supporter of the Royal cause, and at the same time a consistent Catholic.

My aunt Tabitha often spoke of the dalmatics and chasubles with 'Christ in Glory on the back', and cherubims and seraphims upon the orphreys, which were worn by the priests, and which the Puritans now denounced as 'devices worked by the devil', and which brought Mr Hornyold and his fellow religionists into disrepute. Aunt Tabitha nevertheless declared that she preferred the truly magnificent Catholic vestments to the spangles and imitations of Lord Cockayne and his

Church party, which she said "was a poor attempt by Archbishop Laud and his followers to imitate Catholic magnificence after a cheap fashion."

But all the dalmatics, chalice veils, chasubles, stoles, borses, and orphreys were as nothing in the eyes of my aunt compared with the baby clothes[6] of his Majesty King Charles, as mentioned in her Diary:–

"Lo and behold I saw with my own eyes the clothes of my Lord ye Kinge when he was a leetel childe, and ys botes wherin were placed his leetel tose, God bless em!"

Chapter Six

W E WERE now sent by Prince Rupert on a most unpleasant errand. This was to accompany a troop of cavalry commanded by Captain von Grubbe to levy war contributions upon those disaffected to the King, in the neighbourhood of Upton-on-Severn. We first visited Madresfield Court, the residence of Colonel Ligon, brother to Madam Bromley, and a decided Parliamentarian. He lived in a moated manor-house, which occupied the site of an ancient Norman keep. The moat, the strong walls, and the position of this *domus defsabilis*, was suitable for a garrison, and we reported accordingly. Colonel Ligon was absent in London, and we contented ourselves with levying a large quantity of hay and corn to be sent to Worcester for the King's cavalry.

From thence we proceeded to Severn End, the residence of Mr Lechmere,[1] whose wife was a sister of Colonel Sandys, now with the Parliamentarian army in arms against King Charles. Mr Lechmere was from home, at least so said the servant, and I had, consequently, to ask to see his learned lady. Mrs Lechmere was a follower of Richard Baxter, the Nonconformist divine. She loved to hear preaching, and was a great reader of homilies, but she was not yet so bigotted as to object to the harmless recreations of the people, and in her young days had been known to dance a *coranto*, and had even been to a playhouse.

Leaving Giles Nanfan outside with the troopers, I dismounted and was ushered into a room panelled with oak and hung with family portraits in deep frames. Madam Lechmere was seated at a table covered with writing materials. At the window, nearly hidden by the curtain, was another lady, engaged in reading, who remained seated, while Madam Lechmere rose to receive me.

She looked at me earnestly, and told me she would have known me from my likeness to my father, who was her husband's friend before these troublous times. With much hesitation I informed her that I had orders to inquire for Mr Lechmere, and to demand in the King's name, the surrender of four of his horses for the immediate service of his Majesty's cavalry, and that the troopers with me would take charge of them to Worcester.

The colour mounted to her temples as she listened to my communication, but she suppressed her indignation and merely said she had heard that Prince Rupert was using the King's name in levying unlawful contributions, and that as Mr Lechmere was absent, it was not in her power to resist his demands. "It is a shame, Mr Forester," she said, "a burning shame, that a foreign Prince should bring his German mercenaries to levy war upon those who are devoted to his Majesty, and only ask for freedom to worship God in their own way, and to be rid of his tyrannical advisers. As regards yourself, Sir, I know you are only following what you believe to be your duty."

She then spoke to the lady in the window nook, and requested her to order refreshments served immediately. Thus addressed, Mary Bromley stepped from behind the window curtain, and came forward with a serious and sorrowful expression at thus finding me engaged in levying contributions from the intimate friends of her parents and herself.

We were ill at ease, we both felt that circumstances might soon arise, which would undermine the friendship and affection of our youthful days, and with a sore heart I declined the proffered hospitality and took my leave. We requisitioned four good steeds, which we immediately despatched to Worcester, and then rode on to Seller's Orchard, the residence of Captain Bound.

Captain Bound had gained information about the visits we were making to those who favoured the Parliamentarians, and had ridden away on one horse leading the other. Report declared that he had gone to rebellious Gloucester. The reception of Mrs Bound was a great contrast to that of Madam Lechmere. She was so abusive that I feared some of the troopers would souse her in the duck-pond.

When Captain von Grubbe found that she would not listen to the mild remonstrance of Nanfan and myself, he gave orders to the soldiers to search the house, whereupon Mistress Bound succumbed, and found the sum of three pounds eighteen shillings in an old stocking. She also undertook to send two loads of hay to Prince Rupert's quarters on the morrow. In lieu she received the following voucher:

Receaued then of Mistress Bound, the some of three punds eighteen shillings, being in pte composition for Captain Bound's estate at Seller's Orchad, also a promise of delivry of 2 loades of best hay.

I say reseaued by me, VON GRUBBE.

Captain von Grubbe now returned with the troopers to Powick, while Giles and I rode to Hanley Castle for the night, according to our instructions. Our duty next day would be to deliver a letter of protection from Prince Rupert to Mr Bromley, on his undertaking to pay ten pounds a month to the garrison at Worcester.[2] We found Bridget Nanfan at the Castle, paying a visit to my aunt and Isabel. Her black eyes, beaming with fun and good nature were pleasant to look upon after the disagreeable duty on which we had been engaged. She was full of her 'quirps and prattlings'.

She told how she had put a cockchafer into Lord Cockayne's mouth when he was asleep in church, and twitted Giles and myself upon becoming knights-errant, and rescuing royalist damsels from puritan giants. She declared "'Twas a pity that two mere boys should be trusted with such sharp swords and loaded pistols." Yet she sewed hard, with my aunt and Isabel, in preparing the linen and other clothing for our soldiers' kits, and blushed when I entreated that she would work my initials upon my vest in her own bonnie black hair.

With them, in deep consultation with Aunt Tabitha, was Hannah Stubbs, an elderly dame from Upton, short, plump, and active, who was famous as a nurse, for her concoctions of herb drinks and simples, and for her recipes for diascordium and electuaries. At the same time she could brew ale, or mead, or mix sack possets with any innkeeper in the county. Giles made a wry face as he surveyed bottles of rue, wormwood, and masterwort, with dozens of pills of camphor, angelica, and horehound being packed for our benefit.

Then there were zedoanes against infection, and amulets against rheumatism or plague, all of which we were expected to carry about with us wherever the approaching campaign might take us. It was evident that our health and comfort was the great motive of our beloved relations, so we promised to take the physic – in mental reservation as far as the nearest pool.

Then Giles persuaded Isabel to sing the popular ballad:

> *If you ask why Britons struggling,*
> *Fight to conquer or to die ?*
> *Their men are strong, their wives are loving,*
> *Now, you know the reason why.*

And I thought that Isabel's voice trembled, and her blue eyes were downcast as she wished my gallant comrade "Good night," when the evening was over.

The following morning we examined into the resources of our Castle for the storage of gunpowder and arms, and explored the recesses of a gloomy underground passage, which led from what was once the dungeon to an exit near the road to Upton. The dungeon had a bad name, and not a servant would venture near it after nightfall, while the passage was unknown to any one beyond our own household.

With the aid of a couple of lanthorns we traced the passage the entire length, and found nooks which would hold several kegs of powder, and boxes of fuse and match. A hoard of war material collected here might be useful, if at any time the Royalists had to defend Upton, for the inhabitants were too much inclined to the Parliament to allow of any place there being a safe receptacle. Our servants, Jack Sampson and Dick Bonner, a Hanley man, who declared he belonged to the same kith and kin as the Bishop, and was born in a cottage near the church, had been with my father several years, and were both staunch royalists and trustworthy men.

During our ride to Hamme Court, with Prince Rupert's protection to Mr Bromley, we 'two boys', as Bridget called us, talked over a plan to raise a troop of horse in our own neighbourhood. In the centre of Longdon Marsh was a considerable area of hard turf, which was well adapted for drill and cavalry evolutions. This would be preferable to Upton Hamme, as less liable to inquisitive visitors from the town, who reported everything that was going on to their disaffected associates at Tewkesbury or Gloucester.

We had reached an old grange known as the Eades, said to date from the forest days of the Saxons, and were nearly swamped in a dirty lane up to our horses' bellies with mud, when we heard a shout from behind, and saw John Kelly waving his hat as if to recall us, so reining up our steeds we awaited the tidings he was prepared to give.

Kelly had returned to his residence, the Waterside, and had received intelligence that Colonel Fiennes, Colonel Sandys, and a large body of Parliamentarian troops were marching for Pixham Ferry, where they would cross the Severn, and then the Teme at Powick Bridge, with the intention of blockading Prince Rupert at Worcester until Lord Essex should arrive with his whole army.

Kelly had heard of our being at Hanley Castle, where he just missed us, and taking a short route across the enclosures fortunately hailed us near the Eades. His report was of the utmost importance, so setting spurs to our horses we retraced our steps and galloped by Severn End and the Rhydd for Powick. We were not too soon, for the Parliamentarian horse, to the number of at least one thousand, had taken up a position on Powick Hamme.

We had just time to cross Powick Bridge, in hot haste, as some of their dragoons rode up to the river side, and in a few minutes would have cut off our communication with the Worcester Road. We rode up the rising ground beyond the bridge, and on the platform came suddenly upon a regiment of Cavaliers. Prince Rupert, his brother Prince Maurice, Lord Digby, and other officers were lying under a large thorn tree,[3] being utterly ignorant that so large a force was about to march across Teme Bridge. Although the Prince was taken by surprise, he received our communication with apparent sang-froid, and rode amongst his soldiers telling them to tighten girths and draw swords and he would lead them on to victory.

The Cavaliers were forbidden to sound a trumpet, or make the slightest noise, and were drawn up behind a cherry orchard to await the moment when their leader should order them to charge. It was an exciting moment for Giles and myself, and we passed it in rubbing the sweat from our horses and preparing for the battle. Soon we heard the voices of the approaching force singing a psalm[4] as they came up the hill by a narrow lane, and in front rode Colonel Sandys.

Prince Rupert allowed the corps to debouch upon the plain above the slope, when, in an instant he sprang upon his horse, shouted "Charge!" and we were on them like the shock of an avalanche. Giles Nanfan, on an impetuous roan stallion, rode right at Colonel Sandys, before which the Colonel's horse went down and the gallant rider lay prostrate in the dust. In a few moments several officers shared the same fate, many of the dragoons were cut down, while the rest were stricken with panic, and rode some for the river, some for the bridge.

When in pursuit I made straight for the Teme, and a young officer attempted to force his charger into the water, which the terrified animal refused, and threw his rider over his head into the river, where already some fifty men and horses were struggling to reach the other side. The youth cast an imploring look upwards, and I saw he could not swim.

I was young then, and more tender-hearted than at the close of the war, so I jumped off Hanley, plunged into the stream, and being a powerful swimmer, it was little trouble to me to clutch a willow bough which overhung the bank and rescue the drowning man. When we were safe on land I intimated that he must consider himself a prisoner, to which he assented with many expressions of gratitude. I now rode for the bridge with my prisoner behind me, and handed him over to Sergeant-Major Cross, who had already the care of several others.

By this time the fight was over, for the Parliamentarians had galloped away like frightened sheep; some got safe over the bridge and rode to Upton, others swam the Teme, and then rode for Kempsey Ford. Giles Nanfan and other Cavaliers pursued the flying throng, and while some were drowned, others were cut down without resistance; but the larger number escaped, never drawing their bridles until they reached the town of Pershore, where without hats or swords they met the cuirassiers of Lord Essex's lifeguard riding in advance of his whole army.[5]

The battle-field was a sorry sight for youths like Giles and myself, who had rarely looked upon the face of the dead. Fifty or sixty strong, stalwart men lay where they fell, and Colonel Sandys, the brother of Madam Penelope Lechmere, lay by the side of his Sergeant-Major Douglas, both mortally wounded.

Prince Rupert dismounted to examine the condition of these officers, and commanded me to see them carried safely into Worcester, giving me a pass to Lord Essex as attendant upon the wounded. He then marched to St John's, and meeting Sir John Byron with the treasure, they all rode off for Ludlow and Shrewsbury. Giles accompanied them, and I had orders to gather all the information in my power, and join the Prince as soon as possible.

Sergeant Douglas died before we could reach Worcester, but Colonel Sandys survived for a short time. All the other prisoners Prince Rupert took with him to Shrewsbury, and my young officer among the rest. The next day, by noon, Lord Essex entered the city, and with him several thousands in his train, who disgraced themselves by their conduct to the innocent inhabitants.

Lord Essex visited Colonel Sandys, and then sent for me, to question me on the events of the previous day. He recognized the Prince's pass, thanked me for my care of the wounded officers, and gave me an order to withdraw with my horse and accoutrements, when and where I pleased after the lapse of eight-and-forty hours, during which, he said, he must request me on my honour not to leave the city.

At this commencement of the war, little restraint was put upon the soldiers, who set at nought the fine proclamation of Lord Essex, about 'discipline and forbearance'. All who had obeyed King Charles' Commission of Array and had furnished either money, plate, or horses, were treated with severity. The Mayor and many of the principal inhabitants were sent prisoners to London, and every kind of profaneness, insolence and violence was wreaked upon the unlucky city by these religious, psalm-singing Presbyterians. True, their preachers made great fuss of preachments, and turned the clergy out of their pulpits, while some of the dragoons dressed themselves up in surplices and rode about the streets.

They quartered their horses in the nave of the Cathedral, and defiled the choir and aisles. They burst into the chapter-house, tore and scattered about the college papers and old records.[6] They lit fires in the nave, and broke the organ and painted windows, but they all went religiously to their own services on the Sunday, and thanked God for their great successes.

My own quarters for the night were at the Earl's Post at the corner of Copenhagen Street, a modern house underneath which are the remains of some ancient ecclesiastical building, and, if report is to be trusted, an underground passage to the nunnery of the White Ladies. The Earl's Post is now turned into a tavern, and the chapel below is a cider cellar. It was kept by a verger of the Cathedral, who was horrified at the excesses of the Roundheads.

The ancient Cathedral crypt, built in Wulstan's time, was filled with straw; saddles, and harness covered the tomb of King John; and the Chapel of Prince Arthur, 'sonne of the right renowned King Henry the Seventhe', became a depot of dirty linen. The Vandals had defaced the 1481 monument of Judge Littleton, and maltreated the figures of Sir John Beauchamp and his lady.

But most of all the verger mourned over the total destruction of the organ and the smashing of the beautiful painted windows.[7] The townspeople who frequented the tavern had all some tale to tell of barbarous treatment and devastation. "A nation bad lot are these cussed, sanctimonious scrummigers," said a countryman to our landlord, "and I hope yor zider will give some of 'em the jerry-go-nimbles before they goas."[8]

While listening to these complaints, and sorrowing that such things could happen among Englishmen, I saw Captain Bound ride by on Hell Cat in earnest conversation with Lord Essex. With them, too, was Mr Gaston from Hanley, which much surprised me, as his son at Oxford was reported to have taken a decided part for the King. I retired into the house as they passed by and thus escaped observation. My dreams were not pleasant that night in desecrated Worcester, and I was awoke by the heavy tolling of the Cathedral bell. In the grey dawn of the morning corpses were carried past for burial; the victims of civil war.

When I recollected the fiery nature of Prince Rupert, and many of the Cavalier officers who were with him, I feared that retaliation would speedily follow these deeds at Worcester, and I was right glad when my eight-and-forty hours had passed, that I might no longer be the un-willing witness of abominable excesses.

I rode back through St John's on my way to Hanley Castle, to ascertain the feeling of the country people on this occupation of Worcester by a Parliamentarian army, and report thereon to Prince Rupert. The ground near the bridge of Powick still showed evidences of the late struggle in the broken hedges, the trampled soil, the battered helmets, and torn clothes of the troopers. But the inhabitants had buried the bodies of the slain, save those which were never recovered from the river.

As I passed Severn End, I thought of Madam Penelope Lechmere, whose brother, Colonel Sandys, I left dying, and who was soon to be laid with his wife,[9] in the cathedral his followers had defiled. Full of gloomy forebodings, I took the turn to Hanley Castle.

After a night's refreshing rest at our quiet home, I found from Aunt Tabitha that most contradictory reports had been spread respecting the transactions of the last three days. According to some, the troops under Prince Rupert had been annihilated, others said Lord Essex was killed, and his army in full flight, so that neither party in Upton knew what to believe. Captain Bound had been active in levying horses and money for Lord Essex, while no one had moved on the side of the King.

I now wished that Giles Nanfan had been sent back with me, that he might have assisted in beating up recruits among those who were known to support the cause of King Charles, and I was just starting to consult Sir Giles Nanfan, at Birtsmorton Court, when a letter was brought to me which proved to be an epistle from Madam Bromley, and was worded as follows:

Dear Sur, I hear that you are return'd from the bloody battaile in wh
you were engaged and in wh that malignant Prince was totally
defeatd and driven from y field. It would appr from y accounts of y
battaile by one present, even y gallant captain bound, that your
horsmen ran away and never stopped until they reachd y town of
ludlow, and that y malignant Prince saved his life by gallopg there in
front of his men. It was reported to captain bound that your dead
body was found on Powicke bridge, but it seems he was mistaken, as
I hear you are safe and sound at Hanley.

Yours truly,
MARTHA BROMLEY

P.S. You may have heard that our son Richard was in y dredfull
battaile of Powicke and is now a prisoner of y malignant Prince. How
he was takn is not known, but captain bound thinks that he rode too
far and too fast, in pursuit of y malignants, and so got takn at last near
unto Ludlow.

P.S. My daughter Mary has been sick; she feinted clean away at y
bloody accounts of y slauter of y malignants, by captain bound.

P.S. Should you write to y Prince you might say a good word for
Dick.

Chapter Seven

THE PITH of Madam Bromley's letter evidently lay in the post-script. Her son had been taken prisoner, and she thought I might negotiate terms with 'ye malignant Prince'. I had not seen Dick Bromley since we were boys, and it was a question if we should recognize each other; but Mary was ill, so I determined to go to Hamme Court and inquire after her. I rode first to the Waterside to see John Kelly, whom I found, in his scholar's garb, busily engaged in screwing up an engine which bubbled and spluttered, making a tremendous smoke, and one would not have guessed that the philosopher, whose energies now seemed concentrated upon strange experiments with boiling water, could suddenly assume the garb and bearing of an active Cavalier.

With Kelly was Mr Gaston, whom I had seen the day before with Lord Essex; he took his leave as I entered, and I soon found that Kelly was acquainted with all that had happened at Worcester since its occupation by the Parliamentarians. He smiled when I told him that Mr Gaston was associating with the Puritans, and handed me a letter from my father which Gaston had brought, which announced that the King had marched to Shrewsbury. How Gaston came by the letter he did not say. Isabel, who accompanied me on her palfrey, was not a little amused at the condition of the philosopher's den, while she was amazed at the performances of his engine, and thought it no wonder that the Earl of Worcester had travelled many miles to see it.

A short gallop soon brought us to Hamme Court, and we learnt that Madam Bromley had gone to Mr Bartlett's to see his Uriel's magic stone, but that Mr Bromley and Mary had walked down to the Severn. It was a bright September morning, a slight autumnal tint burnished the foliage of the oaks, and the great elms had here and there put on the sere and yellow leaf. The red cliffs of Ryall and the Mythe rose above the Severn, and beyond was picturesque Bredon Hill and the long line of the Cotteswolds. A covey of partridges rose from the green sward and whirred rapidly towards the harvest stubble. We approached a great oak by Severn's side, and beheld the flutter of a woman's dress. Drawing nearer, we stopped for a moment, as we heard a gentle voice reading aloud the words, 'And a man's foes shall be they of his own household'.

Then the voice trembled, and there was a sob and silence. When we reached the tree, Mr Bromley was seated with an open Bible upon his knee from which Mary had been reading. They both rose, and Mr Bromley held out his hand with the grave demeanour he now wore whenever I met him. Mary kissed Isabel and curtsied to me, but I sought in vain for one kind glance of her dove-like eyes, or one glad smile of recognition, as in days gone by. Mr Bromley listened to my assurance that I knew nothing of the capture of his son, but shook his head as I said he had nothing to fear from Prince Rupert. He pressed us both to take refreshments, and questioned me on our return to the house on the events of the skirmish at Powick. Before we parted he pressed upon my acceptance the Bible out of which he and his daughter had been reading.

"It is a good old book," he said, "and of greater value than ever in times like the present." I thanked him. Mary's eyes met mine as I received the sacred volume from her father's hand, and they wore the old expression of heartiness. We now remounted our horses and rode away by Eastington, the home of the old family of Brydges, for the residence of Mr Rowland Bartlett at Castlemorton.

Hill End commands an extensive view of the surrounding country. Northwards rise the Malvern Hills, their base dotted with forest trees, the relics of the Chase. Westward we behold May Hill and the crests of the uplands of the Forest of Dean, and below the house are the Longdon marshes, the haunt of the heron and bittern, where Mr Bartlett and Sir Giles Nanfan loved to follow the sport of falconry.

Both these gentlemen were now engaged in a very different pursuit. They had been drilling some newly levied recruits on the broad green expanse in the centre of the marsh, and the troop had ridden up to the house to feast upon bannock cakes and foxwhelp cider, while Hafod the Fool was jesting and handing round the big silver tankard to the toast of "King Charles, God bless him". I rejoiced greatly that some of our royalist gentlemen were raising recruits and drilling them, for hitherto there had been much talk and no performance. Some fine, gallant-looking fellows were there, the sons of farmers and yeomen, but they had no uniform, as in the regiments raised by Mr Hampden and other Parliamentarians.

Some wore red handkerchiefs round the waist, from which dangled a sword, others carried their swords under their arms in a most unsoldierlike fashion, and some had pikes only. The horses were of all shapes and sizes, some fresh from the plough or the cider-mill, while here and there was a black nag, known to have done duty in a hearse. This was the Longdon troop that Giles Nanfan and I had talked of drilling into a regiment of dragoons. Sir Giles was the only man present who looked like a soldier. Mounted on a grey horse of great strength and action, old as he was, he had a firm seat and martial bearing, and had been engaged all the morning in endeavouring to inspire the rough materials around him with the spirit and action of a cavalry regiment.

After dismissing the Longdon troopers with an admonition to assemble on the following afternoon, Sir Giles led the way to the old hall at Hill End. The house was an old moated timbered dwelling of forest days, with a central hall and many small apartments opening into it. The Red Earl was said to have slept in one of the bed-rooms, and the Princess Joan d'Acre to have danced in the hall. The great gables were black with time and storms, and the little latticed windows told of days when glass was a rare luxury in the houses of country gentlemen.

As we drew near we could hear the merry voice of Bridget Nanfan, and on entering we found the two lassies endeavouring to persuade Mr Bartlett to show them his celebrated talismanic stone; the wonderful crystal which was reported to have been given to his father by the famous Dr Dee.

As the possessor of this wonderful stone, Mr Bartlett was frequently consulted with respect to the future; sometimes by a great lady on the subject of an heir to the family; sometimes by the anxious peasant or farmer on the brooding of hens, the birth of a cow calf, or the omen of some planet; sometimes, as by Madam Bromley, respecting the fate of a friend.

The old Squire listened to the prattle of the girls with a smile, but he did not like the mystic stone being made a subject of joke by Bridget, and it was with an air of deep and solemn gravity that he at last yielded to the softer entreaties of Isabel, and went to the secret drawer where lay the Crystal of Uriel.[1]

On his return he handed to Isabel a small, black casket, covered with mathematical figures, and opened by a hidden spring, which Isabel tried in vain to discover, yet in Mr Bartlett's hands it fled open with a burst that startled us, disclosing a polished pebble about the size of a dove's egg, with a peculiar grey glitter.

Bridget wished to handle and examine the stone, but this Mr Bartlett decidedly objected to, so the casket lay upon Isabel's lap. In the mean time Sir Giles questioned me upon the events at Powick Bridge and Worcester, and we had well nigh forgotten the crystal, when Isabel uttered an exclamation of surprise, and rising from her seat as if in terror, placed the casket upon the table. The colour of the stone was entirely changed, it had become as crimson as blood, and seemed to shoot out red rays; Mr Bartlett grew pale and troubled, then seizing the casket, he closed the spring, which snapped like the crack of a pistol.

We were all anxious to learn what this strange change portended, when our attention was diverted by a trumpet blast on the arrival of some soldiers, and Giles Nanfan shortly entered, bringing important tidings from Ludlow and Shrewsbury. He had been entrusted with a commission to raise, equip, and drill a troop of horse for the King, and had brought half a score of cavalry officers with him to assist in drilling our village peasants and country clods; and truly there was no time to be lost, for the Lord Grey of Groby had already occupied Hereford with Parliamentarian forces, while Lord Essex was in possession of Worcester, from which place his troops had plundered and raided Sir William Russell's house at Strensham.

With Giles Nanfan rode the Earl of Cockayne, whom I had before seen at Birtsmorton Court. I was not favourably impressed with this specimen of the British peerage, though he had the ear of both King and Queen. He was 'thorough' as a politician, was a member of the Star Chamber, and had joined in advocating those personal tortures of British subjects which had brought Strafford to the block, Laud to a dungeon, and the King to his present condition of war with his own people. He professed to belong to the Anglican Church, but he was more than fussy about ceremonials and spangles, and had advised Archbishop Laud to prosecute Dr Williams, the Bishop of Lincoln, for his 'Tract upon Tables', declaring that "A man who could call the Altar a Holy Table, was fit only for a prison." In personal appearance Lord Cockayne was handsome but effeminate. Nothing could exceed the elegance of his dress, but a doublet of slashed satin, velvet breeches and yellow boots of doe-skin, was a style of apparel ill-suited to our muddy lanes and commons half covered with water.

When he saw that Bridget Nanfan was at Hill End, he dismounted and entered the house without ceremony, ordering his frill, pulling his lace cuffs, and mincing and pippiking like a love-lorn girl. His language was remarkable for the strong expletives he used against all Parliamentarians and Nonconformists. Even Sir Giles was astonished at his vocabulary, but he was to command our Longdon troop and it was our duty to obey.

The end of September and the beginning of October 1642 was occupied in raising recruits for the service of the King. Sir Giles Nanfan, Mr Honeywood Yates of Bromesberrow, and Mr Richard Dowdeswell did their utmost to enlist men, and drilling went on all day, and sometimes by moonlight well into the night, on Longdon Marsh. Giles held a Captain's commission, while I was Lieutenant and Aide-de-camp to Prince Rupert.

As money was not spared by the Royalist gentlemen of our neighbourhood, our Longdon troop was changed in appearance by the beginning of October. Jackman of Pendock, who had come to drill in a cuirass which his ancestor wore at the battle of Tewkesbury, and riding on a cart mare, was now a well mounted swordsman, while Jack Tandy, the host at the Wind's Point, who bestrode a Welsh pony and wore scarlet breeches, was now riding a good flea-bitten grey, which belonged to Mr Cocks of Castleditch. We were arrayed in a kind of uniform of leathern jerkins, with strong, long boots, and the horses had been taught to stand the fire of muskets and petronels. All carried good sharp swords, and knew how to use them.

Giles and I worked like horses, but our noble commander preferred riding over the country – recruiting, as he termed it, with Bridget Nanfan – to superintending our drill performances. On one of these excursions he made a blunder which might have proved awkward. The passage I had heard Mary Bromley reading, was even now being fulfilled. The Earl of Denbigh was a staunch Royalist; his eldest son, Lord Fielding, had declared for the Parliament, and was arrayed against his own father. Sir Richard Hopton, of Canon Frome, among the Herefordshire woodlands, beyond Ledbury, had one son, a colonel in the King's army, and another a major in the militia forces of the Earl of Essex.

Mr Honeywood Yates, of the Hook House, in the parish of Bromesberrow, was a good Royalist,[2] his only brother was a decided Parliamentarian. Now it happened that early in October Lord Cockayne went over to Ledbury to attend a gathering of Royalist gentlemen in the

Market House by the Bull Ring, and challenged Bridget Nanfan to ride
with him. As Bridget never failed to get much fun out of My Lord, she
agreed to accompany him, although she was wearying of his long-
winded stories about minuets and *corantos*, and the dancings and
prancings of the noble Earl's father with Queen Elizabeth.

They rode by the Holly Bush Pass, where the berries of the mountain
ash vied with the coral necklace of Bridget, and the dewy sloes emulat-
ed her flashing dark eyes. But the beauty of the scenery, the trailing
tresses of the old man's beard, and the lingering flowers of the purple
loosestrife, were all thrown away upon the Earl, for when he was not
looking at Bridget, he was engaged in admiring his lace ruffles or his
velvet hose. Even the towers of Branshill Castle, as they loomed below
the hills of Eastnor, failed to elicit a word of appreciation, and so they
rode on until they reached the Upper Hall, the residence of Mr Skipp, a
Royalist descendant of Bishop Skipp, the first Protestant Bishop of
Hereford. Here Bridget waited while her companion attended the
royalist meeting at the Market House. He met there Lord Scudamore,
Mr Skynner, Colonel Lingen, Mr Hall of Highmeadow, Mr Cocks, and
several other royalist gentlemen, who requested Lord Cockayne to see
Mr Yates of Bromesberrow, and ask him to assist in recruiting in the
neighbourhood, as well as to serve himself.

On this My Lord went to the Plume of Feathers Inn and enquired of
every one "Had they seen Mr Yeates? How far was it to Mr Yeates?"
These enquiries were overheard by Mr Yates the Parliamentarian, and
Mr Higgins of Eastnor, another Roundhead, and expecting that he had
just left the meeting of Royalists, they determined to find out what had
transpired there. So Mr Roundhead Yates introduced himself, and over
a flagon of canary listened to Lord Cockayne, as he dilated upon our
Longdon troop, our drill, the King's movements at Shrewsbury, and
other subjects we particularly wished to keep from the knowledge of
our adversaries.

This loquacity of the Earl's might have been disastrous had not Mr
Honeywood Yates, the Royalist, been with us on Longdon Marsh at the
moment the Earl was quaffing canary and being pumped by his
Parliamentarian brother. This being the case, when Lord Cockayne
informed Sir Giles that he had set all right with that 'good fellow Yeate'
at the Plume of Feathers, the murder was out, and that the Roundhead
had taken in our commander.

Soon after this occurrence Prince Rupert sent word that the King had
broken up his camp at Shrewsbury on the 12th of October[3] and was
marching towards Oxford; also that Lord Essex had left Worcester to
intercept the march of the Royalists. Prince Rupert entreated Lord
Cockayne to wait on the rear of Essex, and to keep him acquainted with
his line of march. The King's route would lie by Wolverhampton,
Birmingham, and Kenilworth, as he would endeavour to strike a blow
at London before Lord Essex could come up. Such was the information
we received, and it was agreed that all should assemble by daylight next
morning, at the Cross at Upton-on-Severn. Every man was supplied
with a box of simples made by the fair hands of Dame Nanfan, and of
Bridget.

> *Yarrow, wherewithal to stop the wound made gore,*
> *The healing tutsan then, and plantane for a sore.* [4]

I was ordered to ride ahead, to trace the march of the Roundheads, and
to communicate to the Prince that Lord Cockayne would join him with
our Longdon men as soon as possible. I started the same evening on
Hanley,our best charger, accompanied by our groom Sampson, who
rode Black Harry, and carried our kits on the crupper. We first visited
The Cat and Cauliflower, at Pershore, and there learnt that Lord Essex
and his army had arrived at Evesham. I therefore determined to cross
the wild district of the Lenches to Alcester, and thence to Stratford-on-
Avon. In this way I should get between the forces of the Parliamentarians and those of the King.

Arriving at Stratford, we took up our quarters at an inn near the
church; and while Sampson was looking to our horses and questioning
the ostler, I paid a visit to the grave of the illustrious bard, Will
Shakespeare. Even the Puritan had shrunk from the curse which awaits
those who desecrate this tomb and monument. Here I fell in with Sir
William Croft, of Croft Castle, near Leominster, a gentleman of excellent ability, and gallant and noble bearing.

I had seen him as a visitor at Birtsmorton Court, and his arms were
among the heraldic shields in the old oak dining chamber. One of his
ancestors had assisted in the escape of Prince Edward at Hereford,
before the battle of Evesham. Another had fought at the battles of
Mortimer's Cross and Tewkesbury and, at the latter, had taken prisoner
the unhappy son of Queen Margaret.

Sir William recognized me, and gave me the important information that the Parliamentarians, Colonel Hampden and Lord Brooke, were at Warwick with their 'green coats',[5] and that the King had advanced as far as Southam.[6] He said that he had encountered much annoyance from some of the Court 'Thoroughs', but was on his road to join the royal forces. Of these, most of the regiments were raised in Wales, and were only half-clad or armed, while many of the militia troops of the Roundheads were in uniform.

I now perceived that Lord Cockayne's advance would be blocked by Colonel Hampden's green coats, unless he proceeded more rapidly than I was inclined to give him credit for. I therefore sent off Sampson with a letter to My Lord, giving an account of the King's position at Southam, and the advance of the Parliamentarians from Warwick; telling him that I should accompany Sir William Croft, who was on his way to join His Majesty, as far as the little town of Kineton.

I advised Sampson to take the left bank of the Avon on his way to Evesham, and cross the river at Offenham, to avoid meeting with Parliamentarians. In my despatch I recommended Lord Cockayne to march to Kineton with all speed, by Broadway and Alderminster, and avoid Alcester and Stratford.

On the evening of the 21st October we reached Kineton, a poor place and small, but ancient. Sir William Dugdale says it belonged long ago to the Kings of England. It was in the possession of Edward the Confessor and William the Conqueror. Nevertheless a duller place than it is now it is difficult to imagine, or one less likely to have been visited by the kings who owned it. It is situated to the north-west of Edgehill; the elevated range which stretches like a great terrace five miles in length above the adjacent vale.

It was midnight, but the host of the Cow Tavern informed us that some feathers[7] and troopers were quartered at various houses in the town, and sentinels had been placed on the castle tump to the west of the town, also at King John's Well, at the foot of the hill, where an ancient castle stood. We were preparing to retire to rest when we heard a horseman ride up at full gallop to the door, and then the voice of Sampson shouting for admission. I asked him from the casement, "What tidings, Sampson!" and he replied in a low tone, "Get up, Sir, get up, the Roundheads are coming."

Fortunately it was moonlight, and we had little difficulty in arousing the royalist officers and troopers, and in less than an hour we were on the road to Southam. In two hours from that time Lord Essex was at Kineton. As we rode along Sampson told me that Giles Nanfan was not a little annoyed at the slow movements of Lord Cockayne. He declared it was impossible to get him into bed at night, or out of it in the morning, and that his dressing and undressing occupied precious time that should be employed in marching.

Sir William Croft was anxious to make his way to Chesterton, on the Roman fossway, and here we breakfasted and halted until we heard that Prince Rupert had marched from Southam at the head of several regiments of cavalry to Wormleighton, a few miles to the eastward. We therefore thought it better that I should join him, while Sir William Croft carried the news of the occupation of Kineton by Lord Essex, to King Charles at Southam. Here then I parted with the gallant Croft, soon to meet again on a bloody field.

Wormleighton once belonged to the celebrated Simon de Montfort, whose tomb I had seen at Evesham, but it now was the property of Lord Spenser, at whose Tudor mansion I found Prince Rupert quartered,[7] with several other officers, among whom was Sir William Dugdale, the Rouge Croix Pursuivant.

I was ushered into a spacious room hung with old tapestry, on which King David and King Solomon figured largely, and there I found the Prince carousing with his officers around him, one of whom was singing, 'Hey then, down go they'. The Prince raised his hand to warn me not to interrupt the ballad, and when it was finished, handed me the goblet he had filled with wine. He listened with attention to my account of the occupation of Kineton and the plain below by the army of Lord Essex, and of the march of the regiments of Lord Brooke and Colonel Hampden in his rear.

I was in hopes he would send troops to check this advance, and told him of the position of Lord Cockayne, but it was the fault of this gallant Cavalier general to make light of his foes, and on the present occasion he contented himself with moving towards Kineton and sending a message to the King.

A regiment was quartered at Farnborough on the night of the 22nd, and I was sent with orders from Prince Rupert to their Colonel, to march to the westward on Sunday morning, the 23rd, and block the Stratford high road. On my return, I found the King had occupied the steep bluffs of Edgehill with his whole army. The King's standard floating on the breeze, gave the first intimation to the Earl of Essex of the proximity of the Royal army. It was carried by Sir Edward Verney on Ballet Hill below the old British Camp of Norbury. It was at this great fortification, as Sir William Dugdale calls it, that 'was found a sword of brasse and a battail axe', and here, on that Sabbath morn, I beheld the flag flying in the hands of him who was so soon to be numbered with the dead. I joined Prince Rupert near to Radford Church, and at a cottage hard by the King was reported to be at breakfast.[8]

Here the Prince Rupert, the Earl of Lindsay, the Earl of Denbigh, Sir Jacob Astley, Sir Edward Verney, and Lord Wilmot were summoned to a council of war, and a long council it was to those who, like myself, had to wait outside! At last my honoured father came forth. We had not met for months and our greeting was hearty and affectionate, but I could see something was wrong, and he told me that there had been a quarrel between the impetuous Rupert and Lord Lindsay. The Prince wished to attack without a moment's delay. Lord Lindsay advised waiting in our advantageous position, as the Parliamentarians would be broken if they attempted to charge up hill. Hours passed away, the two armies gazing at each other, when at last Prince Rupert's advice prevailed.

King Charles now came forth from the cottage, clad in splendid armour. His vizor was up, and I saw for the first time the face of that King for whom thousands were to die on the battle field, and for whose sake widows and orphans would soon be weeping over their dead.

My father presented me to the King's notice as he was mounting his horse to ride to a rising ground a little way west of Radway Church, when he surveyed the army of Lord Essex. Soon afterwards Prince Rupert threw himself, hot and excited, into the saddle, saying something to Lord Lindsay, who shook his head, and shouldering his pike prepared to lead his men into the plain, contrary to his own wishes and advice. The Prince, shouting to me to follow, galloped rapidly to the westward to join our cavalry at a place called Sunrising, on the Stratford road.

It was now two o'clock,[9] and the bells of the village churches were summoning the inhabitants of the surrounding parishes to evening prayer and praise, when another sound aroused both hill and dale on that Sabbath afternoon. The great guns of the army of Lord Essex awoke the echoes in the vale of the Red Horse, to which we replied with all our artillery, and this exchange of great shot continued for the space of an hour.

In the mean time Prince Rupert sent me to the Earl of Denbigh, who was in command of a number of half-armed Welshmen, to beg of him to lead the Welsh down the slope of Edgehill, and thus hasten the action of the Earl of Lindsay. Lord Denbigh at once complied, followed by the gallant Lindsay, pike in hand, and soon the masses of infantry were hand to hand in mortal combat. Mr Harvey[10] took the Royal Princes, Charles and James, under a bank until the whistle of bullets compelled them to withdraw, and a cannon ball drove them from their retreat.

I galloped back to Prince Rupert, and was just in time to follow him, as he charged with headlong fury, at the head of his cavalry, into the left wing of the Parliamentarian army. Lord St John fell in this impetuous onslaught, and four regiments of the Parliamentarians, with the whole of the left wing of horse, turned their backs and fled. The Prince pursued them, driving them into Kineton, and out of Kineton, and had it not been that some of his German followers would stop to plunder, and whom it was impossible to rally, the victory of Edgehill would have been more assured than it was.

While the Prince and his officers, myself among the number, were vainly endeavouring to rally the plunderers, Sir William Balfour seized the opportunity, and attacked the King's infantry thus abandoned by the cavalry, charged with all the reserve, horse and foot. Here fell Sir Edward Verney, the King's standard bearer, and the standard was taken. Here, the brave Lord Lindsay was mortally wounded, shouting to the last, "March on, boys!" Here Lunsford and Vavasour were made prisoners, and all this happened because it was impossible to keep our men from pillaging.

At last, when this was done, we found the King's left wing broken, and the centre in the greatest confusion, while we charged the enemy again and again to prevent a panic from spreading among the King's forces. The close of day was now at hand, the King resumed his former quarters, and darkness shrouded the battle field, where nothing was heard but the moans of the wounded who lay where they fell. We remained under arms during the night, and in the grey dawn of morning Lord Essex withdrew his troops to Warwick, leaving to us the wounded, the dead, and the blood-stained battle field, which was all we could claim for victory.

Early in the morning, the King, attended by my father, rode to the summit of Edgehill, and gave orders for the burial of the dead, of whom about 1400 lay slain,[11] with some 3000 wounded, mostly near the spot where the standard was taken. I saw the King knight Captain Smith for his valour in recovering the royal standard,[12] and I was then sent to superintend the burial of the fallen below the crest of the hill.

Alas! with saddened heart did I behold this sepulchre of Englishmen slaughtered by Englishmen. I had heard men begging for quarter in the tones of my native country. I had seen the father lead his men against a regiment commanded by his son. I had heard my own companions cry, "O God, I am shot!" and seen those whom I had talked with but a few moments before, grasping the bloody grass as they rolled in agony; and now I was looking on, while hundreds of dead bodies were being thrown into a great quarry hole which served as a pit for the slain.

Full of sadness at these reflections, I heard a trumpet sounding on the heights above this grave-yard of more than a thousand Englishmen, and I saw King Charles ride among the troops of Rupert, and lift his plumed hat, as "God save the King" rung out from the thinned ranks of his army.

Chapter Eight

GILES NANFAN was furious at the slow movements and delays of his commander, which prevented the Longdon troopers being present at the battle of Edgehill. Still they had been of some service in checking the advance of the regiments under the command of Lord Brooke and Colonel Hampden, who heard of this march through Captain Bound, and did not reach the shattered army of Lord Essex till the day after the battle.

We accompanied the King as far as Banbury, which surrendered without striking a blow, and here Prince Rupert, after a consultation with Giles Nanfan, advised the King to appoint Lord Cockayne Master of the Wardrobe, as being more fitted to his taste and energies than that of Colonel to a regiment of rough soldiers. We then received orders to occupy Upton-on-Severn, Giles commanding the troop and I holding the commission of Lieutenant under him. The Prince desired me still to act as his aide-de-camp, and keep him acquainted with the movements of the enemy, especially around Gloucester and Tewkesbury.

The close of the year 1642 was chiefly remarkable for the battle of Brentford, where, through want of ammunition, King Charles failed to gain a signal victory, and he had to fall back upon Oxford. My honoured father remained with him as his private secretary, with the rank of Colonel, and thus from time to time, we were informed of the proceedings at the King's head quarters.

Our first care, on occupying Upton, was to recruit our numbers and raise our troop into a regiment, drilling continually on Upton Hamme. In spite of the expostulations of Aunt Tabitha, we stored gunpowder and fusees in the underground passages of Hanley Castle, with as much secrecy as possible, for many of the Upton residents were ever ready to play the spy upon us, while we had the greatest difficulty in obtaining any tidings of our adversaries.

And now, Christmas time had come again, and alas, even this season, ever hailed with joy and gladness, had become a source of dispute and heartburnings. The dressing of our churches with holly, the hanging of the mistletoe bough in hall and kitchen, the yule log, the merry dance, the wassail bowl, and the boar's head decked with rue and rosemary, were all now voted by the Puritan party to be superstitious, heathenish ceremonies, and unworthy of Christian men and women.

All the country games, such as the Cotteswold Sports, of which Ben Jonson wrote:

> *They advance true love and neighbourhood,*
> *And do both Church and Commonwealth good,*

were to be put down and discontinued; nay, Mistresses Bound and Cocktail, with other female Roundheads, went on a deputation to Mr Woodforde, to represent to him that the decoration of Upton Church with holly and banners was rank Popery, and savoured of the rites of Baal, rather than the Babe of Bethlehem.

Notwithstanding these Puritanical murmurs, we kept Christmas right merrily at Hanley Castle. Giles Nanfan and I helped to drag in a great yule log across the drawbridge, and we had plenty of fun and no wrong under my Lord of Misrule and the Abbot of Unreason on Christmas eve. Sir Giles gave the toast of Church and King, and Isabel and Bridget carolled like angels. Still there were some omens the girls feared, and Isabel whispered to me that no bees hummed on Christmas eve, and the yule log smouldered and sighed as if in sorrow, instead of crackling and spitting forth old heartburnings and ancient enmities.

We all went to church on Christmas Day, dressed in our very best, and the vicar preached on the song of the Angels, and the blessings of peace, but it was sad to see empty seats, and miss many familiar faces.

New Year's Day of 1643 brought us a news-letter from Oxford, the *Mercurius Aulicus*,[1] as well as a private epistle from my father. From these we learnt that Queen Henrietta Maria, or Queen Mary, as we Royalists loved to call her, was expected to land on the coast of York-shire, accompanied by considerable reinforcements and a large sum of money. The Queen had been absent in France for some months, and report said she had sold every jewel she possessed to raise an army for her husband's cause.

Earnest request was made that we should send tidings to Oxford respecting the position of affairs at Gloucester. This we found great difficulty in doing, although we well knew that a system of espionage was exercised over ourselves for which we could in no way account. We suspected Captain Bound, but he was in Gloucester, and had not been in Upton for weeks; we were therefore completely puzzled, but felt that we must redouble our watchfulness. Sir William Russell being Gover-nor of loyal Worcester, arranged plans for raising money to prosecute the war. Collectors were appointed, the King's Commissioners of Array

met weekly at the Guildhall, and the nobility, gentry, and clergy were
exhorted to assist the King with loans exclusive of the monthly
contributions. In the mean time Parliamentarians were not behind in
making requisitions on their side.

Early in January, Captain Bound and his friends, Zion-build and
Help-on-high Fox,[2] of Tewkesbury, intrigued with Colonel Massey, the
Parliamentarian Governor of Gloucester, and put Tewkesbury in his
possession. In consequence of this, two messengers we sent to Prince
Rupert with despatches, were waylaid and deprived of the letters they
carried. No one was aware of these messengers having started; save our
own household at Hanley Castle, not an officer or trooper was acquainted with their departure, and our own servants knew little more than
that messengers had been sent somewhere.

At last suspicion fell upon Hannah Stubbs, the Upton nurse and
midwife who, although she declared she was for the King, attended the
wives of all the Roundheads in the neighbourhood. Hannah had a son
living in Gloucester with a Parliamentarian brush-maker, with whom
she might communicate from time to time, and though Hannah was a
very unlikely body to turn spy, and could neither read or write, still she
had been much at Hanley Castle assisting at our Christmas festivities.

Towards the end of January, John Kelly received information from a
friend at Gloucester that Captain Bound had been made acquainted
with the storage of gunpowder at the Castle, and Hannah Stubbs was
the only person, save our two grooms Sampson and Bonner, who knew
of this storage, which had been carried on at night. In these men I had
every confidence, as they had been with us from boyhood.

We determined to watch Hannah closely. She lived in a narrow
street, called Dunn's Lane, down which we had to march daily for our
evolutions on Upton Hamme, and being a favourite with the troopers,
they often chatted with her, when not at drink, as she stood at her
door.

On one occasion, as I passed by Hannah's domicile, I heard the voice
of Mary Bromley; I could not resist entering, and found her talking to
her old nurse. On the table was a letter addressed to 'John Stubbs, with
Master Wilkins, Gloucester', this Wilkins being a friend of Captain
Bound. Reminded of the espionage which was our bane, and acting on
the impulse of the moment, I said, "Hannah, that letter must go with
me to my commanding officer."

Upon this Mary arose and said calmly, though blushing, "Mr Forester, this letter was written by me."

"It matters not if it was written by the Queen," I replied hastily, "we have reason to believe that correspondence most prejudicial and injurious to the cause of the King has gone forth from this house, and I must insist on carrying that epistle to Captain Nanfan, that no more treasonable reports may be sent to our enemies."

Mary looked at me in astonishment, her eyes flashing with indignation, while Hannah angrily asserted that the letter contained nothing save what a mother might write to her absent son, and that Mary merely held the pen and wrote to her dictation. With a quivering voice, Mary asked me if I really believed that my old friend and sister's companion would stoop to the meanness of a spy, and waited for my answer with a look of scorn I have never forgotten.

I hesitated and stammered about suspicion of Hannah, and our messengers being stopped and robbed, when she interrupted me saying, "Stopped and robbed through Mary Bromley's artifices you mean!"

Then taking the letter she broke the seal and handed it to me with a profound curtsey, requesting that I would read it. It contained a message to Jack Stubbs respecting some warm stockings, and a present to his master of some pig's souse, which would be sent by barge down the Severn, with a small sum of money from Mary, to help a poor widow woman who formerly lived at Upton.

I apologized and expressed sorrow for my hasty conduct, but Mary interrupted me, saying, "Pray withhold your excuses, Mr Forester, it is not for an old friend to interfere with your devotion to your King, but for the sake of days gone by, think twice before you connect the name of Bromley with foul play, or suspect one, like Hannah Stubbs, whom you have known from your childhood, of acting as a spy over those she once nursed on her knee!"

She then passed into the street, her cheeks still crimson with indignation. I would have followed and entreated her to listen to my explanations of various circumstances which caused Nanfan and, myself to suspect Hannah, but from her look and manner as she swept by me, I judged it better to allow her angry mood to pass, and trust to time to set us right once more. Nurse Stubbs soon forgave me and I left her bewailing the times and the estrangement of friends, but when I mounted my horse for our cavalry manoeuvres, I would gladly have ridden a charge against the enemy with Bound at their head. I fear also that this worthy's style of expostulation was more rife from my lips than usual, for Nanfan inquired as we rode off the Hamme, "What is the matter, Dick? You have been swearing like a German trooper."

Exciting events now followed in rapid succession. The citizens of Gloucester had been from the first opposed to the royal cause, and declared for the Parliament in 1641, when they raised a company of militia, procured cannon from Bristol, and strengthened their fortifications.

Early in the year 1643 Prince Rupert demanded the city for the King, but Governor Massey replied that he would defend it to the last extremity. Soon afterwards Massey laid siege to Sudeley Castle, the famous seat of Lord Chandos, and which was defended by Captain Bridges with so little energy that, after a slight bombardment, he sounded a parley, and the garrison 'passed out to their own homes, leaving their arms behind them'.[3]

Prince Rupert now manoeuvred around Sudeley, as if he would attempt to regain it, but 'instead of this he stormed Cirencester with great fury, fired the surrounding barns and ricks, and put to the sword all the soldiers of the Earl of Stamford who occupied the town'. The defenders 'stood like men amazed ... eleven hundred were taken prisoners', and a large magazine of arms was captured by the victors. After this great defeat at Cirencester the Roundheads abandoned Sudeley and Tewkesbury, and Sir William Russell sent Sir Matthew Carew to occupy Tewkesbury with a regiment of dragoons.

It had been a white St Valentine, and, although the middle of February, the whole country lay deep under snow. The Severn and Avon were still frozen, and not even the robin redbreast had ventured upon a song. The blackbirds and thrushes flocked in the court-yard of Hanley Castle to be fed by Isabel, and the rooks cawed, as if in distress, from the elms above the moat. As Sir Matthew Carew was a stranger to the country, I was sent to Tewkesbury with a troop of horse, and Giles Nanfan received orders to guard the passage of the Severn at Upton Bridge.

I took up my quarters at the Swan Tavern and reported myself to Colonel Carew, who said that he sadly wanted information respecting the whereabouts of the active Parliamentarian general, Sir William Waller, who had earned the soubriquet of the Owl, from the frequency and secrecy of his night attacks, and who was said to be accompanied by a clever Upton spy known as Captain Bound.

We also received information of the important success of an army of Welshmen raised by the Earl of Worcester, who were marching upon Gloucester under his son Lord Herbert. They had been opposed at Coleford in the Forest of Dean by a regiment of Parliamentarians under Colonel Berrowe, but although the Royalists lost one of their chief officers, Sir Richard Lawdy, they drove the rebels before them to the walls of Gloucester.

Two miles from Gloucester, to the westward, situated on a hill and surrounded by beautiful trees, is Highnam House, then the residence of Sir Robert Cooke, who married the widow of the poet, George Herbert, and was himself a man of literature, but had unhappily espoused the cause of the Parliament. Here the Welshmen halted, and were commanded by their leaders to entrench themselves, while Lord Herbert and Colonel Brett sent a trumpeter to Colonel Massey to demand the surrender of Gloucester for the King within four and twenty hours. But the summons 'was received with scorn'[4] by a garrison who had twice declined to listen to the overtures of Prince Rupert, and answer, was made that 'the leeks were not yet planted for Taffy's broth'.

On learning these important tidings, Sir Matthew Carew lost no time in sending to Oxford for instructions, and strongly recommended that Prince Rupert should march himself, or send a force to co-operate with Lord Herbert and surround Gloucester. Had he done so, probably the whole character of the war would have been changed.

While Sir Matthew's messenger was on his expedition to Oxford, I rode to Highnam and had a personal interview with Lord Herbert. The Welshmen had fortified the mansion with spade and mattock, on the Gloucester side. Lord Herbert, like ourselves, hoped that the King would command that Massey should be shut up, by an investment on the south, especially as we held Tewkesbury and Cheltenham on the east, so he determined to await the result of our message to Oxford.

A whole fortnight of March passed away, and no reply, no orders from the King or the Prince, and we all thought the messenger had been killed or taken prisoner, when one evening he rode in with despatches. Fatal mistake! No troops would be sent to assist at the siege of Gloucester, they were required to march northwards to meet the

Queen. The King's Council considered that the Welsh army would be sufficient to cope with Massey.

In a letter from my father I learnt the reason of so little attention being paid to the request of Lord Herbert and Sir Matthew Carew. The Queen had landed at Burlington Bay, in Yorkshire, with troops, munitions of war and money, and had well nigh lost her life the night of her landing, owing to the bombardment of the house in which she slept by some Parliamentarian vessels under Admiral Batten. She had written to the King an account of her danger in words which I am enabled to quote:[5]

> 'One of these ships,' wrote the Queen, 'did me the favour of flanking upon the house where I slept, and before I was out of bed the balls whistled so around me that my company pressed me to go out of that house, the cannon having totally beaten down the neighbours' houses, and two balls fell from the top to the bottom of the house where I was. So clothed, as well as in haste I could be, I went on foot to some little distance from the town of Burlington and got into the shelter of a ditch like that at Newmarket, whither before I could get, the cannon bullets fell thick about us and a servant was killed within seventy paces of me; one dangerous ball grazed the edge of the ditch, and covered us with earth and stones, the firing lasting until the turn of the tide.'

These war experiences of his loved Queen determined King Charles to use every effort to enable her Majesty to join him at Oxford. This prevented the siege of Gloucester being undertaken, when all was ripe and ready, and Lord Herbert was left to his own devices, a dangerous business with such a fine soldier as Colonel Massey, Governor of Gloucester, and just returned from a high command in Holland.

On the 20th of March I had been to visit our outposts at Tewkesbury Park, Boddington Manor, and Fiddington Orange, and on returning to the Swan Tavern, I saw our groom Bonner, arm-in-arm with a tottering old man, conversing with Mr Zion-build Fox, who lived at Clarence House just opposite. As I did not approve of such communication with one of the most virulent Puritans in all Tewkesbury, I questioned Bonner, who stated that his grandfather, a first cousin of the Bishop's, which did not elevate him in my opinion, had a fit of the staggers, and Master Zion-build had just relieved him with a horn of decoction of wormwood. I bid him look to his horses as soon as he was rid of his respectable grand-parent, who wore a very dirty wig, and a big patch over one eye, then handing him his crutch, he led him down the street.

Soon after this occurrence, when drilling on Tewkesbury Hamme, we heard the continuous booming of cannon in the direction of Gloucester, as if at some siege or battle. Sir Matthew Carew ordered me to ride off and report what was going on. I proposed to take my soldier grooms, Sampson and Bonner, in case I wished to send them as scouts or return messengers. The Colonel immediately consented, when Bonner declared the horse he rode was not fit to carry him, and begged to go to the Swan for my best charger, the Prince. To prevent delay, Carew mounted him on his second charger, and we then started on our expedition.

We crossed the Severn at the Upper Lode, skirting the right bank of the river by Tirley and Ashleworth. Notwithstanding a white St Valentine, the springtime had now awakened the flowers; primroses and violets blossomed beneath the hedgerows, and Sampson declared spring was come, for he could put his foot on nine day's-eyes. The basket-makers were busy by Severn side in the osier holts, wagtails were bobbing on the banks, and fishermen were dragging their nets for the silver salmon or early shad, while boom, boom, went the cannon in its work of death and destruction, as all nature was bursting into life.

Leaving the Severn at Ashleworth, we rode for the hill above Hartpury, and learnt from some countrymen that Massey had marched from Gloucester with 500 foot, several big guns, and 200 horse, crossed the Severn at Over, and was now attacking the Welsh in their entrenchments at Highnam. Diverging to the right, we crossed the Leddon by a wooden bridge between Hartpury and Lassington, and rode for Highnam Church.

Here we found Lord Herbert and the Royalist cavalry, while Colonel Brett, the second in command, was at Highnam House superintending the defence. Leaving my two men with the Welsh horse at the Church, I accompanied Lord Herbert to survey the besiegers and the besieged, and I felt satisfied that no assault by Massey, with such forces he had with him, could prevail against the strong earthworks the Welshmen had raised for the protection of the encampment. Massey kept up continual fire the whole day, and made no attempt to withdraw his troops and re-enter Gloucester. At this Lord Herbert and Brett rejoiced, as they proposed to attack him early next morning in the rear, and for this purpose a body of men were sent to a village called Rudford, by Tibberton, from whence to march round and fall upon Massey's forces, while Lord Herbert and Brett attacked in front.

On our return to Highnam Church and village, I found the groom Bonner was missing. He pretended that I had given him a letter of parley to carry to the Westgate Bridge at Gloucester. In short, he had deserted, and taken with him Colonel Carew's charger, while I strongly suspected that he had gone with information to Captain Bound, the 'aged and crippled grandfather' I had seen at Tewkesbury. I was bitterly mortified, as indeed was Sampson, who declared that he had doubted his comrade ever since he attended the preacher Cocktail's discourses in Upton Chapel.

As night drew on the firing ceased, and I rode to Newent to join Lord Herbert next morning. On our way we saw two corps of the Welsh troops under Colonel Powell, posted between Lassington and Rudford, and night fell before we reached the tavern of the Royal Charles.

The inn was full of farmers and countrymen, who had been to Over and Lassington to watch the cannonading, expecting to behold a battle. Among them were the Messrs Clark, royalist farmers, who were afterwards of great aid to the cause of the King.[6] The greatest excitement prevailed; and many were the questions I had to answer, until I sought refuge in my bedroom, ill at ease about the desertion of the scoundrel Bonner. I awoke early next morning by Sampson rushing into my room, to tell me that heavy firing was going on by Highnam, and I lost no time in getting to horse, but when we reached Rudford it was evident that Lord Herbert's troops had met with a sad reverse, and the road was so blocked by excited and victorious Parliamentarian forces that I was glad to escape by Tibberton and Taynton.

The history of all this was that the 'Night Owl' Sir William Waller, and Colonel Massey had laid a well concerted scheme, which was admirably carried out. Waller had taken Malmesbury, and persuaded Massey to bombard the Welsh at Highnam, and, while Massey occupied the attention of the Royalists by cannonading, Waller crossed the Severn on pontoons at Framilode. He then marched by night to Huntley, and being well informed by spies of the position of Lord Herbert's forces, he divided his troops into two brigades. With one he marched straight upon Highnam House, the other he sent by Taynton to fall upon the Welshmen at Rudford. Great slaughter took place in this attack, on a common near the turn to Tibberton village, between Rudford and Ludman's Hill. Here the dead lay in heaps; 500 Welshmen were slain,[7] and Waller lost many men in the general carnage. A brook hard by was so stained with blood that men still call it the Redbrook.

While this scene was enacting to the west of Highnam, Waller marched by the Ross road, and the Welsh Royalists found themselves hemmed in between the Gloucester troops and Waller's two detachments, and now a most humiliating occurrence took place. No entreaties of Lord Herbert or his officers' could induce the Welsh soldiers at Highnam to show fight. They stormed and swore, not a man would move. Their hearts failed them, they longed to be among their sheep and their mountains, and hung out a flag of truce, and, quarter being promised, capitulated to a man. I found Lord Herbert and his cavalry wandering hopelessly in the lanes between Highnam and Huntley, and persuaded him to ride to Tewkesbury, and hope for better times and braver soldiers.

One thousand strong and able Welshmen left entrenchments they might have held against Waller and Massey combined, and were marched as prisoners across the Westgate Bridge into the city of Gloucester. They were shut up for some time in the Cathedral and other churches, and 'having been refreshed with boiled turnip tops and cabbages', were dismissed to their mountain homes, on taking oath not again to leave them.

Within two days after my return to Tewkesbury, Sir Matthew Carew determined to abandon it, and I returned to our Longdon regiment.

Ripple Cross

Chapter Nine

I FOUND THAT, during my absence, nothing could exceed Giles Nanfan's kindness and attention to my Aunt Tabitha. Notwithstanding the emergencies of our position at Upton, and the necessity of watchfulness against spies, or a sudden raid from the ever active Massey at Gloucester, Giles never missed a daily visit to Hanley Castle from his quarters at Upton. As the spring time drew on he won my aunt's heart by his love of gardening. I never understood before that my friend knew one weed from another! But Giles told Aunt Tabitha that he believed, with Lord Bacon, that 'it is the purest of human pleasures'.[1]

We had two flower gardens at Hanley Castle, forming one long flower-filled border along the slope which rises from the inner moat. One, which Aunt Tabitha loved to call Master Chaucer's Garden, she would work in for hours, all the spring and summer through; the other, separated by a box hedge, was the property of Isabel, who gardened almost as industriously as our aunt, but she loved new and various flowers, and sometimes angered her fellow gardener by calling Master Chaucer's flowers 'weedlings'. I could not make out that Giles ever dug or planted; he sat upon the box hedgerow, and would sometimes dibble awhile for Aunt Tabitha, but more often for Isabel, who was easily affected by the heat of the sun, and loved to insist on Giles working.

The Chaucer garden had trellis-work covered with roses and honey-suckles, trained in the spring. Giles got the thorns in his fingers, and asked Isabel to take them out. Here grew the blue iris from the wild woods of Sarnhill, and the Monkshood from Teme-side, Golden Rod and Dames Violet, Sweet Ciceley, Feverfew, Canterbury Bells, Hose in Hose, Primroses, and Cowslips, red as well as yellow, Daffodils, Stars of Bethlehem from Bromesberrow, and a hundred others which blossomed in succession in Master Chaucer's Garden.

The garden of sweet Isabel was more ambitious, and contained wall-flowers which, for perfume's sake, Lord Bacon would have 'set under a parlour window', and the Herbe de la Reine, lately imported from the gardens of the French Queen,[2] with streaked Gillivors, Lilies, Larkspurs, and Golden Jasmines. But greatest of all Isabel's treasures was the Spider Wort,[3] lately sent from America by King Charles' travelling gardener, John Tradescant, who beheld the Dodo in the Isle of

Mauritius,[4] and wild turkeys in their native woods. This flower was given Isabel by Mary Bromley. It was sent to her by Andrew Marvell, who became known in after years as Trusty Andrew, and as a sweet singer about gardens, but who was a terrible Roundhead. The only flowers that Giles himself planted were Forget-me-nots, and a large patch of pansies, which Aunt Tabitha declared were fit for nothing but to make plasmers to put over a girl's chest when she had the heart-ache.

As a consequence of the spring time, and Master Giles' newly acquired love for horticulture, I did not find my commanding officer drilling his troops on Upton Hamme, or examining into the accounts of the regiment at his quarters, but dibbling in his Forget-me-nots upon the sunny banks of the garden slopes, with Isabel looking on laughing, and declaring they would never grow.

On my saluting him and enquiring how long he had taken to this culture of flowers, he coolly declared ever since he heard my father say that Julius Caesar gardened at Tusculum and Xenophon at Toscana. Aunt Tabitha could not stand this, and came up to the box hedge to inform Giles that it was Pliny who was at Tusculum, to which he replied by vigorously watering the plot of pansies. He looked flushed and excited, which gave my aunt an opportunity of pressing upon him a hornfull of distilled pepperworts and hedge garlic, so good for purgings of the blood and spring pimples.

As we walked back to our quarters at the White Lion I told Giles of the desertion of Bonner, and that I had little doubt he had joined Bound at Gloucester, a serious matter, as Bonner was well acquainted with every nook and corner of Hanley Castle, as was also Bound with every place near Upton.

But now when the disaster at Highnam had given the Roundheads much encouragement, the King's Council at Oxford thought fit to send Prince Maurice to Tewkesbury with an army of 2000 men and 26 cornets of horse.[5] It was hoped that he would cut off Sir William Waller, who had marched on a foray into Herefordshire and Monmouthshire. The fiery Rupert was better fitted for such an expedition than the over-cautious Maurice, the last of our generals who should have been selected to catch such a man as Waller.

Prince Maurice did not delay long at Tewkesbury, but marched by Ledbury and Ross into the Forest of Dean. Giles Nanfan was to remain at Upton, and I was ordered on a foraging expedition to Newent to obtain the aid of Mr Edward Clark, of Oxenhall Court, who had already shown his wish to assist the Royalists by sending his team with corn for Prince Rupert's cavalry horses when he summoned Gloucester in January.

Before I left Giles Nanfan told me of his love for my sister Isabel, but I cannot say that I was enchanted at the announcement. I knew that Isabel, when she once gave her affections, would love to the hour of her death. Giles was too young, too thoughtless, and too general an admirer to bind himself in the fetters of matrimony. Young as he was, I knew he had already fancied himself deeply attached to half a dozen of our fair neighbours, and he was too handsome and fascinating to be much with a generous-hearted girl like Isabel without danger to her peace of mind. Love-making with Giles had been hitherto a harmless and pleasing excitement. If Isabel loved him and he became untrue, it would break her heart!

So when Giles told me of his hopes and fears I gave him a patriarchal exhortation, and pledged him, on his honour, to give up gardening until he had consulted my father's wishes and those of Sir Giles. Not content with this I had a long talk with Aunt Tabitha, and entreated her to lock up the watering pot and the dibble, until my father's return.

Accompanied by honest Sampson I soon found myself at Oxenhall, a rude hamlet near Newent, surrounded by woods and deep red sandstone lanes. Mr Clark was a true English yeoman, a man of powerful frame, and a candid, open countenance. No man had a higher reputation for honour and honesty than 'Eddud Clark', and I do not forget the grip he gave my unlucky fingers when I told him that I had ridden over on the King's service, or the "Dang it man, but y're welcome", as he assisted me to dismount from my horse.

He insisted upon my taking up my quarters at Oxenhall, instead of the Royal Charles at Newent, and promised to lend his own team and obtain the use of others to haul hay and corn into the Forest of Dean for the use of Prince Maurice's horse. I passed the night at Oxenhall Court, and heard from my host how the war had already affected the cultivation of the land. The toil and labour of the farmer was too little respected by both sides, hay and corn had been carried off without payment, and the young corn trampled under foot by horsemen who would not ride a hundred yards round by road to spare it. The hedges were:

> *Like prisoners wildly overgrown with hair,*
> *Put forth disordered twigs; the fallow leas,*
> *The darnel, hemlock and rank fumitory,*
> *Doth root upon.* [6]

And so the husbandry did 'lie on heaps'. Clark's great wish was to see
the King, and he looked upon me with great respect when he found I
had conversed with his Majesty, and kissed his hand. He loved his
Church, which he considered 'the heart of England', and was by no
means charitably disposed to the 'ranting, canting, snuffling, hypocritical Roundheads', as he indiscriminately termed all Dissenters. Good
Mistress Clark was loyal too, but not so devoted as her husband. She
wished King Charles to regain his own, but she objected to the hay and
corn going without the money down. She would have willingly given
his Majesty a couple of pullets, but she insisted that her husband ought
to have ready cash for the grain. Right famous was the Styre cider
made from the Oxenhall orchards, and over our pipes the host told me
more than once how he had shaken hands with Prince Rupert. [7]

The expedition of Prince Maurice into Herefordshire and Monmouthshire came to nothing. Instead of cutting off and surrounding Sir
William Waller, that general marched his army across the southern
extremity of Dean Forest, crossed the Severn at Aust Ferry, and arrived
safe in Gloucester. While Waller was executing this movement, Prince
Maurice was at Newnham, and it became a very serious question
whether the forces of Waller and Massey combined would not intercept
the return of his army across the Severn. Mr Clark gave valuable
information respecting the route for the return march, and Prince
Maurice decided to cross the Severn at Upton Bridge as soon as he could
call in his troops, which were scattered over the Forest of Dean waiting
to surround General Waller.

I was sent back to Upton without delay to make preparations for the
passing through of the army, and with orders to report the present
position of affairs to Sir William Russell at Worcester.

On the long open common, so lately forest land, now called Longdon
Heath, I overtook Bridget Nanfan on her palfrey, riding to the town for
tobacco for Sir Giles, and right glad was the merry girl to see an old
friend and to hear of my adventures in the Forest. Riding side by side
we reached the steep, red hill, on the Ledbury Road, just above Upton
town, when we saw before us Mr Bromley and his daughter. Mr

Bromley's parole to Prince Rupert did not extend beyond twelve months, so he was again active on the side of the Parliament, and I knew that he was in communication with the Gloucester Roundheads. After what had passed between Mary and myself respecting Hannah Stubbs, I did not care to pass them, so they trotted on in front.

As we rode up to the Cross in the middle of the town, we found the Squire engaged reading a letter which had been handed to him by a man who was standing by his horse. Mary, who had turned her palfrey round, sat facing us as we rode down the street, and returned a slight bow in recognition of my soldier's salute. As we passed, the man who was standing beside Mr Bromley nearly ran under our horses, and I saw, to my astonishment, the deserter Bonner. No sooner did he catch my eye than he rushed like wildfire down the New Street, and I galloped after him as wildly. About the centre of the street, on the left, is a narrow alley, leading to some suburbs and gardens, impassable to horses. Up this place Bonner bolted, like a rabbit into its hole, and as soon as I could pull up, I dismounted and ran after him, leaving my horse running loose in the street. Jack boots are bad things to run in and I was heavily armed, so when I reached the top of the alley Bonner had disappeared among the gardens.

When I returned to the street I found Bridget in a state of wonder at my proceedings, and a man holding my horse. Mr and Miss Bromley had, she said, ridden rapidly across the bridge, and seemed somewhat amused at the race they witnessed.

It did not take long to make Giles Nanfan acquainted with the position of affairs, nor was he surprised, as he entertained a poor opinion of Prince Maurice's capacity as a general. He set off to consult John Kelly about the bridge defences, but not before he told me that he had been but once to Hanley Castle with a spring salmon for Aunt Tabitha. I rode on with my despatches for Worcester without further delay. Two nights afterwards Prince Maurice entered Upton at the head of six thousand men, the dragoons encamping at Bury Field, the site of an old Saxon station, while the foot soldiers took up a position on the Hamme. Our greatest difficulty was that we were surrounded by espionage. Not a corps could be moved that Massey was not made aware of it. Thus spies having informed Massey and Waller of the arrival of Prince Maurice at Upton, a bold attempt was made to prevent his crossing the Severn.

We received intelligence[8] that Waller had crossed the river at
Tewkesbury, on the bridge of boats built by Prince Maurice himself,
and was marching with a strong force up the right bank by Pull Court
and Coomb hill, and that Massey was marching with another force up
the left bank by Ripple. It was plain that the endeavour was to place us
between the two forces. Not a moment was lost; the infantry on the
Hamme broke up their encampment and marched across the bridge at
Upton, taking up a position on the other side the river. In dragging the
cannon over the narrow bridge it got blocked, for a time, with the rush
of men and horses, and in the midst of this confusion the scouts in the
rear announced that Waller's horse were advancing by the Rectory.
Giles Nanfan and I were ordered to keep them in check with our Longdon troopers, and the aid of a couple of guns we had placed on Bury
Field.

The Parliamentarians came steadily on past Seller's Orchard, and I
could see Waller himself in armour riding side by side with Captain
Bound on Hell Cat. The first discharge from one of the carronades
knocked over a couple of their men and evidently took them by
surprise; a second shot threw the leading files into confusion. General
Waller immediately began to deploy his men to the right and left
among the gardens and fields, before attacking the guns which commanded the narrow lane by which they were advancing.

We now saw that we were engaged with a force that must soon have
overwhelmed our Longdon troop, when an aide-de-camp arrived from
the Prince commanding Nanfan to withdraw our men instanter, in
short to make a run for it, and cross the bridge, as the rest of the army
were safe over the Severn. Giving the rebels one more dose from the
cannon, we abandoned the guns and joined Prince Maurice across the
river.

It was not a moment too soon, for we could hear the Prince's van
engaged with Massey's troops at a little hamlet known as Holly Green,
while there was still much confusion among the Royalists, owing to the
difficulty of moving the cannon in the deep and miry lanes. Fortunately
Waller advanced very cautiously, expecting to fight hard in the streets,
but when he found we had all crossed the bridge he prepared to follow
and give us battle on the other side. We were not in good order to
receive them, so entangled was the rear with the guns that it was
difficult to move backwards or forwards. In fact, it was a most awkward

position, especially as the Parliamentarians mounted a gun in the church-yard commanding the opposite side of the narrow bridge.

We were soon relieved from any anxiety with respect to Waller's force. A terrific explosion took place, masses of earth, wood, and stone were hurtled high into the air, and the archway of the bridge next the town disappeared in the rushing waters of the Severn.[9] We could see, from the other side, General Waller examining the gap, and Bound venting his disappointment upon his mare until driven back by the fire of our musqueteers. Amidst this scene of excitement a fisherman paddled across with an armed man in a flat-bottomed boat, and John Kelly, in the uniform of a Cavalier, ran up the bank and mounted a led charger belonging to Prince Maurice.

The cavalry were now ordered to the front to attack Colonel Massey, as Waller's force was disposed of for the present by John Kelly's well-timed destruction of the arch next the town. Trumpets sounded, horses neighed, and one troop of horse galloped for Holly Green, while another rode by the Severn banks for the red cliffs of Ryall. Massey witnessed the disaster at the bridge from Ryall cliffs through his espying glass, and withdrew his men without delay. He sent his dragoons to protect his foot soldiers, and told the infantry to make good use of their legs and get back to Tewkesbury.

A few fell on both sides in a sharp skirmish between Holly Green and Ryall, but the principal conflict took place on a wide plain known as Ripple Field, which adjoins the wild heath of Brockeridge Common. Here the Parliamentarians met our charge with much bravery, but they were outnumbered and beat a retreat, while many a good soldier on both sides lay extended on the plain. Here Bonner the deserter was cut down, and hand-to-hand fighting went on as far as the Mythe hill above Tewkesbury.

We now heard the trumpeters sounding the recall and, riding slowly back towards the village of Ripple, I came upon several men who had fallen near a newly planted avenue of young elm trees on the Tewkesbury side of Brockeridge. Among these was a Parliamentarian officer clad in old armour, not in the iron plates worn by the 'Lobsters', as we called the Roundhead dragoons. He was seated against some railings erected to protect an elm, groaning, but apparently insensible. His helmet having been struck off, he was bare-headed, but his features were so smothered in mud they were hardly discernible.

I dismounted, and assisted by a trooper got some water in my helmet, and we bathed and washed the face of the wounded man. I then recognized the features of Mr Bromley. We lost no time in unloosing his cuirass, but it was evident the injury was in the head, for a deep gash was laid bare at the back of the right ear, and the hair was matted with blood. Fortunately Prince Maurice and his staff rode by as we were thus engaged, and enquired if he could render any assistance. I told him that the wounded officer was a country gentleman of the neighbourhood, and begged for a brief leave from duty in order that I might see him carried safely to his home across the Severn. The Prince acquiesced without a moment's hesitation, and ordered some soldiers to assist us in conveying the wounded man as far as Ripple village.

I sent Sampson ahead, across the ferry to Upton, to summon Dr Trash, the chirurgeon, to Hamme Court without delay. Then with the aid of some villagers we laid Mr Bromley on a hurdle covered with straw, and bore him as tenderly as possible to the ferry boat. He lay as motionless as death, occasionally breathing a deep sigh. We bore him past the great oaks, and by the plantations and young elms in front of the house. Here I bid the bearers of the litter rest awhile, that I might go forward and acquaint Madam Bromley of the sad occurrence.

On the greensward before the house I met Mary, little thinking, amidst the anxieties of the situation, of the figure I presented to the alarmed girl. My face was streaked with blood, and I had lost my helmet. I had taken off my scarf, one worked by Mary's own hands in happier times, to wrap round my head, having been slightly wounded, and I was besmeared with mud from head to foot. No wonder Mary was alarmed! All she said was, "Oh Richard!" and sank fainting at my feet.

I bore her in my arms to the house, her face close to mine, and I thanked God I could feel the beating of her heart. At the entrance we met her mother, and to her care I consigned her. It was a hard task for one so young and inexperienced as I then was, to tell the loving wife and daughter – when she recovered from her swoon – of the state of their beloved one who lay nigh unto death close by.

How I told the tale I know not, but bidding Mary remain on the couch Mrs Bromley accompanied me to the litter on which her husband lay still utterly unconscious. She bore the sight with more composure and determination than I expected, and held his hand as we carried him to the house. Sampson arrived soon after with the surgeon, who immediately set to work to foment his head and bathe the wound.

After a time Mr Bromley recovered consciousness, and raised himself on his arm as he recognized his much-loved wife and daughter. Surgeon Trash had him carried up to bed, remarking to Mrs Bromley, "Head like a Yorkshire bull, he'll get over it." He then turned to me, saying, "You, Mr Forester, have been cut and slashed also, let me examine your caput." Thus I was obliged to undergo a fomenting and plaistering, which I bore with equanimity, as Mary was sufficiently recovered to hold the basin while the chirurgeon bathed my skull. It was soon done, but Mary laid aside the stained and blood-sodden scarf, replacing it with one of her father's. It had once been her own; I remonstrated, and then I saw in her eyes that she had forgiven me for my suspicions about Hannah Stubbs' letter.

I now rode off for Upton, where the inhabitants had been brought face to face with the results of civil war. Some stood at the doors of their houses talking over the events of the day; a few fishermen hung about the broken bridge looking at the waters as they glistened in the setting sun; others crowded in the church-yard, looking with anxious faces upon an ominous line of dead bodies. The corpses of those who fell in Bury Field, and at the entrance to the town, had been carried to the church-yard, where they were laid side by side. Most of the bodies were those of strangers, but here and there a well-known face was recognized. For the moment religious differences were forgotten, and the Catholic priest from Hanley and Mr Woodforde spoke words of comfort to a bereft mother, or offered a prayer for the soul of one who was rapidly passing to another sphere. The great bell of the church was tolling the death signal as the shades of evening were falling upon the living and the dead.

In the old church porch, through which many a Beauchamp and Despenser had passed to hear High Mass in bygone days, Surgeon Trash was amputating the leg of a wounded Parliamentarian, while Mr Gaston made notes for the benefit of his friend Dr Harvey. Leaving the dismal spectacle, I rode off to join Prince Maurice at Pershore. Tewkesbury was now occupied by Parliamentarians from Gloucester under Sir Robert Cooke of Highnam, who destroyed the walls and ancient defences of the town.[10]

Chapter Ten

THE ARMY of the Earl of Essex assembled at Windsor, now marched to lay siege to Reading, which fell, some said through bribery, on the 26th April, and thenceforward was for some time the head quarters of the Parliamentarian forces. In the mean time Sir William Waller and Colonel Massey marched from Gloucester and attacked Hereford with an army of three thousand men.

Sir William Waller belonged to an old family in Hampshire, and laid claim to the ownership of Winchester Castle. He had served with credit in the armies of the German Princes, and early in these miserable dissensions he wrote an affecting letter to his old friend Sir Ralph Hopton, who was destined to be his constant opponent in war, saying, 'My affections to you are so unchangeable that hostility cannot violate my friendship to your person, but I must be true to the cause wherin I serve. We are both on the stage, and must act those parts that are assigned to us in this tragedy; but let us do it in the way of honour and without personal animosity.'

It caused much wonder amongst us Royalists that a man of the character of Sir William Waller should join the Roundheads. On the 24th of April assaults were given at Bister's Gate on the north side of Hereford, at Wye Bridge, and the gates of St Owen and Widemarsh. At the latter Massey discharged 'two sakers', and the first cannon shot which entered the gate 'took an officer's head from his shoulders and slew some besides. More shots scoured the streets',[1] when the garrison sounded a parley, and 'most of the common soldiers ran over Wye Bridge into Wales', leaving the officers and gentlemen to shift for themselves. The city then surrendered with fair conditions, and among the prisoners were Lord Scudamore, Colonel Coningsby, and Sir William Croft.

Sir William Waller behaved with his usual courtesy, which was afterwards brought against him by the blood and thunder Puritans, who if they could have had their way would have dealt with their brother Englishman as did 'Saul with the Amalekites'. Notwithstanding Waller's courtesy of demeanour and generosity of character, he never interfered to prevent the destruction of those ecclesiastical edifices treasured by Anglican Churchmen, and there was much fear that his troops would deface and damage the venerable Cathedral.[2] In March his army ransacked the stately church of Romsey, which had escaped the ravages at the dissolution of the monasteries, and a ranting minister hounded on the zealots from the pulpit. We therefore rejoiced to hear that the Gloucester troops had spared the Minster at Hereford, with the exception of some monuments and the painted glass.

About this time there was much preaching on the part of the Parliamentarians 'that the heavy wrath of God was visiting the nation for sin', and the sin of us Royalists in particular. They prayed for the abolition of the Prayer Book, and for the removal of the brutish ignorance and palpable darkness of every one in the kingdom, save themselves. They wrested Scriptural phrases to bolster up the wickedness of civil war; Waller's entry into Hereford was 'as the Israelites passing through the Red Sea'; the success of Essex at Reading was 'no lesse a miracle than the razing down of the walls of Jericho with pichers and rams' horns'. Plunder, when they plundered, was the 'gift of God', but 'hellish thievery' if we Royalists carried off a hay-rick. In short, it seemed to me that both sides forgot the charity of true Christianity, and accepted, for example, the cruel deeds of some of the heroes of the Old Testament. Slaughter, like that of Samuel, was preached more than the forgiveness taught by Christ.

Meanwhile matters looked serious for us at Worcester. Prince Maurice and his army retired to Oxford, and with him went Sir William Russell, leaving Colonel Sandys of Ombersley, Governor of Worcester in his stead. No sooner did Colonel Sandys receive intelligence of the surrender of Hereford than he summoned our Longdon troopers to assist in garrisoning the loyal city.

All hands at Worcester were now at work strengthening the city walls, which remained much as they are described by Leland in the days of Henry VIII. Two cannon commanded the Severn by St Clement's Church and the bridge, and several guns were in position between Foregate and St Martin's Gate, as also between St Martin's Gate, Friar's, and Sidbury Gates. Of the six gates two were posterns. The Castle had long been destroyed, but the Castle Mount[4] commanded the lower reaches of the river, and here we placed some of our biggest guns. Colonel Sandys received the garrison and volunteers on Pitchcroft, and the Council of Array met frequently at the Guildhall. The Earl of Cockayne presided, and strongly advocated putting the Parliamentarian Generals in the pillory and cropping their ears. He would also punish the Puritan clergy by making them masticate their own Bibles, and recommended a levy of stores for the garrison on every Roundhead in the neighbourhood. Pepper had risen to six shillings an ounce, and hops we had none, so Lord Cockayne advised immediate requisitioning.

About the end of the month we were surprised by the intelligence that Sir William Waller had evacuated Hereford and retired to Gloucester. We therefore naturally supposed that Worcester was safe from investment, and our Longdon troopers made many forays into the country to provide provender for man and beast. All nature was teeming with beauty, and the town children ventured forth from the monotonous drudgery of piling turfs, to gather flowers in the surrounding hedges and bring in bunches of May.

The Puritans in the town had to put up with a May-pole which was erected on May-day at Worcester Cross, and round it danced a May Queen crowned with flowers, and a Jack in the Green half hidden in herbs and posies. Many a gallant officer laid aside his sword 'to helpen the ladies their May-bush to bear', so that the citizens declared that 'good old times were coming back again'. These May-day revels, however, were soon over, and we had sterner sounds and sights by the middle of the month, when the cavalry of the rebels appeared on the slopes of the Malverns, raiding and plundering the farm-houses all around.

When on a scouting expedition with Giles Nanfan in the neighbourhood of Madresfield, we were riding towards Pixham Ferry by the Old Hills among the blossoms of the golden gorse, which ever displays its yellow flowers from May until the snows of December. Giles was sentimental, and whenever in this mood he always talked about the power of a woman's influence, the effect of a woman's smile. In vain I endeavoured to turn his attention to a Peregrine falcon soaring high in the air, he was thinking of the eyes of a dove, when he checked his horse so suddenly that the charger reared and plunged.

"Surely," he said, "that is Bridget on Daisy!" and he directed my attention to a lady galloping up the hill with an armed groom behind her. And Bridget it was; the gallant girl was riding from Birtsmorton to Worcester, charged with a letter to the governor from Sir Giles, which he would not trust a domestic to deliver. Bridget's eyes sparkled and her cheeks flushed as she overtook us, and claimed our attendance until she had delivered the epistle according to her father's instructions, "with her own hand."

We escorted her to the Bridge gate, and soon the important intelligence she carried spread like wild-fire through the city. Sir William Waller was marching upon Worcester with 3000 men and 10 guns! But Worcester was now full of Cavaliers as true as steel, and of citizens as loyal as King Charles' children, so crowds of men armed and arming appeared in the streets and in front of the Guildhall; soldiers and musqueteers marched to and fro through High Street, and the drum and fife re-echoed in every alley. Ladies occupied the balconies wearing King's scarfs, and Rupert kerchiefs, and the royal standard floated from the steeple of the cathedral.

Bridget was conducted in honour to the care of the Governor's lady, and that night Lord Cockayne toasted her at supper as "The Rose of Birtsmorton, the brave, the beauteous Bridget." Alas, chivalrous as were our Cavaliers, truth compels me to declare that they were often reckless, underrated their enemies, and too much given to toasting and roystering. While we were quaffing flagons of canary to the health of the King, and wives and sweethearts, the Parliamentarians contrived to admit Captain Bound, who scattered handbills abroad, signed William Waller.

The copy of this document appeared in *Mercurius Aulicus*[5] for May 30th, thus:

> To all Gentlemen and other Inhabitants of the City of Worcester. As
> many of you as are sensible of the danger of your religion, your
> persons, and goods, and the priviledges of your corporation, are
> desired to declare yourselves sensible of them at this opportunity. It
> being my errand (by the helpe of God) to rescue them from the
> oppression of your present governours. And I promise that all such as
> shall appear willing to welcome my endeavour, shall not only be
> received to free quarter, but protected to the utmost of my power.
> WILLIAM WELLER

But all these tricks would not draw the honest and loyal inhabitants of Worcester from their allegiance.

In the grey dawn of morning, on the 29th of May, the front squadrons of Waller's celebrated blue regiment were seen marching down the hill on the Kempsey and Tewkesbury high road. I was on the Cathedral tower with Colonel Sandys, when Giles Nanfan galloping in with a scouting party, gave the alarm with a fanfare of trumpets, and soon all the bells in the churches were ringing, and hundreds of volunteers rushing to assist the garrison at the walls. Sir William Waller, taking up his station on Green Hill summit, sent his trumpeter to the eastern gate at Sidbury to summon the city to surrender.

Colonel Sandys went to meet him, and the trumpeter being somewhat saucy, the Colonel gave him an unceremonious reply, telling him he was not now in Hereford, and ordering him to take himself off. But the trumpeter refused to stir, and said he must carry back a civil and explicit message. Again the Governor ordered him to retire, and then turned away and went towards his quarters at the Commandery.

Still the trumpeter refused to leave the gateway, and the guard sent for instructions how to act. Colonel Sandys returned, accompanied by Colonel Beaumont, and enquired why the man refused to depart. He received a most insulting answer, and fired at the fellow's impudence, Colonel Beaumont, in the heat of the moment, called out,"Shoot the black-guard," when much to our regret, one of the sentinels shot him dead. The news letters[6] afterwards justly complained of the trumpeter's being killed when engaged on an act of duty, but the man brought it upon himself by his unbounded insolence.

Soon after this unhappy circumstance, Waller attacked in force, but our cannon did good service and he lost many of his Blue regiment early in the day. He tried first one gate, then another, and everywhere was repulsed with loss. The walls were lined with the garrison and volunteers, while the women frequently came under the fire of their petronels as they ran to and fro with food, fuses, and powder. The attack had lasted well nigh sixteen hours,[7] and no breach had been made, at last Giles Nanfan begged Colonel Sandys to allow him to head a charge of dragoons.

After some consultation the Colonel consented, and with trumpets sounding, drums beating, and men cheering, to make believe there was to be a sally at the north gate, we rode quietly down to the east gate at Sidbury. Here we saw a crowd of horse and foot endeavouring to bring up a petard. The sentinels opened the gate, and following Nanfan two by two we were soon in the midst of the enemy, who gave way in great confusion at our unexpected attack upon this position. Sir Robert Cooke, of Highnam, the Parliamentarian governor of Tewkesbury, was slain,[8] and many a fine dragoon fell in that sharp skirmish before Sidbury gate. Waller was about to charge in person with a large force of horse, when Giles gave us the recall from his own bugle, and in a few minutes we were safe back within the city walls.

As we were preparing another sortie, Waller demanded a parley. He found Worcester was 'a nut too hard to crack', and already his troops were falling back on Tewkesbury. He asked to be allowed to send his wounded in boats down the Severn unmolested. This was granted immediately, for the time was not yet come for such merciless butchery as that of Marston Moor and Naseby. King Charles had written to Prince Rupert, and bid him observe that 'Mercy is the highest attribute of a King', while Waller, Massey, and Essex avoided unnecessary blood-shed, and quarter was granted, when asked, on both sides.

But I must not leave unrecorded what the news letters said of the honest, brave behaviour of the good women of the town, 'who did not only encourage their husbands to stand it out bravely, telling them they would die with them in this just cause, but did also themselves run out of the town – as soon as Waller was gone – and with their own hands slighted the works that had sheltered his musqueteers, and the day after levelled all the ditches in and about the town, which will make them so famous that no honest maid of that Corporation should hereafter want a good husband'.[9]

During the months of June and July the war was prosecuted in different parts of England with various success. A battle was fought at Bath, where Waller was defeated and Sir Bevil Grenville killed upon the heights of Lansdowne. Prince Rupert rode forth from Oxford and carried Birmingham by assault. Here the Earl of Denbigh, whom I had seen fighting so gallantly at Edgehill, was killed, and his Puritan heir succeeded to his father's title and estates. Mr Hampden, the leading spirit of the Parliamentarians, was wounded to the death by the burst-ing of a pistol at Chalgrove near Oxford.[10] Colonel Cromwell, a cousin of Mr Bromley's, was reported to be active in a 'sharp fight horse to horse', at Stamford and Gainsborough, and to have been appointed Governor of the Isle of Ely.

What provoked all good Royalists most, now, was that the Parlia-ment, destitute of all feelings of chivalry, impeached their Queen of high treason at the instigation of Mr Pym, a man who, born and bred a gentleman, should have had more knightly honour. True it was that

Henrietta Maria had landed troops and money on the Yorkshire coast, and like a brave woman had marched at the head of her troops and shared with them the hardships of the field. For this the Puritans, in their gallantry and nobility of heart, talked of setting a price on her head, and impeached her in their House of Commons..

We now learned from *Mercurius Aulicus* of a great tumult raised in London, and the discoverers of a horrible treason had 'all the prisons in London searched, and the imprisoned ministers robbed of their sermon notes, taking from one man – Dr Oldsworth by name, above sixty – several papers of collections for sermons'. On which Giles Nanfan and I thought what a fine thing it would be to make a bonfire of the notes of Messrs Cocktail, Baxter, Vicars, and some of that class of preachers who loved to affright poor people with blazing devils and the fires of hell.

In the mean time the Queen was still separated from her husband, whom she was most anxious to rejoin. This was no easy matter, as Lord Essex, with a large army, lay between the Queen's forces and Oxford, and my Lord Essex was no more of a true knight than Master Pym.

In the month of July I was ordered to meet Prince Rupert with fifty horse at Stratford-on-Avon, on a secret expedition; and I set forth with some of the most gallant of our Longdon troopers. The corn was ripening in the fields as we rode up the Garden of England, as the Vale of Evesham is well termed, and in many places the wains were being loaded with hay by Avonside; that Avon which had borne the ashes of Wyckliffe to the Severn and the sea; on whose banks died the stout Earl Simon; and by whose waters lived and died the bard of Stratford.

The peasants leant on their hay forks to watch the troopers as they trotted by, and blessed their stars that they had not been impressed for the wars. The nightingale 'in July away doth fly' so its trill was no longer heard in the groves of Cracombe, and the cuckoo, having 'bought his nag horse at Pershore fair',[11] no longer flitted above the Fladbury meadows, but the sky-lark soared above Evesham's battle-field, and the swallows swept to and fro above the graves of De Montfort's army.

We found the Evesham folk out in the sunshine among their gardens, or trundling their hay, and those within the town did not seem disposed to show us much civility. Indeed, we had reason to believe that the landlord of one of the taverns played us a scurvy trick, and mixed wormwood juices with his beer for verily it was so bitter we could not drink it, and those who did had manifestations of the gripes. He had better have let this alone; for, although I was very strict in preventing my men from plundering, I had orders to make any necessary requisitions for the support of my troopers from the disaffected towards his Majesty, if I could find them out. From his Royalist supporters we borrowed what we wanted, promising full payment when the war was over.

We had not ridden further than the hill above Harvington, on the road to Alcester, before some of my troopers were ill from the effect of the bitter ale quaffed at mine host's of the Leland Arms, on which I rode back with half a squadron and we requisitioned him of some gallons of strong waters, and two very fine Cotswold sheep. Arrived at Alcester we found the inhabitants still more uncivil; afterwards we learned Waller had been before us, so I requisitioned a goodly quantity of hay and corn, beef and mutton, and saw it off in carts under the protection of my troopers, for the loyal town of Stratford-on-Avon. Before I left I endeavoured to impress upon the citizens the high honour of contributing to the cause of his gracious Majesty.

My quarters were at the Red Horse, a tavern said to be much frequented by Shakespeare, the celebrated player and bard, and it was pleasant to sit in the kitchen corner he once occupied, and to quaff ale from the mug he was reported to have given to the host. Having seen men and horses in comfortable quarters, I started to visit the house in which 'glorious William', as my father called him, was born. It was a poor place inhabited by a pork butcher, who was a crusty Roundhead, who would hardly allow me to enter the room where Avon's bard first saw the light.

He sat upon a dresser reading the Puritan tracts, 'Hooks and Eyes for Believers' Breeches'; while, 'Eggs of Charity, layed by the Chickens of the Covenant, and boiled in the Water of Divine Love', was open on the shop-board. His wife was as surly as himself, so the next morning my men requisitioned some of his pork for his Majesty's service, and his wife's pullets for their own. No messenger having arrived with orders from Prince Rupert, I went forth to visit other places of interest in the town. Among these was the Charnel House,[12] attached to the church. It was probably the contemplation of this mass of dishonoured bones which filled Shakespeare with that horror of the violation of the tomb which led to the stern inscription on his grave stone:

Blese Be Ye Man Yt Spares Thes Stones,
And Curst Be He Yt Moves My Bones.

Human relics lay there in thousands, no one could guess how long, and the sexton said that the oldest inhabitant in the town knew nothing about them. Requisitioning took me with some of my troopers through the small village of Shottery, the home of Ann Hathaway. The cottage remains exactly as it was when Shakespeare sat in the courting chair, still shown to the curious; also a purse and inkstand, and a pair of fringed gloves[13] which once belonged to the Warwickshire beauty, to whom he inscribed the refrain: *She hath a way, Ann Hathaway.*

Ducks and fowls strayed about the garden where the Bard of Avon told his tale of love, but we did not requisition them.

After going to Shurdington, where the bard was married, I determin- ed to pay a visit to my father's friend Sir Thomas Lucy, a descendant of Justice Shallow, in whose park Shakespeare killed the deer. Charlcote is a fine house with Tudor casements, great gables, turrets, and stacks of chimneys. The three *luces*, the arms of the de Charlcotes, which Justice Shallow declared to be an old coat, were carved in stone above the entrance. Whatever the Justice of the furred gown might have been, the present Sir Thomas was a courteous gentleman. Hospitable and a Royalist, he would have entertained with good cheer a whole squadron marching for his King. With Sir Thomas was his brother, Squire Lucy, who lived in a fine house in Stratford-on-Avon, and invited me to the christening feast of his little daughter, to be held on the morrow, when he declared they would have a masque and a merry dance for all the 'chickens of the Church, and the sparrows of the Spirit' under the sun.

As I dearly loved a dance, and Bridget Nanfan had taught me the *coranto*, and to strut the *pavo* bravely, I gladly accepted the invitation, provided no orders arrived for our march, but a difficulty arose concerning dress, as Mr Lucy insisted that every one should appear in Shakesperian character, and wear a mask until midnight and supper time.

The buff coat and jack boots, breast-plate and helmet of a soldier were not the garments in which to dance a *coranto* with a Stratford beauty. Sir Thomas solved the difficulty by offering to lend me a dress for Coriolanus, which Sir Walter Raleigh had worn at a great masque given after the rebuilding of Charlcote in the time of Queen Elizabeth.

On my return to Stratford I walked up to the New House, where Master Shakespeare passed the last years of his life, now the residence of his daughter, Mrs Hall. I had looked over the garden wall at his mulberry tree, and was standing by the Chapel of the Gild of the Holy Cross, when Mary Bromley leisurely walked up the street supporting an elderly lady who leant upon her arm.

They were about to enter a house, when, yielding to the impulse of the moment, I crossed the street, hat in hand, and accosted Mary, enquiring after the health of Mr Bromley. She appeared somewhat taken aback, but smiled kindly, saying that her father was nearly recovered, and presented me to her aunt. My Cavalier's feathers, and smart sword belt worked by Isabel, evidently offended the eye of the stern old lady, who merely gave me a short, jerking nod, and no curtsey, while she told Mary to knock at the door, and when it was open, slammed it in my face. I walked back to the Red Horse, apostrophising Puritan aunts and Puritan manners. In the course of the evening Sir Thomas Lucy sent down my Coriolanus garb, with a mask which hid my face more completely than the Roman garments hid my limbs. Indeed, the habiliments of the noble Roman were so few of them, that I was very thankful the masque was in July and not in December.

The next morning brought no intelligence from Prince Rupert, but in the mean time we accumulated a goodly store of provisions for soldiers and provender for horses. As the evening drew on, and it was time to prepare for the masked ball, I wished heartily that Mr Bromley had not contracted those Puritanic notions that a merry dance was a sinful amusement, for I felt that there was no hope of a jig with Mary. I covered the Coriolanus garb with my horseman's cloak, and, rapier in hand, proceeded to the place of entertainment. This was a wooden building erected for the occasion on the banks of the Avon. A crowd gathered around the doors, looking with great interest at the arrival of Macbeth arm-in-arm with Banquo. Then came a tall and portly Friar, with Romeo and Juliet. Sir John Falstaff appeared attended by Richard I and King John; and great cheering arose as a gentleman passed arrayed in the dress of Shakespeare, as he appears in the church, with ruff and scarlet coat,

Entering the great booth, I beheld such a scene as my eyes never before encountered. A spacious amphitheatre was decked with garlands of summer roses and trellis of honeysuckle. Holly was there and ivy, so

that the wooden walls were converted into a large bowery, with nooks
and green corners where the dancers might rest themselves, partake of
refections, and Romeo tell his tale to Juliet.

From the villages around, as well as from Stratford itself, came Mr
Lucy's guests; from Charlcote and Shottery:

> *Piping Pebworth, Dancing Marstan,*
> *Haunted Hilbro', Hungry Grafton,*
> *Drudging Exhall, Papist Wicksford,*
> *Beggarly Broom, and Drunken Bidford.*

With the exception of Mr Lucy and our hostess, everyone present wore
masks sufficiently effective to prevent any personal recognition.

The musicians sat in an alcove green with boughs of oak and holly,
and festooned with marigolds. There were lutes, citherns, and fifes, and
in their midst was a Welsh harper, with long grey locks and dazzling
eyes, and a beard as white as snow. As I surveyed the motley throng,
Mr Lucy, recognizing the attire of Coriolanus, came up and said, "Invite
Lady Macbeth to the *pavo*, most illustrious Roman; she danceth like
Queen Bess, of glorious memory, high and disposedly." I obeyed our
host's commands, and was received by the dire Scottish Queen with
stately demeanour. We must have succeeded in the 'dignified showing"
of this celebrated dance, for a crowd collected around us. I now
observed a figure in the dress of Dame Quickly, closely masked, making
as if she would address me, but a crowd parted us, and Miranda
challenged me for a Henri Quatre maze. In this same maze there
meandered Hamlet and Cleopatra, and overhearing the Dane saying,
'Theewte things; thweetly', I recognized my Lord Cockayne.

Miranda danced well and nimbly, so thinking I might discover who
my fair partner was, I led her to an evergreen recess and bowered seat.
Here sat a Nun, motionless and alone, telling her beads, so we left her
and tried another, when we found the tall Friar I had seen at the
entrance. Shrouded in a long cloak and cowl, and wearing a mask
striped with red and white bars, he rose hastily as we entered, and
stalked solemnly away. While seated by Miranda's side, Mistress
Quickly again made her appearance, and this time she curtsied as if to
challenge me for the minuet. I might have responded, but there came
mincing by Katherine the Shrew, and it took my fancy to address her as
'Bonny Kate, the prettiest Kate in Christendom, Kate of Kate Hall, my

superdainty Kate', and entreat her sweet hand for *le danse*. But she jeered and flouted, and replied, "'Do what thou can'st, I will not dance to-day, no, nor tomorrow, nor till I please myself'."[14]

I now withdrew to a niche of ivy which was unoccupied, and was admiring the evolutions of a fandango, when the Friar, not seeing me among the greenery, entered with the Nun, and I heard him say in a low tone, "We have as yet no news of the Plunderer," a soubriquet given by the Roundheads to Prince Rupert. Her reply I could not catch, save that I heard distinctly the word "Walsall."

The dance music ceased, and every one listened with wrapt attention to the air of Merrie England, ringing forth shrill and clear, as a solo upon the fife. To me this was of especial interest, for I knew there was but one person who could play those wonderful quavers and runlets upon the reed, and that was John Kelly. What brought him there, and what for? I looked among the musicians and saw it was the white-bearded harper who was piping. I also fancied his black eyes were fixed on me.

And now the great clock struck twelve, a trumpet sounded and bells jingled, the signal to unmask. A large tapestried curtain in the amphi-theatre was drawn aside, and revealed supper tables laden with a feast of good things. Many were the dainties:

> *Beef, mutton, pork, and shred pies of the best,*
> *Pig, veal, goose, capon, and bustard so well drest.*

Then there were summer fruits, jellies, spices, sauces, and flagons of good wine and sack. The supper, like the dress of our hostess, was of the days of Good Queen Bess, and there were none of the petites choses, kickshaws, and comfitures which came in with the boozy banquets of King James. Like Master Stow, 'I lack the head of wit and also cunning in my bowells to declare the wonderful devices' of that Shakesperian banquet by the soft-flowing Avon under a July moon.

I stood wondering at the strange scene before me, as kings seated themselves by the side of shepherdesses, and queens by fools and jesters, when a cry of "Unmask, a fine, unmask!" arose, and I perceived that I and the burly Friar were both still wearing our masks. Confused at my own forgetfulness, I laid aside the velvet mask, when I was hailed by the merry-eyed Bridget Nanfan, who, dressed as Ophelia, called out, "Good morrow, 'tis St Valentine." She was seated by Lord Cockayne, who was displaying the rings on his fingers and quaffing canary.

I was making my way to Bridget full of astonishment at her appearance so far from home, when my arm was pressed significantly by Dame Quickly, who was still masked and appeared to tremble with trepidation. She addressed me in lisping tones of foreign accent, and said, "Captain Forester should now be at the head of his troops. His Queen is in sore danger." Before I could reply, she was lost among the surging crowd, now leaving the supper room for the renewal of their pastime. I followed the retreating steps of Mistress Quickly as best I might, when I encountered the glittering eyes of John Kelly, who whispered, "To horse! we have no time to lose in love speeches. To horse! Queen Mary is beset by traitors."

Thus I had to leave Bridget, and the fun and dancers, and hurry off to the tavern and arouse Sampson from his midnight sleep. I soon exchanged my Coriolanus gear for my war harness, and our bugles sounded in the streets calling our troopers to boot and saddle. Then as I stood at the tavern door waiting for Sampson and my charger, the Friar dashed by on horseback. His cowl was thrown back, there was a jingle of armour beneath his gown, and the horse was the Ghost. Soon after, John Kelly rode up in haste, and telling me he would enter into explanations as we journeyed, led us on the road to Walsall.

Earl's Croome Court

Chapter Eleven

As we rode forth from the birth-place of Shakespeare on this July morning, we approached the Heart of England, a land famous for its records from times when fierce tribes of Britons roamed over the dense forests which covered the country from the Avon to the Dee. Beyond us were Warwick's ancient towers, and Kenilworth, the haunt of England's kings and queens, Taworth Keep, Guy's Cliff, and the home of the Black Dog of Arden.

I now heard from Kelly that Prince Rupert had formed a secret expedition to enable the Queen to join King Charles without encountering the danger of a conflict with Essex. Notwithstanding every precaution, information of the Prince's plan had reached Massey at Gloucester, and Captain Bound had volunteered to make an attempt to take the Queen a prisoner. The interception of a letter had put Kelly partly in possession of Bound's scheme, and he offered his services as a musician at Mr Lucy's masque, expecting that Bound would endeavour to be present for the purpose of learning Prince Rupert's movements, but he failed to discover him under the Friar's garb.

Kelly heard at Evesham that a troop of Parliamentarians had crossed the Avon at Harvington, but he had been unable to trace their destination. When I told him that I had recognized the Ghost in the streets of Stratford-on-Avon with the Friar on his back, he said, "We must push on, as there is no knowing what mischief that spy is bent upon."

At King's Norton we found a coach, containing three ladies, escorted by a dozen dragoons. My attention was arrested by a beautiful lady with a spaniel in her lap, who gave orders to those around her with a manner of exceeding authority. This was no other than Henrietta Maria, Queen of England, and one of the most fascinating women in the world.

Fixing her radiant black eyes on Kelly, she recognized him as one of the Earl of Worcester's devisers of strange engines, and beckoning to him with her little hand, she addressed him as "Monsieur Keely," and leaning over the side of the coach, asked with her peculiar silvery laugh, "Why he left his smokers?"

I could see by in friend's countenance that something was wrong after she had spoken to him for a few minutes. On returning he said to me, "That fellow Bound has had the impudence to pass himself off as an aide-de-camp of Prince Rupert's, and has possessed himself of some important despatches to the King at Oxford." And such was the fact! Bound had discovered that our squadron was to meet the Queen and escort her to Stratford, and, fearing to be outnumbered, had given up the plan of taking her Majesty prisoner. But he had the impudence to meet the Queen's escort from Walsall, watched his opportunity to ride up, and giving the pass-word, "God and Queen Mary," was permitted to approach her Majesty.

With a glib tongue he asked for some important papers, and coolly waited while the dragoons searched for the parcel and gave it him without hesitation. With a profound salutation he galloped away, as it was supposed, on his return to the Prince, but in reality on his road to Gloucester with his prize, papers from the Marquis of Ormond and the Earl of Antrim.

Prince Rupert, who arrived with a regiment of dragoons, was furious with rage and pale with anger. I was despatched in pursuit of Bound, but he had an hour's start, and rode by a circuitous path through the forest of the Lenches to Pershore.

The Queen, now protected by a large body of troops, proceeded to Stratford, where she was entertained at New Place by Mrs Susannah Hall, Shakespeare's daughter. She lived, during her stay, in the rooms Shakespeare frequented in his later years, and slept in the chamber in which he died.[1]

On my return to Stratford, after a fruitless expedition in search of Bound, I was ordered, with my Longdon troopers, to keep a strict guard at New Place, and was presented to her Majesty by Prince Rupert as the son of the King's private secretary, Colonel Miles Forester.

We had now in and around Stratford 3000 foot, 1500 horse, 150 waggons, and a train of artillery, so that our requisitions in the neighbourhood soon disappeared, and every house was filled to overflowing. My own quarters were in Dead Lane,[2] near New Place.

Lord Cockayne now joined her Majesty's suite, and took upon himself the superintendence of the supply of provisions for her table. He was often engaged in the pursuit of Avon eels, Bidford cherries, and Shottery chickens. Never to be forgotten either was his scarlet velvet coat, blue breeches slashed with silver, and ostrich feather in his hat. The yokels in the streets looked upon him with perfect admiration, as he passed by, followed by two servants carrying fruit, eggs, or other dainties.

The Queen commanded my attendance at New Place almost as soon as I mounted guard, and asked me many questions respecting my last letters from Oxford, what my father said about the appearance of the King, how he bore himself, and what the state of his health. I was amused with her broken English and pronunciation, as in the days of the Tudors. She 'seyde gude' and 'maister', and 'tway' for two, very different from the fashionable talk of high personages. She was somewhat petite, as the French term it, of beautiful features and delicate complexion, with black hair almost as luxuriant as Mary Bromley's. Her apparel was a simple white gown worked with summer roses, and slashed sleeves drawn up with broad green ribbon; her bodice was laced with gold chains and pendant pearls.[5]

As General of the forces assembled around her – after landing on the coast of Yorkshire in February – danger and fatigue, and the sight of death, had not daunted her. She was present at the taking of Wetherby by storm, had generally ridden on horseback on the march, and taken her meals in the sight of the army. She spoke much of plans for carrying on the war, too much so for a woman, and the word peace never once crossed her lips.

As I paced to and fro, overlooking the sentries and attending to other duties, thoughts of the great responsibility of the Queen often crossed my mind, and how the best and worst men have been influenced for good or evil by good or bad women. Every one near King Charles knew how his Queen had wound herself around his heart, and now she was about to rejoin him, would her influence be exercised for the nation's weal or woe! Would she plead for the voice of the people to be heard, or for the 'divine right of kings', and for her own Popish religion, which the people hated?

Then I thought of all that poets said and sung of woman's love, and an inner voice whispered the question: "What is the worth of wealth, or ambition, or the gallantry of a Court, or the triumphs of a battle-field, if one is doomed to face the battle of life alone, and can never hope to gain the love of the one woman the heart has gathered to itself?"[7]

As these thoughts were passing through my brain, Mary Bromley issued from her aunt's house and half stopped when she saw me, as if she had something on her mind she wanted to say; she hesitated, then, with a serious air, expressed a wish to ask a favour. I was going to inspect the guard at the boat ferry on the Avon, and proposed to Mary to accompany me thus far, so we strolled together beneath the great elms which line the river bank. I was somewhat dismayed when I heard that she wished me to obtain an audience of the Queen. I asked her what Mary Bromley, a Puritan's daughter, could possibly have to say to the Queen of England?"

"It is for peace, Richard, that I would plead, aye, plead on my bended knees, as a woman to a woman. The Queen has much, all say, in her power; her solicitations ever influence the King; I would entreat of her, by all that is holy in woman's nature, to endeavour to arrest this horrible war. Oh, Richard, I implore you to aid me."

It was impossible for me to refuse such entreaties from Mary, but I told her of the Queen being present at the bloody storming of Wetherby, and of the warlike tenour of her conversation. She still implored me to obtain an interview, and finally confessed how her aunt had become acquainted with Bound's plot, and that, stern Puritan as she was, she nevertheless was disgusted at an attempt to entrap the Queen by a sneaking ambush. Thus it happened that she allowed Mary to go to the Shakespeare dance, disguised as Mistress Quickly, in hopes that she might give some warning of the Queen's danger. Mary recognized my long curls, and tried to attract my attention.

Soon after I saw the Queen walking in the garden at New Place, looking at the mulberry-tree the great bard had planted, so, putting on a bold face, I bent the knee before her, and requested an audience for a few moments for a fair friend I had known from my earliest youth. The Queen laughed heartily when she understood it was for a young lady I thus entreated, but immediately consented to my request. I then led Mary, blushing and almost weeping, into her presence, when seating herself on a garden chair, she held out her hand to be kissed. I was retiring, but the Queen commanded me to remain, and addressing Mary, said "Eh bien, fair maiden, what would you say to Queen Mary?"

Mary Bromley knelt before her Majesty on the green grass. and as soon as she could compose her utterance, replied, "Oh, deem it not presumptuous, our England's Queen, that a poor maiden should implore you, on her bended knee, to lend your powerful aid in restoring peace to our unhappy and distracted country. It is rumoured that the Parliament have offered to entreat. What influence must his beloved Queen have upon the kindly heart of his Majesty! What greater blessing than to be able to reflect that you have prevented the slaughter of Englishmen by Englishmen, and the rending of thousands of English homes and hearths! For pity's sake, gracious Madam, save us from more war!"

Henrietta Maria bid Mary Bromley to arise, and her cheeks flushed and paled, then flushed again. She spoke in a hurried manner and somewhat passionately, as if she had listened to pleadings she heartily disapproved of. She declared that rebels against 'God's own anointed' must be punished as they deserved; the laws of God and man demanded this, and the despisers of all Church government and Church doctrines must be taught that heresy was a sin no Government could endure or sanction.

When the Queen ceased to speak, she arose from her seat, as if to put an end to the audience, but Mary remained still kneeling, her hands clasped together, as if she was praying, and she said gently, "Oh, your gracious Majesty, what have these human doctrines ever done to establish that peace and goodwill on earth which our Master Christ died to teach? Was it not the splitting of miserable straws about doctrines that made Sir Thomas More, the good Catholic, fierce and unrelenting in his religious animosity against Master Tyndall? Behold the fruit of quarrelling over doctrines in Queen Mary's time; in the fires of Smithfield; the massacres of St Bartholomew; the burning of Servetus by Calvin. Our Master's doctrine was a *noble life* not a theory of creeds. Away with doctrines, if they are thus to be the curse of our common Christianity."

I was startled at Mary's boldness and enthusiasm, and the Queen drew herself up, and with much hauteur and stateliness commanded me to lead 'Mees Bromley' from her presence.

I conducted Mary back to her aunt's house, and she wept bitterly and would not be comforted. I took her little hands in mine and even dried her tears as they rolled down her cheeks; but Mary's heart was sore, and well it might be, when I reflect, now, how differently matters might have ended had Queen Henrietta Maria thrown her influence on her return to Oxford, for the cause of peace, instead of the continuance of the war.

The following day a flourish of trumpets announced the return of Prince Rupert who had gone to Oxford. He came prepared to escort her Majesty to Wroxton Abbey, and we soldiers of Worcestershire were to accompany the escort. The Queen took a kindly leave of Mistress

Susannah Hall and Mistress Quiney,[4] thanking them heartily for their reception of their wandering Queen. She carried away for the King some relics of the poet's birth-place, and a leaf of his mulberry. She had a kindly and forgiving heart too, for she enquired for 'leetle Mees Bromley', and gave me for her a form of prayer by Bossuet. But I saw no more of Mary, although I looked up at Madam Bourne's window as we rode past in front of the Queen, who was mounted on a grand charger belonging to Prince Rupert, and appeared in high spirits at the thought of again meeting her Royal husband.

When we reached the village of Kineton, the King's standard was drooping in the July sun, the Queen rode to the front and King Charles galloped up to welcome his beautiful wife. They met at Kineton[5] for the first time since their long separation, and the Queen's journey to France to levy foreign aid and money. A bad omen this meeting so close to the slain at Edgehill. It is recorded that ravens were croaking the live-long day above the house where their Majesties slept, and voices were heard that night; shouts as of strong men still striving in the tempest of battle. Then these would pass away, and the sobs of the dying came back in the whistle of the winds.

It was arranged that their Majesties should pass the night at Wroxton but, as the rain came down in torrents, they took shelter and remained at Kineton. Every precaution against surprise was taken by the officers in command of the escort, and I bivouacked with our Worcestershire squadron on the edge of the hill between Ratley and Radley. Notwithstanding the rain and discomfort the men were in good spirits, eating their drenched rations contentedly, and drinking to the toast of "God save King Charles and Queen Mary!" Before us lay the battle-field with the memory of the dead.

At night I wrapped myself in my horseman's coat, and recalled the scenes on the plain below, twelve months before. Were these scenes to be re-enacted in other parts of England? Already women were wringing their hands and wailing over their dead in many an English homestead. Was England to be turned into a charnel house? Then I thought of Mary Bromley's weeping figure as she knelt before the Queen. The night seemed long and wearisome, and a dense mist covered the battle-field below.

I was glad when morning came, and with it the passing of the rain cloud and return of sunshine. The sound of a bell tolling at Radford

Church came across the lea, and I saw two figures standing upon the mound from whence the King watched the strife at Edgehill. It was King Charles showing the battle-ground to his wife, and the quarry hole under the hill which had been filled with the bodies of the slain.

The arrival of their Majesties at Oxford was the signal for the renewal of operations. It was evident that the Queen and the Council were for continuing the war, and no more was heard of peaceful messages to the Parliament. From Oxford Prince Rupert emerged again and again, slaughtering in skirmishes, but winning no decisive battle.

Intercourse of trade between Oxford and London was forbidden by royal proclamation, and great despondency prevailed among the Parliamentarians. At a general council of war it was determined to besiege Bristol, which Colonel Fiennes surrendered within three days to Prince Rupert. The King visited the conquered city and resolved to take possession of Gloucester, which would have been easy when invested by Lord Herbert, but was now stronger than ever owing to the enthusiasm of the citizens and the capacity of Governor Massey.

In the mean time the news-letters of the Parliamentarians had alarmed the whole country with calumnious reports of the conduct of the Cavalier cavalry. Not only were Prince Rupert, Colonel Lunsford, Lord Digby and other Cavalier officers called Plunderers and Blazers, but it was currently reported that they had 'seized infants in the streets, stuck them on their pikes, and afterwards devoured them'. The gallant Lunsford was said to have a dried child's tongue and ham ready for any caller at his quarters.[6]

Early in August I was sent by Prince Rupert to occupy Tewkesbury with a squadron of horse, and to watch and report, as far as it was possible, upon the state of things at Gloucester. Soon after I had taken up my quarters at the Swan Tavern I received a communication from Squire Jeffreys, of Earl's Croome Court, near Upton, respecting the raising of some recruits. I therefore rode over, attended by Sampson and Jack Tandy.

Mr Jeffreys resided in an old timbered dwelling house near the Norman church, which is well nigh hidden with clustering ivy. An avenue of fine oaks leads to the entrance, and cattle were grazing in the rich, green meadows. Mr Jeffreys was a lover of paintings, and his hall was nearly filled with portraits, among which were several by Holbein, and two by the celebrated modern painter Vandyck. When I entered,

Mr Jeffreys was sitting for his own portrait to his clerk, Mr Samuel Butler, a native of Strensham, who afterwards became much more distinguished for the efforts of his pen than those of his brush.[7] In later times Butler described himself in his portrait of his hero:

> *He was in logic a great critic,*
> *Profoundly skilled in analytic,*
> *On either side he would dispute,*
> *Confute, change hands, and still confute.* [8]

He had a dry kind of humour about him which entertained his patron, and he sang a royalist song with a melodious voice.

Before we departed Mr Jeffreys insisted upon carrying a tankard of sack with his own hands to Sampson and Tandy, and as they quaffed it Sam Butler trolled out:

> *Bring the bowl which you boast,*
> *Fill it up to the brim,*
> *Tis to him we love most,*
> *And to all who love him.*

Then we all doffed our steel caps, and when Mr Jeffreys said, "King Charles, God bless him!" We gave an English Hurrah, which made the welkin ring. Nor did this content our host; he insisted upon presenting my troopers with a sucking pig which was hanging in his larder, and which is generally considered most succulent, wholesome, and delicious victuals. Sampson and Tandy carried the pig by turns, and as we passed through the streets of Tewkesbury, the pig's hind quarters were exhibited from under Tandy's buff coat as he carried it under his arm.

When we rode into the yard of the Swan Tavern, the Roundhead brothers, Help-on-High and Zion-build Fox, were standing together at the door of their domicile, the house said to have been occupied by the Duke of Clarence after the battle of Tewkesbury. Notwithstanding their Parliamentarian proclivities they saluted me, and I observed that Zion-build's nose, which resembled the knocker of a door, was redder than usual.

The day following, thinking I might hear some news about Gloucester, I decided upon paying a visit to Mr Snip the barber. Barbers have generally a wonderful store of information, and are ready to discourse on politics, on religion, on things in general, and, particularly, on the sayings and doings of their neighbours. Master Snip had shaved Sir William Russell and Mr Richard Dowdeswell, curled the wigs of Mr Bromley, Sir William Waller, and Governor Massey, and had touched with diamond powder the fair cheeks of the Earl of Cockayne. In religious matters Mr Snip had a habit of adapting himself to the customer for the time being.

He had a Prayer-Book in one drawer given him by the Vicar of Tewkesbury, and a large series of tracts by Baxter, presented to him by the Foxes. He rarely used the party phrases then so common, but had been heard to say "Je-hosha-phat", as he carefully drew aside Zion-build's nose in order that he might get at his chin. He had also been heard to whistle 'Hey for Cavaliers, Ho for Cavaliers', as he heated the tongs for curling Mr Dowdeswell's peruke. I wore my own hair, and although I had then very little beard, I called upon Snip in hopes of some information about our enemies. I announced that I wished to be shaved, and, while he was making up the lather, looked out into the street.

I was about to put some leading questions about Roundheads in general, and Gloucester Roundheads in particular, when I saw Mr Bromley ride by with Mary, and with them the youth I had saved from drowning in the Teme at Powick fight. There was no mistake about it! There was the same bright face and laughing expression, which even the danger from which he had been rescued could not obliterate. He was smiling, and looking right lovingly at Mary, and Mary – it made my heart ache – looked lovingly at him! My first impulse was to rush into the street and accost the party, but I refrained, when Mr Snip remarked, "Grand hair, Miss Bromley's; would make a wig fit for Mr Lenthall, the Speaker! Thousand pities that Mr Bromley should be obliged to leave Hamme Court!"

"Mr Bromley obliged to leave Hamme Court," I said, in astonishment. "Yes, Sir," he continued, "could stand it no longer, dangerous proximity to Hanley Castle!" Here I flinched, and received a gash for my pains. Then Snip said, "Young Captain Forester has joined Prince Rupert's 'Eatalls', and he and his soldiers have kidnapped several fat children and supped on them! The bound I gave from the bench on which I was sitting, and the Cavalier expletives I let forth in a volley, did not appear to discompose Mr Snip one whit. He merely simpered out, "Good lack, good lack, you are never Captain Forester!"

On my questioning the Barber as to the origin of such calumnious and ridiculous reports, he said that everybody in Tewkesbury knew that they were true; that Captain Bound, a gallant officer in the Parliamentarian army, well known and highly respected at Upton, had stated as an undeniable fact that a 'squab baby' was the favourite food of Prince Rupert's Own; that Gabriel Guzzle, the mustard and stocking merchant, and the well known Brothers Fox, Hopewell, Help-on-High, and Zion-build,[9] all men of letters and learning, although now deprived and silenced, had seen with their own eyes the hind quarter of a fat child protruding from under the buff coat of one of Captain Forester's men as they rode in from a foray."

As Master Gabriel Guzzle, of mustard repute, lived directly opposite the Barber's, I said no more to Master Snip, but walked straight to his dwelling and gave a loud rap at the door. Gabriel not only sold mustard but was a usurer, and a hard one, in these hard times. The room into which I was shown was full of furniture and plate, once the property of, alas! now, needy gentlemen. There were mirrors, and family portraits, one or two by the celebrated Vandyck; there were silver crosses and precious relics, showing the destitution of some family who cherished the old religion, wedding rings, and the much loved Bible of the Puritan.

Gabriel received me with a smirk and a smile, thinking, no doubt, that I came to negotiate a loan. With his hands in his pockets, he jingled some pistoles as if they were at my service when the pound of flesh was settled. I disappointed him by enquiring with a stern countenance what he meant by daring to circulate calumnious reports respecting the King's officers. Gabriel bowed and simpered, and referred me to the Brothers Fox with the wonderful baptismal appellations, two of whom were now passing down the street.

I knew these gentlemen by repute, for their father had once been Curate of Forthampton, and was suspended for Nonconformity. Bishop Goodman, too, of Gloucester, had a strong belief in the 'froward and subborn disposition' of the Fox family. It was therefore in somewhat angry mood that I crossed the street and interrogated Help-on-High and Zion-build on the reports they had disseminated. Help-on-High, who had learned to be 'cannie' in Scotland, allowed Zion-build to reply, and he looked as if he wished that his Brother Hopewell, the fighting priest had been there in his stead. Nevertheless, after fumbling and twisting for some moments, he muttered something about Captain Bound.

"And what about Captain Bound, Sirs," I said in a downright fury, and in a tone that took the colour out of Help-on-High's nose. That "Esteemed and highly religious officer of the Parliament's army," they declared, "so well known and so much respected at Upton-on-Severn and the surrounding neighbourhood," had told them, and every one around, of the favourite dish of Prince Rupert's Own. And not only so, but Captain Bound was standing at their window when I rode into the Swan followed by two troopers, one of which had a fat baby under his arm, whose features the Captain believed he recognized. At this sight Bound was well nigh distracted and would have rushed to see if his surmises were correct, had he not been restrained, as he certainly would have been made prisoner by the royalist dragoons. As it was he left Tewkesbury in tears!

I could stand this no longer. "Do you mean to tell me, Sirs," I shouted, "that you or Captain Bound really believed that a sucking pig presented to my troopers by Mr Jeffreys, of Earl's Croome Court, was a human child!"

"Pig! oh, indeed," said Zion-build; "Pig, hugh, hugh," grunted Gabriel; "Pig, hah, hah," said Help-on-High.

"Yes, Sirs, *pig*!" I replied; "and I give you my word and honour, as an officer and a gentleman, that if you do not, within an hour, contradict the atrocious statements you and your friend Captain Bound have circulated respecting the soldiers of your King, I will quarter a dozen of my reputed Baby-eaters on you for the next month at your own charges."

Saying this I departed in high dudgeon; but I had reason to know that forthwith the brothers Fox made a peregrination throughout the town. Nevertheless, the women of the lower class ever looked askance as we paraded up and down the streets, and, what was still more significant, and has never happened before or since, not a child was to be seen in the streets of Tewkesbury for several days.

Chapter Twelve

WHEN THE Benedictine monks of Tewkesbury were driven forth at the suppression of monasteries by Henry VIII, the Abbot's house was preserved, though the cloisters were wrecked. The Abbey Church itself was deemed superfluous, and would have been pulled down and sold for building materials, as was Winchcombe and others, but the parishioners implored and bought it from the King in 1539.

A Royalist, Mr Copfold, now lived in the Abbey House, and cultivated a garden upon the site of the ruined cloisters, while a Roundhead had built a cowshed where once stood the Lady Chapel. Mr Copfold loved the grand old Church, which for long centuries had thrown its shadow towards the meeting of the waters of the Severn and Avon, and it went to his inmost soul to behold its desecration by the Parliamentarian soldiers. He called upon me respecting some wounded men who were lying in the Church, and among them two of our Longdon troop, who had fallen in a skirmish with Massey's men close to Queen Margaret's camp.

Alas for the Abbey Church! The building Kings loved to visit, and the burial-place of the Plantagenets, de Clares, Despensers, and Beauchamps. The nave had been turned into a stable full of straw and litter, and the choir and chapels into sleeping apartments and a hospital. The beautiful Beauchamp chapel had been shattered and knocked to pieces by the emissaries of Thomas the Mawler[1] and it was now occupied by a narrow couch, on which lay a dying soldier.

Another youth lay stretched in the Despenser chapel. He had fallen in an attack upon the fortified house at Beddington Manor, and wished to see me and send a last message to his mother, who lived in the quiet village of Longdon. Shot through the lungs, the surgeons gave no hope that he would ever see his beloved home again. Poor boy! he was not yet twenty, and but for the war would have been leading a peaceful, useful life among the kine and sheepfolds above the Longdon mere. I had been the means of persuading him to become a soldier just a year before.

He raised himself on the stretcher as I entered the narrow little chapel, and, whispering an entreaty that he might be buried in the churchyard by the old home, sent a last message to the mother who bore him, and to a young girl who had promised to become his wife when the war was over. It was not soldier-like, but my eyes filled with tears as I promised to attend to his request, and bid him think of that better world where there should be no more war, no more sin. Mr Copfold had attended to the dying man's comfort, and I passed onwards to another scene.

Loud cries of anguish burst forth from the chapel of St Margaret, where stands the monumental effigy of Guy de Bryan, the standard-bearer at Crecy and Poitiers. Here were three or four couches occupied by wounded Parliamentarians, among whom the two chirurgeons of Tewkesbury laboured with their coats off and their arms bare. The man who was shrieking with pain had just had his arm cut off, and the hot iron applied to the raw stump. It was all they could do, the surgeons said, to save the limb from mortification.

This victim was a tenant of Mr Bromley's, and had joined the Parliamentarians at Gloucester. Sitting on the side of the couch, and bathing his face with strong restoratives, sat Mary Bromley, the picture of sorrowing pity. Squire Bromley had assisted in holding the patient during the necessary operation, and was now telling him "to bear a brave heart, as the worst was over."

Mr Copfold and I stood contemplating the scene for some time, as all engaged were too much occupied with their mournful work to observe us. Then as the man rallied, and the surgeons left to attend another sufferer, I stepped forward to tell Mr Bromley I was for the time the military governor of Tewkesbury, and begged of him to accept my services in any way he thought proper. Mary looked up, her eyes suffused with tears; and pale and trembling from the scene she had just witnessed, while her father thanked me in a kindly manner.

For some weeks I visited this hospital daily, and with the aid of Mr Copfold and the Bromleys, the wounded were well cared for and sustained. We had just heard at Tewkesbury of the good news of the surrender of Bristol to the Royalists, when Giles Nanfan rode in with a troop of horse, accompanied by Mr Dowdeswell, of Bushley Park. Soon after a trumpet sounded, announcing the arrival of a deputation from Gloucester. With the Gloucester burgesses, was a cousin of Giles Nanfan's, Mr Edward Harley,[2] who had joined the army of the Parliament under the command of Sir William Waller.

He was a singularly handsome young man, with an air of hauteur, and an eye of fire, and he and his cousin Giles met with but a very slight token of recognition. He was the son of Sir Robert and Lady Brilliana Harley, of Brampton Bryan Castle, proud of his ancient descent from Saxon lineage, and of belonging to a family recorded by the leger book of Pershore to have defeated the Danes before the days of Canute. [3]

He appeared to be on very intimate terms with Mary Bromley and her father, and I was not by any means delighted at the ease and familiarity with which he addressed Mary, and carried her off to look at the grand Norman tower of Tewkesbury Abbey. Mr Richard Dowdeswell and Mr Hill, a burgess of Tewkesbury, endeavoured to persuade the citizens of Gloucester to avoid the dangers of an assault from the Royal army, and perhaps the ruin and sack of the city. [4]

The negociations failed! Captain Harley made a profound salutation to Mary, and a very slight inclination of his head to Giles and myself, then marched away to Gloucester with his burgesses and trumpeter.

In the evening the latter returned to declare that it was determined to defend Gloucester against the King. Giles now told me how Sir Robert Harley was a man of wit, learning, and piety, but austere, and in his religion deeply imbued with the views of the Puritans. He had delighted in the suppression of much that we Cavaliers reverenced in the Church of England, and hated even the name of an altar or a cross. But he had paid dearly for his rebellious conduct. His wife, Lady Brilliana, and her younger children, had been closely besieged in Brampton Bryan Castle; his village, his church, his parks, and farms had been raided and destroyed, and even now Lady Brilliana was expecting again to be besieged by our forces.

Reports of various omens and prodigies – sure tokens of stormy times – were now rife in Worcestershire and Gloucestershire. At Upton –on-Severn Mistress Bound's white cat brought forth black kittens. The owls among the ivy at Hanley Castle hooted in the day time, and two were seen flitting in the face of the sun. Aunt Tabitha's latest batch of cowslip wine turned sour, and no amount of honey would disguise its acrimony. The Tewkesbury carrier was passing over the Cotswold hills, with his men and pack-horses, a little before the dawn of day, and they 'saw most sensibly and very perspicuously in the air, muskettiers, harnessed men and horsemen moving in battel array, and assaulting one another in divers furious postures.' [5]

My duties took me much from Tewkesbury day, having outposts at

Boddington Grange, at Strensham, and the village of Cheltenham, when I received orders of the Governor of Worcester to intercept the importation of some bags of gunpowder which a spy reported the Roundheads were about to move in a barge from Tewkesbury to the faithless city of Gloucester. In order to throw dust in the eyes of the Royalists, the barge would carry bags of mustard, as freight for Bristol, and the powder was to be sent to Deerhurst for embarkation. I was also to search the house at the New Park above Tewkesbury, where a suspected Sergeant-at-arms resided, whom, the spy declared, had lately purchased large quantities of ammunition for fire-arms.

Wishing to avoid unnecessary annoyance, I determined to go to Tewkesbury Park accompanied only by a couple of troopers, and sent von Prig, the German Captain, with a score of arquebusiers, to Deerhurst, giving him orders to stop any boat or barge passing down the Severn. I rode by the ruins of Hamme Castle, once the residence of the Earls of Gloucester, and above which now waved, not the proud banner of de Clare or Despenser, but the arms of a windmill, and I crossed the Bloody Meadow, where fell in heaps the wearied troops of Margaret of Anjou before the victorious legions of the Lion of York.

The house at the New Park is that which Leland saw, and where then lived 'my Lord Spenser and late my Lady Mary'. It stands where Somerset, in his anger, is said to have 'stroke out the brains' of Lord Wenlock, whom he thought false. A beautiful garden, tended by a fair maiden with flowing hair and carolling a royalist ditty, now covered the green slopes where Richard of Gloucester led his men of the ambuscade, and, watching his fair daughter, was the suspected Sergeant at arms, looking very little like a Roundhead and a rebel.

My duty was to search the house from attic to cellar for the reported ammunition, but I found nothing save some casks of excellent cider and a butt of canary, which the hospitable Sergeant insisted upon broaching, and himself gave the toast of "King Charles, God bless him." Shaking my entertainer by the hand, and doffing my plumed hat to his daughter, we galloped by the Duke of Gloucester's oak for Deerhurst Church, across the lea, when we heard von Prig's musqueteers firing heavily on the banks of the Severn.

On reaching the river I saw to my horror Mr Bromley, in the stern of a barge, waving a white kerchief from the point of his sword; his daughter Mary standing up facing my musqueteers as if she courted the line of shots from the banks, and two boatmen making frantic efforts to bring the lumbering barge to the river banks.

I had arrived in time to prevent a sad catastrophe, or at least, a worse than what befell us. Mr Bromley and Mary were taking their wounded tenant to Gloucester for better advice, and had stretched an awning with iron stanchions, over the stern of the barge, to protect the sufferer from rain or wind. The boatmen, not understanding von Prig's strange shouts to "Bring the sheep to shoor," paddled in the middle of the river, and thus drew on them the fire of the soldiers, who thought the vessel was laden with gunpowder bags for Gloucester.

At the very first shot both Mr Bromley and Mary threw themselves between the line of fire and the wounded man. Nevertheless, as the barge did not come in shore, the troopers continued to fire until I rode up and commanded them to cease. The barge now approached, and although Mary looked pale and excited, she was brave and quiet. Mr Bromley was justly most indignant until I entered into explanations, which fully excused the action of von Prig. But alas! alas! Mr Bromley's poor tenant was mortally wounded, as he lay on his stretcher beneath the awning, and this escaped our notice until I had boarded the barge and finished my conversation with Mr Bromley.

A slug which would certainly have struck Mary, as she stood forth to shelter the unfortunate patient, hit one of the iron stanchions, and deflecting downwards, lodged in the throat of the wounded man. The blood welled from the orifice as we carried him from the barge and laid him upon the Severn bank, his face turned towards the Malvern Hills which rose above his old home, and his eyes, now rapidly glazing with the film of death, were fixed upon the scenes of his youth. Suddenly he rose upon one arm, and holding forth his hand to Mary, he murmured something about "bless" and "goodness", when his spirit fled, and his head sank upon the green turf beside.

We carried his corpse and laid it in the village church in the aisle, near the old Saxon doorways, until it received 'a metely burial'. Sorrowfully and sadly Mary and her father set forth to walk back to Tewkesbury, and sorrowfully and sadly I mounted my charger at the head of my troops. Even von Prig was moody and silent, and the men conversed in hoarse whispers on the way.

We then rode for Newent, to join the Welsh and Herefordshire Royalists under Sir William Vavasour. Sir William was quartered at

The Castle, a fair sized house near the Castle Tump at Dymock, and we occupied Newent and the Royal Charles. In a few days we were joined by Mr Hall, of Highmeadow in the Forest of Dean, and with him came six servants well armed.

Lord Herbert, afterwards Earl of Glamorgan, then arrived, bringing his eldest son, a lad of thirteen.[6] Mr Cocks, of Castleditch, near Ledbury, and Master Eddud Clark. We established communications with Dymock, Ledbury, and the Forest of Dean, and Clark reared a great beacon of gorse and fir wood on the summit of May Hill, which would show a dense smoke by day, or flames by night, should Massey attempt one of his favourite flank marches. In the meantime Massey set fire to Highnam House, and burnt it to the ground. This caused much wailing and lamentation on the part of the Church clergy, for George Herbert's manuscripts were consumed in this doomed manor-house.

The first blood shed before the arrival of the King was at Brockworth, the residence of Lady Gyse, the widow of Sir William Gyse, of Brockworth and Elmore. She was entertaining Lord Chandos, of Sudeley, who ventured there on a visit to ascertain how matters stood at Gloucester. A sortie was made from the city, by the Parliamentarians, but Brockworth was a *domus defensabilis*, and the citizens lost several men in the attempt, but did not catch Lord Chandos.

On the memorable 10th of August, we saw from Lassington Hill many men and women running along the walks on the city walls, and soldiers occupying the battlements. All the eight drawbridges were up, and then appeared large bodies of troops encamping upon Tredworth field, and the King's standard floating in the breeze. The land was covered with standing corn, which before night was trampled into mire and mud by the King's cavalry under Prince Rupert.

On the afternoon of the 10th August, the King sent a message requiring the city to surrender. John Philpot, the Somerset herald, proclaimed it in the Tolsey, as General Massey would not permit it to be read in the street. The answer was delivered by Sergeant-major Pudsey to the King in person on Tredworth field, to the effect that the citizens of Gloucester had determined to keep the city "according to the commands of his Majesty signified by both Houses of Parliament." The King was accompanied by the Prince of Wales, the Duke of York, then mere youths, Prince Rupert, General Ruthven, the Earl of Sunderland, and Viscount Falkland.

In the meantime we Worcester troops marched from Lassington to the slopes of the Vineyard, and a sorry sight met our view. Massey had ordered the suburbs to be sacrificed, and two hundred and forty-one houses and a large church were in full blaze.

The next day the King's army commenced entrenchments at Gandy Green,[7] the trenches being within musket shot of the city walls. They also cut the pipes which conveyed the water from Robin's Wood Hill. Sir Jacob Astley took up a position on the east, and Lord Ruthven occupied a front facing the ruins of Llanthony Abbey. The Hereford-shire men, under Sir William Vavasour, had possession of Maisemore and Vineyard Hill, and the Worcestershire troops were sent on to occupy two meadows at Longford and Kingsholm.

The Reverend Mr Wilse, Rector of Newent, rode in Lord Somerset's troop, equipped for battle like any soldier, with petronel and pole axe,[8] and accompanied by my gallant friend, Eddud Clark. The investment was now complete; all around the beleaguered city might be seen soldiers pitching their tents and plying their entrenching tools. The fire of musketry was continual, and now and then thundered forth the fire of cannon from the town, to be replied to by that of the King. Thus opened the famous siege of Gloucester.

Being an unusually wet season, we passed the first night in pouring rain, a thick fog rising in the morning, shrouding alike besiegers and besieged. When the fog cleared, those who occupied the high grounds, commanding the view of the city, little thought that it could long hold out against the formidable array which begirt it on all sides. But unfortunately, in the King's army, there were too many gentlemen and cavalry officers,[9] amateur soldiers riding fine horses and attended by fine servants, who never put foot in the trenches. From the first day of siege to the last, their chief occupation was riding over the country levying money, provisions, and forage, in a manner which often brought us great discredit.

I had been at Longford little more than a day when I was summoned to the King's quarters at Matson House, under Robin's Wood Hill. Matson House is beautifully situated, overlooking the vale of Gloucester. It is a modern structure, built in the days of Queen Elizabeth, surrounded by fine trees, and the little old church within a few paces of the garden gate. That humble room at Matson has often since recurred to my memory, for in it I beheld three royal personages, all destined to be Kings of England, Charles I, Charles II, and his present Majesty James II.

King Charles welcomed me with his accustomed grace and dignity, and gave me the latest tidings of my father, who was with the Queen at Oxford, before he questioned me upon the position of matters at Worcester and Tewkesbury, or the forces of Vavasour. The Prince of Wales was then a swarthy, strong-built youth of thirteen, and took great interest in my description of the disposition of the troops from Herefordshire and Worcestershire.

He expressed himself in a very determined manner respecting the conduct of the Gloucester citizens and garrison, saying, "If I were King I would not leave one stone standing of their boasted walls," a destruction which in after years he lived to carry out. The Duke of York, then a lad of eleven, was very zealous for the rigorous punishment of every one opposed to the royal cause, and very active in running to the top of Robin's Wood that he might bring us an account of all that could be seen.

As I knew the surrounding country and every hillock and dale within sight of Robin's Wood, the King was pleased to command that I should attend the Prince of Wales during the siege; I therefore remained at Matson House, and had been there only a day or two, when I discovered that the slow work of a siege was altogether unsuited to the character and disposition of the fiery Rupert.

He interfered with Ruthven in the working of the mines, and was constantly moving bodies of men who were employed with spades and mattocks in the trenches, so that sallying parties from the town watched their opportunities and inflicted great loss upon the foot soldiers in the trenches, with comparatively little to themselves,

The King was General and Commander-in-Chief, but unfortunately many other Generals had plans of their own which they attempted to carry out without proper consultation with each other, and with his Majesty.

Thus, for example, on the morning of the 12th August, Prince Rupert rode down to the Worcester regiment stationed at Kingsholm, and without any consultation with Lord Ruthven or Sir William Vavasour, carried off half the men for a raid on Cheltenham village, and a rich manor-house at Leckhampton. 'Too many cooks spoil the pottage', as we found to our cost and loss.

Watching their departure, Governor Massey with two hundred musketeers attacked the position at Kingsholm, now left with only 60 soldiers to defend it. In consequence of such bad management we lost nine of our best soldiers and Captain Corles.

The Earl of Cockayne now joined us at Matson, dressed in gorgeous array, scented with Dame Nanfan's lavender, his hair in long curls, and his fingers sparkling with rings. He took Prince James under his charge, and played scoperils[10] with him all day, at which I much rejoiced, having great difficulty in preventing the Prince of Wales from running into danger under the city walls.

Attempts were made to create breaches in the walls by undermining, but any success could not be followed up, for want of soldiers on the spot to storm. On the 15th, at the south side of Friar's Orchard, a mine exploded, and a considerable gap was the consequence, but the cavalry were not dismounted to storm the breach and the infantry were too few to attempt it, so the Parliamentarians quickly went to work with wool-sacks and baskets, women and boys assisting right heartily and braving the cannon and musketeers.

On the 18th of August the Worcester regiment was joined by the Herefordshire men, who crossed the Severn from Maisemore on a bridge of boats and marched to Kingsholm. It was agreed between Lord Edward Somerset and Lord Ruthven to attack the Awngate, and four cannon were drawn down to Kingsholm. An aide-de-camp galloped to Matson to acquaint his Majesty and Prince Rupert with this sudden decision, but the King had ridden to the trenches opposite Llanthony with Dr Chillingworth, who prepared sermons for Sundays and battery engines during the week, while Prince Rupert had gone to inspect the cavalry.

Lord Cockayne wrote to the besieged advising them to surrender at discretion, or they would be burnt alive in their houses, or hanged, drawn and quartered without mercy if taken prisoners, and he went with Prince James to find some means of sending his letter into the city. The Prince of Wales no sooner heard of the proposed attack on the Awngate than he determined to mount his pony and ride down to see it. Expostulation was useless! He started without me and I had no alternative but to ride after him, fervently wishing that I was at the head of my Longdon troopers instead of playing tutor to a wilful Prince.

On our arrival at Kingsholm I found to my utter dismay that Prince
Rupert had sent orders for at least half our horse to join him on the
Cirencester road. This movement of troops was immediately detected
by Governor Massey, who led a sortie of 400 musketeers through the
North Gate, and sent another force with Lieutenant Pincock over Little
Mead. Thus we had ridden to within five hundred yards of our
Worcester cannon, when Massey 'charged right up to the guns, spiked
them, and killed Captain Basset, two cannoniers, and a hundred
soldiers'.[11]

We must have been taken prisoners or killed, if Giles Nanfan, who
fortunately was left with a few cavalry, had not ridden among the
Royalists and entreated them to save their Prince. Then, charging in his
Rupert fashion, I had time to hurry Prince Charles out of danger, riding
back to Matson faster than we came. It was a most ignominious
proceeding, but far better than that the Prince should have fallen into
the hands of Governor Massey.

After this escapade, the King forbade the Prince of Wales to
approach the trenches, where Lords Sunderland and Falkland exposed
themselves so as to be blamed for unnecessary contempt of danger.[12]

On Sunday, the 3rd of September, we received intelligence that an
army of ten thousand men was advancing from London to raise the
siege of Gloucester, and a council was held at which, as it seemed to me,
no two of the generals were of the same opinion. Lord Cockayne still
clung to the hope that his persuasive pen might have an effect upon the
citizens, but, unluckily, his last effusion had fallen into the hands of the
Governor, who had given orders that no more letters should be allowed
to enter the town unless carried by one of his Majesty's trumpeters. But
my Lord determined to send a letter to the citizens, so, having seen
Prince James safe in bed and given him a sympathetic powder, he
started off to the trenches. Here he arranged that a soldier should shoot
an arrow into the town early in the morning, and attached to the arrow
was a paper containing the following words:

'These are to let you know that your God, Waller, hath forsaken you,
and hath retired to the Tower of London. Essex is beaten like a dog;
yeele to the King's mercie in time, otherwise, if we enter perforce, no
quarter for such obstinate trayterly rogues. From a Well-wisher.'

In the course of an hour the following reply was shot back:

Waller's no God of ours, base rogues you lie,
Our God survives from all eternity.
Though Essex beaten be, as you doe say,
Rome's yoke we are resolved ne'er to obey.
But for our cabbages which ye have eaten,
Be sure 'ere long ye shall be soundly beaten.
Quarter we ask you none; if we fall downe,
King Charles will lose true subjects with the towne. [13]

NICHOLAS CUDGELL-YOU-WELL

This was the last attempt to persuade the Parliamentarians to surrender. It was now determined to try the effect of a machine invented by the Reverend Dr Chillingworth, the King's Chaplain, a celebrated writer upon divinity, who taught the Royal Princes Caesar's *Commentaries*, the Church Catechism, and the multiplication table. The previous Sunday he preached a startling sermon on Saul and the Amalekites, eloquent and warlike, but not of that kind of Christianity which we attribute to Our Master.

The Divine had invented a contrivance, upon the plan of the Romans, 'testudines' he called it, a machine running upon cart wheels and forming a moving battery. It had thick planks to ward off musket balls, and these had apertures through which to fire, but it proved an utter failure as regards killing the rebels. When pushed forward to the town ditch, we lost several men in the operation; here it stuck fast and remained useless until after the siege, when it fell into the hands of the enemy, who made much sport of the Doctor and his 'Pulpit'.

Soon after this failure I was sent by the King to superintend the embarkation of the wounded in flatbottomed boats to carry them to Bristol, and while this was going on a countryman was seized who was the bearer of a letter to Governor Massey which he was trying to smuggle into the city. From this letter we learnt that Lord Essex was advancing with his London train-bands upon Stow-in-the-Wold, on his road to Gloucester.

On my carrying the epistle to Matson House, the King summoned a council of war, when again there arose great difference of opinion. Lord Ruthven wished to attack the south-eastern angle of the city walls and batter it with all our guns. A breach made, he proposed to dismount the cavalry and lead the stormers. Prince Rupert, on the other hand, proposed to take the cavalry to meet Lord Essex on his march and drive him back to London. The Earl of Cockayne proposed to turn the course of the Severn and drown the citizens.

Prince Rupert's plan was accepted by the King, and the next day he marched away with half the army, leaving the rest of us to our own devices and Dr Chillingworth's testudines. Six weeks had passed, and unless the Prince succeeded in defeating Essex, our prospect of taking the city was hopeless. On the 5th September the King sat down to supper anxious and distressed. He had attended service in the little church, with his sons, and was hoping to receive intelligence that the march of Essex was checked.

The night set in wild and stormy, when it was reported that a great fire was blazing upon the hill of Wainlode on the Severn, and that answering lights were flashing from the Cathedral tower. Early next morning a messenger arrived with accounts of the failure of Prince Rupert at Stow-in-the-Wold, and a warning to the King that Essex was almost at Cheltenham and would soon be before Gloucester. A great glut of rain had flooded the lowlands and filled the trenches with water, and it was considered advisable to remove the guns, fire the tents, and march on the crest of the Cotswolds. This done, our army marched up Painswick Hill and encamped upon the ancient fortification on Spone-bed Hill.

Here the King and the royal Princes dismounted and seated themselves upon a heap of stones near the centre of the great square. The Prince of Wales, courageous though he was, looked with sorrowful eyes upon the ground, and maintained a gloomy silence. The King's attention seemed concentrated on the stormy and threatening rain clouds, and on skies which looked as if God's sunshine was banished from them for ever. All around the earth was sodden, all above was tempestuous. The young Duke of York had crept close to his father's side, and, sheltering under his cloak, looked up into his face and besought him to take them away home.

"Alas, my child," replied the harassed monarch, as he still gazed upon the darkening firmament, "we have no home to go to."

Thus ended the siege of Gloucester. We had lost a good many brave men, expended much ammunition, and gained an ill name for plundering private houses and carrying off whole flocks of Cotswold sheep.

I was now sent by the King with a white flag and despatch to Governor Massey. As I passed Matson House I found a number of soldiers from the garrison at Gloucester in possession. Mr Selwyn had fled to Bristol, and several officers were examining the inscriptions left on the stone window sill by the Prince of Wales and the Duke of York.[15] Captains Purefoy and Harley received me with a soldier's greeting, and accompanied me to the city. We entered by the Alvin Gate, and the word 'Essex' was given as the countersign. I was straightway taken to the Tolsey and refreshments were offered, among them being the renowned Gloucester sweetmeats and sugared plums, with which, later on, General Cromwell was likewise presented.

Here I saw the Reverend John Corbet, chaplain to the Governor, and John Dorney, the town clerk, who have both since written their experiences of the siege. From them learnt that Massey had but fifteen hundred men of all ranks and arms to oppose the Royalist army, not enough to man the works and walls. The garrison had but fifty barrels of powder when the siege commenced, of which they fired away forty before the close. Lead was so scarce that round pebble stones from Lassington were sometimes used for bullets, and a mere lad shot a royalist officer dead with one of these.

I found General Massey civil, but with blunt and determined manners. He was of middle height, with brown hair and of a sanguine complexion.[15] He received the King's despatch with a kind of reverence, and said that it was rumoured that his Majesty contemplated employing 'those cursed Irish rebels against his English subjects, tigers who would tear the bowels of the mother who bare them'. He then declared that he would hand over the King's letter to Lord Essex, and directed that I should be conducted in safety to the North Gate.

I was glad to escape from the 'sanctified inhabitants of Gloucester', and their grim elders so loved by Baxter. Sanctified! Alas that the term should ever be employed to dogmatists, whether of Church or Chapel, however enthusiastic. I rode within a short distance of Tewkesbury, but learning that it was occupied by the train-bands of Essex, I returned for the night to the New Park, which the Roundheads had passed by and left undisturbed.

Chapter Thirteen

FROM Painswick King Charles proceeded to Sudeley Castle, famous for the grandeur of its buildings erected by Lord Boteler,[1] and now the residence of Lord Chandos, by whom his Majesty was hospitably received. The royal standard waved from the Portmare Tower, and merrily rang the bells of Winchcombe. In the meantime Lord Essex made his triumphant entry into Gloucester. Great were the congratulations, and greater still the consumption of sack, claret, and sugar plums, which the Mayor and Corporation found freely. On Sunday morning the 10th of September, Essex marched to Tewkesbury, and demanded the twentieth part of all royalists' income for the benefit of Gloucester.[2]

The King's army was now extended on a line of country reaching from Evesham to Winchcombe, his generals expecting that Essex would lead his train-bands back to London via Broadway and Stow-in-the-Wold. Indeed, he made a feint of doing so, for he left Tewkesbury suddenly, marched some distance on the Evesham road, then turned short to the right, and passing through Cheltenham reached Cirencester by midnight.

I now determined to ride to Worcester and report these movements to the Governor; so, avoiding Tewkesbury, I passed through Ashchurch and crossed the Avon at Twyning Fleet. At the little tavern built on the spot where the Danes are said to have turned back with their fleet of war vessels after the sack of Tewkesbury and Bredon, I fell in with Zion-build Fox, who had been paying the fishermen who supplied the eels for a Tewkesbury pastie for my Lord Essex. Zion-build had been quaffing early purl, and consequently was very communicative.

Notwithstanding the great size and excellence of the pastie, the 'elect' had come in for their share of clipping as well as the royalists, and Zion-build was wrathful accordingly. Every London apprentice who passed through Tewkesbury after raising the siege at Gloucester, marched away in a pair of Tewkesbury stockings without paying for them! The only consolation, at this wholesale appropriation of their goods, was that the inside of some of the socks were well rubbed with Tewkesbury mustard commingled with black pepper. I also learnt that Mr Bromley had returned to Hamme Court after an interview with Lord Essex.

I had ridden past Twyning Church and reached the wild waste of gorse and thickets known as Brockeridge Common, when I heard a stentorian voice shouting for aid, and the clash of arms. Placing my sword ready to my hand, I galloped towards the spot from whence the clamour proceeded. With his back against a great elm tree, I beheld a burly, powerful gentleman defending himself stoutly against the attack of four ragged ruffians who had unhorsed him, but whom he kept at a respectful distance by the sweep of a long basket-hilted sword, wielded by a very powerful arm. One of the robbers he cut down before I reached the tree under which he sheltered, but all his dexterity of fence would not have availed him against such odds, had I not struck down another of his assailants as I rode to the rescue.

In the mean time the attacked officer struck a third fellow such a blow across the iron casque he wore, that it fell to the ground and exposed his face, upon which he and his companion took to their heels with such extraordinary celerity, that they disappeared among the thickets and brushwood in a few seconds. It was some time before I could catch the stranger's horse, which had galloped off among the gorse. When I succeeded and led him to the scene of the rencontre, I found his master leaning on his sword and sternly surveying the dead bodies of the fallen robbers. The wide-brimmed Puritan's hat lay on the ground, and a horseman's cloak folded round his left arm had served as a shield when he was fighting for his life.

He gave me a military salute as I approached, and grasping my hand, thanked me, with a rough courtesy, for saving him from being murdered for the sake of his purse. I now perceived that he was bleeding from a slight wound in the neck, and, to staunch the blood, I bound my own kerchief round his massive throat; the kerchief Mary Bromley had worked for me, in days before sons fought against their fathers, and brother against brother.

I had now an opportunity of seeing the face of the stranger. It was one not easily forgotten! It was a face of power! The head massive; the eyes grey and small, but piercing; the nose large and heavy; a countenance that would have been harsh and severe, save that it lit up now and then with a kindly smile. The general character of the expression was that of stern sagacity.

"It was shameful," he declared,"that such scoundrels should infest public highways, and attack travellers in open day with impunity." He then assisted me to drag the dead bodies of the robbers and lay them under the elm tree, covering up their faces with fresh plucked gorse, and told me that he was a poor cousin of Mr Bromley's, and was riding for Ripple ferry on his road to Hamme Court, when thus attacked by highwaymen. He was a stranger to the neighbourhood and enquired the way, so, as I was riding by the same route to Upton- on-Severn, I offered to be his guide.

We passed by Ripple Church and village cross to the river, and the conversation of my companion was continuous. His manner of speaking was energetic and somewhat dictatorial. He never asked my name or whither I was going, although he must have known from my hat and feather that I was a Cavalier. He inquired about the position of Mr Bromley's residence, and admired the blue range of the Malverns in front of us; but without waiting for my reply he began to discourse upon theological subjects, and I heartily wished Aunt Tabitha or Mr Woodforde, had been in my place to listen.

He dilated upon the works of Baronius, but never once reverted to the siege of Gloucester. He spoke of the dogmatism of Cartwright, the controversies of Bellarmine, and the writings of Grotius, with an eloquence and facility of expression which astonished me; at the same time he delivered his utterances as if he were addressing a regiment of horse and preparing them for a charge.

At last our arrival before the entrance to Hamme Court reminded me that it was time to separate. Even then he would have exercised his powers of speech and mine of endurance by another theological dissertation, when I saw Mr Bromley approaching from among the elms. I was in no mood to meet him after our repulse from Gloucester, so I lifted my hat, and bid my companion a good afternoon. I had not ridden many yards when the poor cousin shouted in a stentorian voice and peremptory tone, "Stop, Sir! To whom may I tell my cousin Bromley that I am indebted for such timely aid and much intellectual conversation!"

This was too good! I had hardly spoken three sentences from first to last, so I merely replied by a salute, and setting spurs to my horse, galloped to Upton. I had passed the old farm house, known as South-end, when, standing beneath a large oak tree, I beheld Captain Edward Harley talking with Mary Bromley, and holding his horse by the bridle. I could not avoid passing them, or observing that she was listening with downcast eyes and a perturbed demeanour to his anxious and fervent speech. Looking at Mary, and bowing to my saddle bow, I spurred my charger until he bounded like a wild cat, and we were soon at The Lion at Upton. Alas! I fear my feelings were somewhat sanguinary, for I swore within my inmost heart that if I and Captain Edward Harley ever met upon the battle-field, one of us should never leave it alive.

I had hardly dismounted from my horse, when a trooper brought me a letter which he said had fallen from the pocket of a gentleman as he rode through the streets. It was addressed, 'For Captain Edward Harley, thes with my affection, present I pray at Gloster'. The seal was broken, and I felt that having just seen so pernicious a rebel, fresh from Gloucester, within a mile of a town where we Royalists were quartered, it was my duty to read it. Perhaps he had come over on Bound's business – that of a sneaking spy! At all events I had seen him with Mary Bromley under the Southend oak, so, gnashing my teeth, I opened the epistle, and read as follows:

> 'For Mr Edward Harley. My deare Ned, in triumph to Woster, then in haste in the more courtly to what purpose lately trained otherwise the viccount enriching themselves united under erle Simons and Richards to the hassard of or any when I sent in feareing fell fomented.'[3]

This went on through four long sheets, and was signed, 'Your affectionat Mother, Brilliana Harley'. I could make nothing of this precious epistle, nor did I learn, until years afterwards, that such letters were read by a key of cut paper, the openings of which correspond with the words within the brackets. At the same time I knew that Lady Brilliana was an accomplished letter writer, and that my Aunt Tabitha had once received from her a letter, since which, four years ago, a day seldom passed that Aunt Tabitha did not allude to it. It was an epistle principally about 'fiseke' for children when they were 'cuttin their teathe' – which certainly did not apply to Aunt Tabitha – that 'scurvy grass pounded and strained with beare is a most exclent thinge to purge the blood;'[4] with recipes for 'snipe pye, kyde pasties, and turky pyes'. The great thing about these pyes seemed to be that 'on halfe of the pye is seasned with on kind of seasening, and the other with another'.

At all events we seldom sat down to a supper after the receipt of that epistle that Aunt Tabitha did not say, "My Lady Brilliana Harley says."

Under the circumstances, I magnanimously determined to send Captain Edward Harley his illustrious mother's epistle; so borrowing a very large sheet of paper of John Kelly, I enclosed it, sealed with our great Forester seal, addressed 'To the care of Mistress Mary Bromley, these present, &c.'

On my return to Worcester, we received ere long an account of the bloody battle of Newbury in Berkshire, fought on the 20th September 1643. Here fell the accomplished Carey, Lord Falkland, distinguished alike for his bravery and unimpeachable purity. At first he was opposed to the 'thorough' policy of Laud and Strafford, but, apprehensive that the Parliamentarians aimed at the subversion of monarchy, he embraced the cause of the King, and became Secretary of State. Here died the Earl of Sunderland, and several of my old comrades at the siege of Gloucester. On both sides the losses were very severe. The London shopkeepers fought well, and lost fearfully in rank and file; but the King had to mourn for many more officers of rank and station than did the Puritans.

Hitherto my aunt and sister had suffered very little annoyance from our enemies, owing, no doubt, to the proximity of our garrison at Worcester, and the constant occupation of Upton by our troops. Nevertheless, in these perturbed times Isabel rarely crossed the drawbridge, and Aunt Tabitha's visits to Upton had become few and far between. The kindly smiles with which she was wont to be greeted were turned into sour looks and averted faces, and the very apples with which her pockets teemed, often returned to Hanley. She had been much exercised by a visit from my Lord Cockayne, who rode over from Worcester and asked Aunt Tabitha to accompany him to the church, which contained two ancient chasubles. He mightily offended my aunt by speaking lightly of the principles of the Reformation and Richard Hooker.

"When he came to the church," she wrote, "he krissed and crossed like any Papist, and talked not of praier and prayse, but of albs, challises, chimeres, of rochets of black, and blue, and redde satins, and the directororium anglicanorium.'

Soon after this we heard at Worcester of the Winceby fight near Horncastle on 11th October, and how Colonel Cromwell, Mr Bromley's cousin, had been nearly killed by our dashing Cavalier, Sir Ingram Hopton, who, alas! lost his own life in that desperate charge.

Then spur and sword was the battle word,
  and we made their helmets ring,
Shouting like madmen all the while,
  'For God and for the King'
And though they snuffled psalms,
  to give the rebel dogs their due,
When the roaring shot poured thick and hot,
  they were steadfast men and true.[5]

And now arose those sad Scottish and Irish complications which were to add to the curse already hanging over England. In the preceding year of 1642, when London was threatened by the King, Parliament sought the aid of the Scots, knowing that they loved cash above all things, but it was not until the middle of the year 1643 that these negotiations with the Scots were repeated by the English Puritans. They were now insisted on! The English Parliament sent £100,000 to Edinburgh, and the Scots prepared to march an army against their King and countryman. Thus there arose a very trying and difficult time for his Majesty.

Some among his courtiers, finding the Scots about to march across the border, thought it would be well to enlist the Irish Catholics in his Majesty's cause, and the Queen, Lord Digby, and other English noblemen maintained an active correspondence with the confederate Irish, through the Marquis of Ormonde, the Earl of Antrim, and Lords Dillon and Castlehaven.

When the Queen was at York, the valiant Earl of Montrose and the loyal Randall, Earl of Antrim, met at her Court, and then proceeded to Oxford, where they signed a compact,[6] and together concerted measures. Montrose was to raise the loyalists of Scotland, and Antrim was to make a descent upon the coast of Scotland with an army of Irish Catholics. In acknowledgment of Lord Antrim's services, the King, later on, wrote the following letter:

'Antrim, I have ever bene senciable of your very hearty affections in my service, and now I find the fruites of them likely to prove soe much to the advantage of my affaires by those forces which you caused to be landed in the highlands of Scotland, that it challengeth from mee very particular thankes; and as you have don those, soe I make no doubt but if you shall find it requisite for my service, you will not neglect goeing a thither in person: As on my part I shall give care to give you assurance that I am, Your affectionate friend, CHARLES R.'[7]

Now the Parliamentarians, although they employed the Scots against their King, were furious at the idea that the Irish Catholics should be marched against themselves. And this was not the worst part of the matter; the King found himself in a very awkward position with respect to many Protestant Cavaliers, who hated the very name of Catholic and Papist since the Gunpowder Plot, and the Irish massacres. Indeed, so strong were the representations made to his Majesty, that he had to give his kingly word that he would not hold out any hopes to Papists respecting their religion, or employ Irish Catholics as soldiers.

The scheme of Antrim and Montrose broke down, for Lord Antrim was seized and thrown into prison at Castlehaven, but the Marquis of Ormonde continued his negotiations with the confederated Catholics at Kilkenny, and in the month of November 1643 shipped off five regiments to Chester, and in their ranks were a number of the much detested Celtic Irish.[8] As soon as this news of the treaty with the Papists at Kilkenny reached the Earl of Newcastle's army in the north, many of the men threw down their arms, and refused to fight any longer for the King.[9]

The year was not to close without a sad trial for the Bromleys. From 25th of July their friend, Lady Brilliana Harley, with the greatest courage and prudence, had defended for weeks Brampton Bryan Castle, in which she and her younger children were shut up and besieged by troops under Sir William Vavasour, and her former friend, Colonel Lingen. They soon, as already related, ravaged village, church, farms and buildings, but Lady Brilliana defended the Castle bravely, until the besiegers feared an attack upon their forces and raised the siege, leaving her triumphant.

But now the heroic lady was dead! Broken-hearted at the wrecks around her, at the ruined families, and starving tenantry and peasantry, and worn out by anxiety at the long absence of her husband, and her son, Captain Edward Harley, whom she so dearly loved, she succumbed, and in October her spirit fled. Brampton Bryan Castle mourned its brave defender, and Mr and Madam Bromley lost a loving friend.

The year closed with the death of Mr Pym, a great blow to the Roundheads, and a subject of much rejoicing to us Cavaliers, whom he had disgusted by his unchivalrous charge of treason against her Majesty the Queen. New Year's Day 1644 was heralded by a furious storm and terrific gale of wind. Clouds rushed above the Malverns, as if torn in pieces, and the winds wrought ruin among the shattered walls of Little Malvern Priory, while they whistled mournfully among the deserted turrets of Hanley Castle, though the brave old Keep withstood the bitter blast. This was succeeded by a hard frost, which bound the country as in iron.

There was a lull, as regarded the war, in our neighbourhood, so I obtained leave of absence for a few days, accepted an invitation from Giles Nanfan, and, accompanied by Isabel, went to pay my respects to Sir Giles and his kindly dame. Fieldfares sat pecking berries from the great hawthorn bushes, remnants of Malvern Chase, and cock-robin was huddled up like a ball of feathers. The Old Man's Beard hanging from the trees made the woodlands look colder than even the frost flakes, and 'as the day lengthens, so the cold strengthens', was true of this first of Janiveer.

We carried our New Year's gifts for our friends. I had a pair of turtle-doves for Dame Nanfan, which cooed as I bore the cage, notwithstanding the frost, and a velvet girdle with silver clasps for Bridget. Isabel had her whimsies for every friend, mostly the work of her own little fingers; but there was one which took a ringlet of her beautiful hair – I found her in the act of clipping it – and tears suffused her eyes, thinking it might, ere long, be stained with the life blood of him she loved. Sweet Isabel, that spring time gardening and planting of Forget-me-nots by the side of the old moat at home, had faded the roses from her cheek and the light glad look from her eyes; for in every fight Giles Nanfan was always to the front, with his well-known shout of 'Forwards', and charging like the whirlwind as if there was no Isabel.

Arrived at Birtsmorton Court, we were welcomed with the wassail bowl and the hearty wish for New Year's blessings. Cordial greetings and right good cheer were there as in days of yore; but a sad change hung over the neighbourhood, which was calculated to overshadow the innocent merriments of Christmas and the New Year. Spies were in every household among the servants, and the country clergy were denounced as Popish priests in every village tavern. Some of Sir Giles' tenant farmers declared mince pies to be Popish pasties, and even flouted the sacraments of the Church, while they deserted the edifice in which their forefathers had worshipped for centuries, for some conventicle.

Puritanism had become the fashion, and there is no phase of godliness so convincing to the multitude, especially women, as the fashionable! Nevertheless, we mustered a goodly New Year's party at Birtsmorton Court. The shields of the Crofts and Scudamores, Baskerville, Harley, and Rudhall, Blount and Throgmorton, were wreathed with mistletoe in the old oak room; an ox was roasting in the courtyard; and Sir Giles and Dame Nanfan were clad in their best garments and received their guests right courteously. That strange oddity, Mr Gaston, senior, was there, 'speering', as Bridget said, into every nook and corner, and he brought Giles as a present a one-eyed fitcher ferret, which he declared had killed a score of rats at one baiting.

Giles had invited a handsome young officer of our Longdon regiment, Captain Hasseli, who was remarkable for the splendour of his boots. He was of an old Huguenot family, and had joined the Royalists, notwithstanding that his father was a Puritan. Here, too, was Honeywood Yates, and Mr Cocks of Castleditch, so there was a merry dance and I observed that Bridget Nanfan threw her kerchief to young Hasseli more frequently than was the custom to a stranger. Then came loyal songs and ditties, and we had well nigh forgotten the war, the broken hearts in many a New Year's dwelling, and the wounded in their agony, when above the howling of the wind we heard a woman's scream as if imploring admission by the drawbridge, which was up for the night.

There was a dead silence, and then Giles went forth, accompanied by the domestics, to inquire who was thus entreating admittance so late and so earnestly. He returned supporting a young woman who seemed more dead than alive, and behind her staggered a wayworn man, whose beard and hair were covered with frost rime, and his clothes singed with fire. It was some time before the girl rallied from the effects of the cold, notwithstanding hot peppermints, and rubbing her hands and feet.

Mr Gaston was indefatigable in the latter process, as he was studying the return of the circulation of the blood. It was a sorry tale these poor people had to tell! Both the man and the girl were parishioners of Birtsmorton, and had gone to live as servants with Mr More, of Linley Hall, on the borders of Herefordshire and Shropshire. When Hopton Castle was threatened by the Royalist, Mr More, being a staunch Parliamentarian, removed there with his household, and undertook to defend it with the garrison it already contained.

In the mean time the Irish regiments sent by the Marquis of Ormonde had reached Chester and enrolled themselves under Lord Biron, and these troops were employed in various forays, much to our discredit and the cause of the King.

Hopton Castle had for some time been a stumbling block in the way of Prince Rupert and the Royalist leaders, so Mr More was summoned to surrender the Castle, and this he declined to do. Another formal summons was sent by Sir Michael Woodhouse, who unhappily commanded the new Irish levies.[10] The Royalist forces made an attempt to storm, but were repulsed with loss, the gallant More fighting at the head of the besieged. The assailants then withdrew, but returned in a week's time with a larger force.[13]

After a time the garrison agreed to capitulate, if granted quarter, and the reply was that they should be referred to Colonel Woodhouse's mercy. They yielded, the Irish entered the Castle, and then came the terrible history!

The very maid-servants were wounded, and hardly escaped the butchery which followed. Poor Gregory, the old steward, who was eighty years of age, 'being weak and not able to stand, they put him in a chair to cut his throat'. With the exception of the Governor, More, 'they stripped every man of the garrison, tied them back to back, and put them to death with the utmost barbarity, the dead bodies being thrown into the moat.' Governor More was carried off to prison at Ludlow, and the serving man, having the luck to secure a horse, rode for his life with the poor wounded maiden behind him, arriving at Birtsmorton in the state we now beheld them.

We could not believe Bill Wadley and this tale of our brother Royalists; we thought fright and imagination must have distorted the tragedy. But it was too true, and in a short time the news-letters spread it broadcast over England.[11]

From this time the war was conducted on both sides with tenfold barbarity, and when the Royalists craved quarter, too often came the reply, "We'll give you none but Hopton quarter. It was a sad ending to our gaiety; this example of the atrocities of civil warfare brought to our own homes beneath the Malverns.

England had now two Parliaments, the King's Parliament at Oxford assembled on the 2nd of January 1644, and the Parliament of the Commons at Westminster. The King had about ten thousand men in and about Oxford, and here, amidst halls and colleges was the Court of royalty and the rendezvous of England's proudest aristocracy. Among the stately edifices of Christchurch, Merton, and Oriel, the rank, fame and beauty of England assembled, and in the crowded streets were to be seen many a noble head soon to lie stricken upon the battle field. Here came the bold and hearty soldier Sir Jacob Astley, walking side by side with the ever too reckless Rupert, and Sir Ralph Hopton scarred by the explosion of powder at Lansdowne, the cruel Lord Goring, and groups of Cavaliers clattering in their steel harness among reverend parsons, and court ladies rustling in brocades and pinners.

Here the beautiful Queen held high court, and the noble and gentle loved to offer their homage, while she carried on the intrigues and devices destined to do much injury to the King. While Oxford was filled with divided statesmen, intriguing courtiers, and scheming Jesuits, the Parliament at Westminster raised three separate armies. Of these Lord Essex confronted the King at Oxford; Sir William Waller marched into Dorsetshire; and the Earl of Manchester and Sir Thomas Fairfax marched northwards to co-operate with the Scots under the Earl of Leven, who had accepted the cash of the Parliament to wage war against their King and countryman.

The spring of the year 1644 was early, notwithstanding the intense frost of January and, although a hard winter is said to kill fevers, a terrible plague broke out in many towns and villages, especially in the west of England. In Bath the dead lay unburied in the streets, and in Ross likewise the mortality was fearful. At Upton and Hanley many were stricken, and while Aunt Tabitha almost insisted upon chaining up Isabel lest she should sicken, she was devoted in her personal attention to many a sufferer among the lowly tenements of the poor among whom the disease was most rife. In the general suffering, animosity arising from the spirit of the times vanished for awhile, and Aunt Tabitha knelt by the same bedside with Madam Bromley. But none of these disasters checked the growing war. Tewkesbury had again fallen into our possession, and Sir William Vavasour was made Governor. Prince Rupert became Commander-in-Chief of the Welsh districts, and Colonel Nicholas Mynne the Royalist Governor of Hereford.

March brought us another example of the severity with which the Parliament at Westminster was about to act. Not contented with impeaching their Queen of high treason, on the 12th of March the sick and tottering Archbishop Laud was dragged from his prison in the Tower, where he had been confined for three long years, and was charged with all the united crimes, tyrannies, and follies of the Star Chamber. He no doubt had been dogmatic and obstinate in his endeavours to Catholicise the Church of England, but he was now confronted by wills more dogged than his own, and was accused of 'high treason, treason in all and every part, treason in the highest pitch and altitude'.

Archbishop Laud was an example of a high couraged man become despotic, and in some instances even tyrannical, through the great state error of allowing high ecclesiastics to preside over civil tribunals such as the Star Chamber, and the successor of the Apostles to award sentences of death and torture!

'I am for Thorough', wrote Strafford to Laud, and 'Go on in God's name', wrote Laud to Strafford, and this meant persecution for all who differed from them. It was this millstone of 'Thorough', which was now dragging the worn-out old man to the scaffold, and it was evident to many Royalists that if the Puritans were not soon utterly defeated, Laud was a doomed man; the bloodhounds were on his track. Some English Cavaliers, principally certain weak noblemen who affected to deride the storm they had helped to raise, declared that Parliament 'dared not touch a hair of the Primate's head'; that 'lightning from heaven would strike dead the sacrilegious Roundheads who had the audacity to impeach him'; and that 'he would yet emerge from prison and crush his enemies by his ecclesiastical judgments'.

But some amongst us knew that dogmatism and persecution could be carried out by certain so-called 'Saints', if only they had the opportunity. And the determination of the chosen of Israel to bring the old Primate's grey head to the scaffold, was portrayed in the *Bloody Almanack*,[12] where there appeared '3 gentlemen led by one bearing a pole-axe and one bearing a crosse upon his neck following them, and in the last place a great block'.

April was come again, and a sunny spring time succeeded the hard winter. I was quartered at my own home, while Giles Nanfan and our troops occupied Upton-on-Severn. The news-letters which were sent to Worcester, and an occasional letter from my father at Oxford, supplied us with information from time to time. With the exception of a few raids from Gloucester for the sake of plunder and fresh meat, our neighbourhood had been quiet. The Upton Puritans had become more respectful in their demeanour, and no longer abused the Royalists at public meetings, or made faces at our soldiers as we passed down the streets. Little children once again gathered violets and primroses in the thickets of Longdon Heath, and the fishermen plied their nets below the red cliffs of Ryall for the salmon and the shad.

I had promised Isabel to take her a primrose foray among our woodlands, when a messenger arrived from John Kelly requesting me to go to the Waterside. I lost no time in doing so, and found our old friend, dressed in his scholar's garb, his fingers stained with lotions he had been mingling, and pacing up and down the apartment in a state of great excitement. Seated in the old oak chair, opposite the crocodile, was Mary Bromley, who rose to welcome me with flushed cheeks and a troubled expression. Kelly enquired if I had lately received tidings from Oxford, but I had not heard for some weeks.

He then handed me a letter from my father, and paced the room while I read it. I learnt therefrom that the Queen was in a very precarious condition; she was in ill-health from rheumatic fever, and was expecting her accouchement. Oxford was unhealthy with fever and might be blockaded any day, and there was no surgeon the King could trust, no experienced nurse in whom the Queen had any confidence. Her Majesty was most anxious to leave Oxford; she feared the city would be stormed by Essex, Fairfax, and Cromwell, and it was reported that Essex had set a price upon her head.[13]

She now implored to be taken out of the way of that war and battle which a few months earlier she faced with so much courage. But the Parliament, utterly ignoring that she was a woman in distress, refused to allow her to go to London to seek the aid of Dr Mayerne, the King's physician. Under these circumstances of intolerable anxiety my father had written to Kelly saying that he had formed an opinion that some member should intercede with the Parliament who knew something of the common courtesies and decencies of life, and was a Parliamentarian. There must still, my father thought, be *gentlemen* at Westminster who would have consideration for a woman in that distress when she so much requires gentle care.

Knowing that Mr Bromley had a high respect for Kelly, my father suggested that Kelly should seek an interview with the Squire, for Mr Bromley was a cousin of Colonel Oliver Cromwell, a Parliamentary officer of considerable reputation, member for Cambridge, and who, notwithstanding the abuse of the Royalist news-letters, was believed to be a man possessed of kindly feelings.

Sir Thomas Steward, too, Cromwell's uncle, was a friend of Mr Bromley's, and a most unlikely person to persecute a woman in the Queen's condition.[14] If Mr Bromley could be induced to interest these gentlemen for the Queen, in such an approaching time of pain and weakness, the Parliament might listen to their suggestions.

Kelly was too angry with the Parliament, and their utter want of chivalry and courtesy, to trust himself to speak to Mr Bromley; he therefore summoned Mary to a consultation at the Waterside, thinking it would be well to gain her as an ally before appealing to her father. And he was right! Mary Bromley would have walked barefoot to Worcester to save a beggar woman, in the Queen's condition, from undergoing the storming of a besieged city; she was certain "Cousin Oliver would lend his aid!"

All I knew of this Colonel Cromwell was that he was a cousin of Mr Bromley's, an enthusiastic Puritan, who was said to sing Psalms at the head of his regiment, and one talked of as having drilled a staunch body of cavalry now known as Ironsides. He was said by Royalist news-letters to be the son of a butcher or a baker, but then our news-letters, unfortunately, lied as unblushingly as did those of the Parliament whenever it suited their purpose. When I expressed my doubts respecting the influence of Colonel Cromwell, notwithstanding he was with General Fairfax, Mary told us somewhat of his personal history.

He was of the same family as Thomas Cromwell, Earl of Essex, 'Thomas the Mauler', who lost his head through recommending an ill-looking lady as wife to Henry VIII. His father was a plain country squire, the third son of Sir Oliver Cromwell, of Hinchinbrook House near Huntingdon; a house where no doubt a good deal of butchering, baking and brewing went on when Sir Oliver entertained King James I for three whole days on his coming to England. On this occasion Dame Steward declared that 'Master Oliver gave the Duke of York – afterwards his most gracious Majesty Charles I – a snope on the nose', and in this sense Colonel Cromwell might be termed a butcher, as it was a bloody nose.

"For himself," said Mary, "Cousin Oliver lived, until late years, a country life, farming and grazing kine, and perhaps," she said, smiling, "brewed his own beer. He became a member of Parliament, and at forty years of age accepted a commission in the army of the Parliament. His eldest son, another Oliver, and my only brother Dick, are serving with his Ironsides. Although Colonel Cromwell is a great enthusiast in religious matters, and of stern and grave character where military duty is concerned, no man loves wife and children more devotedly, and he has a heart to sympathize with a woman's suffering I am well assured."

"My father, too," she continued "would gladly lend his aid to relieve the Queen from her present precarious condition, as you both know full well!" Kelly now turned to me and said, "We want you to saddle the Prince and ride forthwith to Chippenham with a letter from Mr Bromley, which Mary will have ready, where we learn from your father's epistle that Colonel Cromwell holds command under the Earl of Essex."

I was not a little confounded at this appeal! I was ready and willing to ride to the world's end to serve her Majesty in such straits, but I was an entire stranger to Colonel Cromwell, and suggested that it would be better for Mr Bromley to go in person and see Cousin Oliver himself. Mary and John Kelly smiled and interchanged glances, as I said this, while she replied, "You are not such a stranger as you suppose, Captain Forester. It was Colonel Cromwell whose life you saved when he was attacked by highwaymen on Brockeridge Common. He is no ingrate, and under such circumstances John Kelly thinks we cannot find a better messenger."

I then inquired how any of them could possibly know that I had the good fortune to aid the Colonel; and here Mary blushed and rose to go, and then blushed again. At last, amidst much embarrassment, she acknowledged that she recognized a kerchief stained with blood around Colonel Cromwell's neck as my property and her own handiwork. In truth the letters *RPF* had been worked by Mary in days before war and religious differences had interfered to separate us.

A short time sufficed to explain to my superior officer that I was about to start on especial service for the King, and I was on my road to Hamme Court with Sampson behind me on Hanley, carrying my valise and well armed. The letter for Colonel Cromwell was penned and sealed, and I found both Mr and Mrs Bromley as indignant as if they had been Royalists, at the treatment of the Queen by the Parliament. Still Mary had not brought my kerchief, which she had promised to return, and which I was determined not to leave behind.

I lingered and lingered while Mr Bromley was patting the Prince, who was pawing and chafing at the door, and Mrs Bromley went in search of her daughter. Mary entered by the garden doorway, and looked as if she had been weeping, but she brought the kerchief cleansed and folded. I longed to kneel at her feet and entreat her lovingly, for the sake of other days, to tie it round my neck again; but a vision arose before me of Captain Edward Harley and the oak by Southend, so I contented myself with bowing stiffly, and taking the kerchief as if it were a matter of no consequence. Mary stood looking at me as if she was sorely puzzled, but cast down her eyes as she curtsied to my farewell, and over-punctilious salutation. I then bade adieu to Mr and Madam Bromley, and rode off, in no very good temper, towards Tewkesbury.

Clarence House, Tewkesbury

Chapter Fourteen

IN MY journey I had ample time to reflect on my interview with Mary Bromley, and my feelings concerning her. I could not disguise from myself that she was the only woman I had ever loved, and I had loved her from my childhood. We were both young, but what unforeseen changes had come over us since the curse of religious animosity was rife throughout the land.

Mary was imbued with strong religious feeling, and was devoted to her father, who had taken his part against the Church of England – the Church of my forefathers and his own. Still I felt persuaded that the Star Chamber, the fires, the mutilations, and the persecution of his fellow-men had induced Mr Bromley to join the Puritans, rather than questions concerning doctrine.

If he had imbibed something of the sternness of Calvinism, it was more for the strict morality it enjoined, than the belief that salvation was granted to the 'saints' alone. The pealing organ, pouring forth its volume of rich sound, or the glorious old hymns of the Church were not objected to by Mr Bromley, but he did denounce as deserving the wrath of God, the loud ostentatious, blasphemous swearing of too many Cavaliers such as Lord Goring, and no splendour or ceremonial in any church atoned, in his eyes, for the want of personal piety. At the same time I knew that both the father and daughter no longer prayed in that Church, for which, as well as for my King, my life was in daily jeopardy.

As these thoughts passed through my brain, there came again the remembrance of the figures under the oak tree, and I must have anathematized somewhat in the Goring style, for Sampson rode up full of concern, and inquired if "summat was the matter, as he heard me cuss 'owdacious."

We rested for the night at Malmesbury, now occupied by Royalist troops, and rode next morning for Colonel Cromwell's quarters at Chippenham. The rain came down in torrents when we reached the out-posts of the Parliamentarians A blast from Sampson's trumpet aroused the sentinels, and on presenting our pass bearing the signet of Lord Essex, they conducted us to Cromwell's quarters in the town.

We found him drilling troops in the rain, and giving orders with a stentorian voice. He did not at first observe me, and allowed us to stand

unnoticcd while superintending some complicated movement, but no
sooner did he recognize his quondam acquaintance of Brockeridge
Common than he came forward holding out his hand, and wringing
mine as that of a friend, he led the way to his quarters. As we walked
down the street, he inquired about his cousins the Bromleys, and rallied
me on my sudden disappearance at their entrance gate. Arrived at his
lodgings, as he called them, Colonel Cromwell ordered a soldier to
bring what provisions the house afforded, and drew from a cupboard a
flask of wine. He then asked to what he owed the pleasure of a visit
from one to whom he should ever feel grateful.

It has been too much the fashion with Royalists to heap abuse on
every characteristic of this celebrated man, but 'the devil is not so black
as he is painted', and, although rough in manner, I ever found in my
dealings with him the consideration of a grave and kindly gentleman.

The belief in God's personal providence was ever strong in Cromwell's heart, and present with him on all occasions of life – in society, in
the army, on the march, in the storm of a siege, in the House of
Commons, in prayer public and private, and in every thought. With
respect to himself and his work, it became almost presumptuous.

I gave him Mr Bromley's letter and waited his reply. "This letter," he
said, "is that of an excellent and high-minded gentleman, and he asks
much of one who is but a poor soldier of the Lord's, and of no great
account with the Parliament." He then denounced in energetic language
the conduct of the Queen in fostering Popery in England when she
knew the people hated it, and enlisting foreign troops, foreign ships,
and money to wage war against her husband's subjects.

Thus he talked until he became angry, when checking himself, he
said, "But you are not concerned with all this, Sir;" and continued in a
gentler tone, "It would be unmanly to refuse the aid of a doctor or
chirurgeon to the Queen in her present condition, notwithstanding her
impeachment for treason against the state. I will write to Master
Prynne, and ask, as a personal favour of the Parliament, that Dr
Mayerne may attend her. But she must leave Oxford at once," he
continued, "and you must urge this upon the King. Her malignant
advice is well known to influence Charles Stuart against listening to fair
offers of peace, and if the city fall, which I expect will happen soon,
there are men in this army who have little affection for the French
Papist, woman though she be."

While Colonel Cromwell was speaking, he paced up and down the room and looked at me fixedly from time to time. Plain and homely as were his features, I was struck with his massive head, the sagacious steady eye, the sturdy frame, and the commanding voice and demeanour.

An officer entered with despatches from the Earl of Essex, and I had an opportunity of listening to the style of conversation indulged in by the military 'saints', a nauseous imitation of language of Scripture, which Cavaliers have ever detested. Thus Lord Essex was 'the chosen leader of God's champions', King Charles was 'Jehu, the son of Nimshi'; the Church 'the house of Baal'; and the Roundhead soldiers were men 'who walked with their loins girded, their lights burning, and their weapons drawn'. A trumpet was the 'pipe of Jezer', and a besieged garrison 'repaired the breaches of Zion'. I observed that Colonel Cromwell adopted scriptural phrases more frequently in conversing with the Puritans than when talking to me, and his discourse was more ambiguous. He dismissed the officer, saying he would attend to the despatches, and bidding him see to 'the drilling of the Lord's lambs'.

After urging me to refresh myself, he said a special messenger should leave in an hour with his letter respecting the Queen's state of health, and recommended me to hasten the removal of her Majesty from Oxford, as the city might be stormed in a few days, and he would not answer for the consequences.

As I approached the great metropolis of learning, with its spires, towers, and various colleges, betokening peace and quiet, it was hardly possible to imagine the banks of the Isis and Cherwell crowded with the pageantry of war. Yet soldiers thronged everywhere; soldiers in the taverns and in the shops, in tents by the river, in the back alleys and in the gaol. Then there was the Court frequented by lords and ladies; some loyal and refined, others full of foppery and frippery; by poets, such as Waller and Davenant; by Papists hanging about the Queen, and philosophers clad in warlike attire; by butterfly men hovering about intriguing women, and going forth from a mask or a dance to a raid in the country in their court hose.

The Colleges were filled to overflowing, not with devotees of the classic muse, but with the members of the King's parliament; officers of rank and title; Frenchmen come to see the Queen; learned doctors in their gowns and bands; and Jesuits who pretended to be anything but what they were. The city was so crowded that often the nobleman was lodged in a garret, and high-born dames were glad to find a bed-room in an attic.

The King was living at Christ Church, the Queen at Merton College, and my father in a small room over Merton College gate. I found the King apprehensive and depressed from the distractions in his council and the bickerings and heartburnings among his adherents. The lawyers asserted the supremacy of civil over military authority; the King's nephews, Prince Rupert and Prince Maurice, with several of the more warlike Cavaliers, laughed at the 'penwipers', and would decide everything by military law and force of arms. The Papists were numerous, confident of the Queen's support, and encouraging her views against any peace save through conquest; while at the same time the priests were so unpopular with the Protestant Cavaliers, owing to the late inhumanity of the Irish Celts, that, notwithstanding his letter to the Earl of Antrim, the King had to take an oath that he would not countenance Popery, or employ the Irish Papists in his army.[1]

Stores were becoming exhausted and powder scarce, thus serious alarm was now felt at the approach of the armies of Essex and Waller, each ten thousand strong. When I told my father of the result of my visit to Colonel Cromwell, he was convinced that the Queen should remove from Oxford without delay, and conducted me forthwith to the presence of their Majesties.

We found them walking in Christchurch meadow, surrounded by a throng of courtiers, and when my father intimated my business, they commanded us to attend them in the Hall of the College, whither they now adjourned. My father halted a moment that I might admire the grand quadrangle where stood Cardinal Wolsey when he laid the first stone more than a hundred years before. The walls of the hall were covered with fine paintings, and it was fitted up with a certain amount of regal state.

It was impossible not to observe that both the King and Queen looked more care-worn and anxious than when I saw them together at Kineton after the Queen's march from York. They both gave me their hands to kiss, and listened with deep attention to the account of my interview with Colonel Cromwell; but I thought that my relation of the circumstances should have been more private, for the Queen's Confessor, and one of the King's chaplains, Dr Gaston, son of the recluse and birdlimer at Merryvale, were permitted to listen to every syllable that passed.

Dr Gaston was the very opposite in appearance of his cadaverous looking father, being fat, fair, and smiling. My father disliked him, for he was a political parson, ever dabbling with the intrigues of the Court, writing anonymous letters, and trying to play the diplomatist. He made himself useful to the King in deciphering letters and copying in cipher.[2] He had a wonderful store of gossip at command, though not always particular about the truth of it, and was ever ready for a questionable joke with the profligate Goring, or a discourse on theology with a Romish priest.

After my interview with their Majesties at Christchurch, I retired with my father to Merton College, and we conversed on the serious attitude of the armies of the Parliament. We had been together about an hour when I received a command to wait upon the Queen in her private apartments at Merton. She occupied the rooms of John Wycliffe, when a fellow of the college, a strange dwelling for so Catholic a Queen.

The room into which I was ushered contained a portrait of the celebrated Duns Scotus, once a scholar of Merton, and as I was kept waiting for an hour, I had the opportunity of cogitating on the subtle, logical disputations of the learned Scotus. At last the Queen entered, attended by two ladies of the Court and her Confessor. The volubility with which she discoursed upon matters which should have been kept secret before her ladies, again struck me as most injudicious.

She was acquainted with the disposition of the forces of the Parliament and the situation of the Royalist troops in the west, and she spoke of them as if we were merely engaged upon a hunting foray and the placing of beaters for deer. She announced that Colonel Cromwell had suddenly left Chippenham to join the Earl of Manchester at the siege of York, and this was told before Lady Carlisle, who already had an indifferent character for sincerity and conjugal fidelity. The Queen then commented on the position of affairs in Herefordshire and Gloucestershire, remarking, in her clever and vivacious way, upon our own loyal Worcestershire, and asking after 'Mees Bromley'. She then reverted to Sir Henry Herbert, Knight, of Ribbesford, in our county, and handed me a letter to read which was written by Mistress Mary Herbert to Sir Henry, her 'Unkle'.

In this letter was an account of a secret plot devised by Lord New-port to deliver her Majesty into the power of the Parliament. The lady concluded her epistle in the following words:

'Thes are mesarable plots. The Lord give all these ploters their disarts, and setile this kingdom in pease again if it be his blesed will. So fering I have ben to troublesom with thes lines, I shall only desire you to present my serves to my ante and my kind love to all my cossens.'[3]

Then the Queen spoke of George Herbert the poet, and 'the little book' he left behind him, when he died at his quiet home at Bemerton, to tell his dear brother Farrer of the many spiritual conflicts that had passed between God and his soul.

It was the Queen's nature to win and charm all who approached her, but again I remarked she never spoke of peace. The bell of the Chapel at Christchurch now gave warning that it was time for prayer, which his Majesty always attended, suffering no business or pleasure to interfere with his religious duties. But these very religious services of the Church of England gave offence to the Puritans of Oxford. When Laud was elected Chancellor in 1630, he established several novel decorations the Puritans considered Papistical, such as 'velvet among the cushions, gold and silver cloth, frankincense, wax candles', and in one year 'the cost of wax candles alone in the chapel was £15 18s'.[4]

The Queen never accompanied her husband to the services of the Church, but had a room fitted up with all the splendour of the Romish ritual; and thither came, from far and near, all the Catholics around Oxford, to the annoyance of the Protestant Cavaliers and clergy, many of them members of the University. Thus some of his Majesty's most devoted followers thought the voluble and excitable Queen would be better away from the royal counsels; and certain Jesuits thought so too, as she compromised them by too much *outward* zeal for a religion already hated by the people, and soon to become more hateful still.

On leaving Merton College Chapel I met Archie Armstrong, the King's jester, to whom King James had granted a patent for the manu-facture of tobacco pipes. Archie brought me a City of London pie, which had been sent by their Majesties' learned physician Dr Mayerne, a delicacy all *bon vivants* set especial store by. I invited Archie to partake of the pastie, an invitation he immediately accepted, as good viands had become rare in Oxford, and there were queer tales about rats caught in the college cellars and the *petites choses* served at the King's table at Christchurch.

The jester was much dismayed by the gloomy days which had come over all England, and it was some time before I could persuade him to tell of the banquets, the orgies, and the joculations he had beheld at the Court of King James. At last he shook off his melancholy, and told droll tales about Will Sommers, who was Fool to Henry VIII, and then trolled forth in a melodious voice to the old tune of Greytail,[5] the famous Cavalier ditty by Sir John Sucklings:

> *The Colonel sent for him back again,*
> *To quarter him in the van — a,*
> *But Sir John did swear he would not come there,*
> *To be killed the very first man — a.*

While Archie was singing, Mr Seymour, once the husband of the unhappy Arabella Stuart, was passing in company with Dr Gaston, and attracted by the ballad drew up opposite our window. I invited them in and ordered another flask of wine, when a company of mummers came down the street. Four girls dressed in Bohemian costume were accompanied by a tall man with a flowing beard and a mask, and mounted upon a pair of stilts, which enabled him to look in at the upper windows. The girls sang ditties and the mountebank carried a box for alms. He had also sundry nostrums for sale and recipes for every malady from the plague to the chicken-pox, for love potions, the gripes, and bad corns. Dr Gaston handed him a groat and received a prescription for curing corns which caused us much amusement:

> *Nevere ware tite bootes.*

A crowd gathered round the mummers, and the mountebank sang a doleful ballad to a cracked fiddle. But his voice was as cracked as the fiddle, and though I felt certain I had heard it before, I could not remember where, or on what occasion, and the mummers passed on to another audience; but the jingle of the uncanny voice of the ballad singer haunted me, nor could I shake off the impression it produced.

We now walked forth into High Street, and there we saw 'many of the greatest gentlemen of divers counties', their ladies, doctors of the colleges, Popish priests, members of the King's Parliament, gallant officers, such as Princes Rupert and Maurice, with other grand peers and soldiers, such as Lord Jermyn, Lord Digby, Lords Goring and Wilmot, all anxious about the proposed departure of the Queen.

After sunset I retired to the tavern and sat before the fire watching the vagaries of those who passed in and out, when the haunting voice of the mountebank seemed again to ring in my ears, and suddenly I recollected that I had heard those harsh tones when Bound was treating his neighbours to what he called singing in an Upton tavern. The next moment I was on my way to Merton College to inform my father that a dangerous spy was in the heart of Oxford.

I found him hard at work, as usual, with his pen, and surrounded by papers and documents. He listened attentively to my statement, and proposed to go with me to Dr Gaston's room at a baker's near Christchurch, where he expected the King was superintending the despatch of some cipher to France.

The door of the apartment was fastened, and although the Doctor acknowledged the knocks bestowed upon it, some time elapsed before it was opened. In this little den many a secret conclave was held at Oxford, and when we entered, Prince Rupert, Prince Maurice, and Lord Digby were discussing the King's intention of dismissing his 'mongrel parliament' and the departure of the Queen.

Here, a year before, had met the daring Montrose and the loyal Earl of Antrim. Here, also, sometimes came her Majesty the Queen, with expostulations respecting some slight shown to her confessor, or her French *femmes de chambres*, or some plan for foreign intervention.

Secret correspondence was the delight of Dr Gaston, he revelled in conducting it, and when not employed by the King or the Queen, would practise it on his own account. Dark contrivances and secret councils were the breath of his nostrils, and as the King often signed papers and warrants on the good faith of his secretary, the question naturally arose, in after years, whether he was always cognizant of the contents of his own despatches.

Prince Rupert expressed himself anxious at the presence of spy of the Parliament in Oxford, and accompanied me, on the instant, to the Captain of the Guard. We soon found the Bohemian mummers, but they asserted that their male companion of the stilts was a stranger, had only joined them for a few hours, and then levanted with the money box. Nor did we learn more of the Gloucester spy, save that a long shambling officer in a dragoon's cloak, on a raking black mare, gave the password at the west gate and rode for Abingdon. This, I believe, was Captain Bound on Hell Cat.

The next morning a trumpeter arrived from London with a reply to his Majesty's request that the Queen might travel to London. This was absolutely refused, but permission was given for her removal to Bath or Exeter, and a promise made that Dr Mayerne should attend her. The King was naturally indignant at the contemptuous answer to his demands, but the Queen's removal now became necessary, and after much consultation it was determined that his Majesty should escort the Queen as far as Abingdon on her route to Exeter, and I was informed that I was to have the honour of commanding the escort to the royal coaches.

On a bleak April morning the rooks cawed around their new-made nests in the elms of Christchurch as the trumpets sounded to horse, and our escort assembled before the gates of Merton. It was too early in the month for the cuckoo and swallow, and too rough a day for any, save the stormcock,[6] to salute her Majesty with a song.

Two coaches, each drawn by six horses, were provided; the first was protected from weather by curtains, the second was a large open caroche for conveying the ladies of the Queen's household. Six running footmen preceded the coaches for the purpose of filling up the ruts and mires, the roads being worse than usual owing to the movements of cannon.

It was nearly mid-day before the Queen and her attendants were ready to start on their long and toilsome journey, and when at last we moved, we could only proceed at foot's pace from the crowds thronging the streets to bid farewell to the kind-hearted, merry, brave, though impetuous and injudicious lady, who for months had enlivened the city by her presence. The King was seated by her side in the coach, his charger being led by a groom; twenty Cavaliers preceded the coaches as far as Abingdon and twenty dragoons followed, which was all the escort the agreement allowed.

Our progress was slow but unimpeded until within two miles of Abingdon, when the Queen's coach, which was ahead, stuck fast in a quagmire, causing the delay of an hour to extricate the vehicle from the depths of black mud in which it was grounded. The other caroche, profiting by the example, left the high road, and found a safer transit across a common. The running footmen, who appeared in Oxford with spotless habiliments, came out of that mud with their fine fringes and tassels black with mire.

Late in the afternoon, we reached the great cross in the market-place at Abingdon, celebrated by Master Camden, and soon after demolished by the ravaging Roundheads.[7] It was a fine structure built by the Guild of the Holy Cross. Archie Armstrong dilated upon the annual feasts of the Guild, how on one occasion they devoured six calves, sixteen lambs, eighty capons, twenty geese, eight hundred eggs, besides many marrow bones, and much fruit and spice.[8]

Abbendun – the town of the Abbey – is but a poor place, although Henry I was educated here, and obtained the name of Beauclerk. Nevertheless, its taverns, the Crown and Thistle in Bridge Street, and the Rising Sun, are much frequented by the country gentry and Oxford ecclesiastics. The ale is bright and the tobacco strong.

The King and Queen passed the night in a good house placed at their disposal by Mr Tumour. Mr Seymour attended to the Queen's suite, while I placed a guard on the bridge over the Thames, and had just gone the rounds for the night when Archie Armstrong summoned me to wait upon the King. On entering the house I was told that the Queen had retired for the night, and was entreated to ascend the staircase with a noiseless tread. I was then ushered into a long low chamber with a recess at the farthest extremity.

In the centre of the room was a table covered with papers and lighted by tapers, but the King was not seated at the table and I looked around, wondering, when a deep sigh emanated from the recess. I started, seeing a figure lying at full length upon a settee, apparently headless, with the arms crossed upon the bosom. It was King Charles! He had thrown himself upon the couch and covered his head and face with a kerchief, which being of the same colour as the settee, gave his body the appearance of being headless. He had evidently been weeping, the traces of tears were still upon his cheeks, and he was pale, worn, and wan. He had just parted from her he loved better than his children; better than his kingdom and subjects; better than life itself, and he felt the uncertainty as to whether they would ever meet again.

He received me with his usual dignity of manner, gave me concise orders with respect to her Majesty's journey, and commanded me to have his horses and escort ready for his return to Oxford by sunrise the following morning. "It is not advisable," he said, "that I should undergo a leave-taking with my beloved wife in her present state of health, I must therefore relinquish the idea of seeing her in the morning, and would take my departure before she is aroused to pursue her journey."

At this moment a lady appeared and requested his Majesty to accompany her to the Queen's apartment, and I was left alone in that gloomy chamber. From the books upon the table I took up a quaintly bound volume containing the mystic prophecies of the French astrologer, Nostradamus. He was a noted mystagogue of the time of Queen Elizabeth, whose prophecies are consulted to this day as foreshadowing future events, and was much sought after by all who could obtain a peep into the volume I saw before me. The custom was to open the book haphazard and read one distich and no more.

I confess that the image of Mary Bromley, associated with my own future, glanced through my mind as I opened the pages and looked upon the first quatrain that met my eyes. Long years have passed away, but I think I see the line now:

Le Senat de Londres metteront à mort le Roi.[19]

Before sunrise next day, I assembled the King's escort at the corner of the street, lest the noise should awake her Majesty, and led the King's horse myself until he appeared ready for the journey. He mounted in silence, not trusting himself to speak, but unfortunately his charger neighed loudly, and before the King had ridden a score paces, the Queen threw open the casement and leaned forward, her beautiful black hair hanging in tresses, and her hands clasped as if in prayer.

The King turned at the sound of the opening window, and waved a white kerchief again and again. I heard a wailing sound of sorrow as I retired, and well it might be, for the King and his much loved wife never met again.

Chapter Fifteen

THE JOURNEY to Exeter was a weary one. We passed through Bath and the Queen would fain have rested awhile and tried the effect of the famed hot springs for her rheumatism, but the plague raged among the poorer inhabitants and corpses floated down the Avon and lay unburied in the streets, so we passed on rapidly to Bristol, a place famous for its defences and fortifications, but ill adapted for an invalid with its dirty streets and unsavoury smells. Right glad was I to see Rougemont Castle, and the broad estuary of the Exe, and to enter the gates of the southern city.

Bedford House was the abode selected for the residence of the Queen, and a house near for the accommodation of her limited suite, among whom were Dr Gaston, who was to act as her scribe and secretary, Sir Geoffrey Hudson – the dwarf – and her Popish confessor. Before returning with my troopers to Oxford, I was presented by her Majesty with a ring which I wear unto this day.

Back at Oxford I was much employed as an equerry to the King, and I was continually sent with despatches to various places, often at a moment's notice. Sampson accompanied me as trumpeter, and we were always well mounted and well armed.

In the last three years Episcopacy had been abolished and the Presbyterians and Puritans had reformed the Church, as they were pleased to term it, but as the Puritan poet, John Milton, wrote a little later, 'New Pesbyter is but Old Priest writ large', and the Independents shouted for liberty of conscience. General Cromwell was called 'the great Independent', and he preached and prayed with his soldiers after a fashion of his own, according to ideas of what he conceived was religious liberty. But the Independents had no more real toleration for Papists and Churchmen than had the Presbyterians, while they were far more hostile to the monarchy and all established order. 'No more lords an' ye love me; they smell o' the Court' was written on papers and scattered about the streets of London, and this was soon to be followed by stronger measures.

Soon after my return to Oxford from Exeter, I was sent with despatches to Worcester, respecting the King's march upon Reading, and the Governor after reading these, sent me with troops to strengthen the garrison at Madresfield. The place was well moated, and supplied with sakers and ammunition, while it was within easy reach of Pixham ferry across the Severn. From Madresfield we rode to Hanley Hall, an old moated Grange, to requisition some horses, then on to Hanley Castle, to examine the ammunition stores in the dungeon, and the repairs of the shattered arch of Upton bridge. As I passed Merryvale, the old timber-ed dwelling where Mr Gaston, senior, resided, or as every one called him, 'Old Gaston', I saw that eccentric individual standing at his gate conversing with bright Bridget Nanfan, who had ridden over to ask for a mashwort for their great bloodhound, Harold, which was ailing and like to die.

It was with sorrow that I heard the sweet mouth of Bridget invoking ill fortune on her Puritanical neighbours, but it was a common feature of these miserable times.

"I am glad to hear," she said, "that the canting Roundheads at Glou-cester have got the plague, and I hope it may kill them every one," while just before she had passed whole nights nursing a sick parish-ioner.

Old Gaston smiled grimly as he listened to her thoughtless speech, and played with two white rats with red eyes which peered from out of his capacious pockets. Like Aunt Tabitha, Old Gaston was great in 'leechdoms and wort cunning', and had recipes for 'footache, heartache, headwark, shingles, elfin haunts, and nocturnal goblins'. He was in possession of the oldest of all recipes from Saxon Leechdom for the Devil's Tabberings, a complaint he was reported to have had more than once himself after a debauch on burnt posset at Hanley Quay. In Aunt Tabitha's Diary, this ancient recipe is given as follows:

'Take bishop's wort, lupin, viper's bugloss, blackberry, pennyroyal, and wormwood, pound all the worts together, boil them in good butter, wring them through a cloth, set them under the altar, sing nine masses over them, smear the man therewith on the temple and above the eyes, above the head, and above the breast. This salve is good for every temptation of the Fiend.'

Bridget received a concoction for Harold, and rode away, when we were joined by Colonel Windebank, who came over from inspecting the garrison at Madresfield to ask Gaston respecting some reports about the spy, Bound. Gaston had two friends in the world he believed in; one was Colonel Windebank and the other John Kelly, who had nursed him through a bad attack of the Devil's Tabberings.

I watched him closely as Windebank questioned him about the spy, for there were ugly reports of Bound having been seen riding the Ghost after midnight hours, away from Merryvale. But Old Gaston's face was imperturbable. His nose assumed a deeper tinge of purple, and his eyes glanced like those of the white rats, but he swore he had not seen Captain Bound for months, and knew not where he was if not at Gloucester. We could make nothing of him, so Windebank rode on to Pershore on his return to Oxford and Bletchington, and I galloped to Hanley Castle, embraced Aunt Tabitha, snatched a kiss from Isabel, and then on to Upton.

Party spirit now waxed stronger and stronger. Delicate women became fiery-eyed and passionate as they spoke upon religious or political subjects, while the men were more cruel towards their opponents. There were thousands of Cavaliers inspired with the spirit of loyalty and devotion for their King, while the Independents so little regarded royalty that they cheered General Cromwell when he declared that 'if he met the King in battle he would discharge his pistol upon him as upon any other man'. The Presbyterians were not prepared to go to such extremes, and wished to trim between loyalty and king-slaying, which in truth led to their final overthrow. The Earl of Essex and the Duke of Manchester were too loyal for the Independents.

Prince Rupert was active in the field, and all we wanted was a bold commander who could have concentrated the King's forces and improved the advantages as they were won.

I was enabled to pass Mothering day at Hanley Castle; a great day in Worcestershire, when all the children and godchildren meet the head and chief of the family and have a feast.[1] Alas, our feasting now was more like a fast, seasoned with the bitterworts of religious controversies.

We had a new Governor at Worcester, Sir Gilbert Gerrard, and another change at Hereford, where Colonel Nicholas Mynne succeeded to Sir William Vavasour.[2] Colonel Mynne learning that General Massey at Gloucester had a plan to invade Herefordshire, determined to hold him in check by occupying Newent and Upleadon with troops. As we knew the country, Giles Nanfan and I were sent with fifty of our Longdon troopers to support Colonel Mynne, whom we found occupying Prince Rupert's old quarters in Church Street.[3] We had only arrived a day or two, when information came from Mr Skippe, a royalist gentleman at the Upper Hall, Ledbury, that a considerable force was assembled on Huntly Heath, a wild uncultivated district below May Hill.[4]

Scouts were sent out to the new plantation of Scots firs on the summit of May Hill, and the Gospel Oak of Clifford's Mesne, and reported the force to be about six hundred horse and as many foot, with thirteen colours, under the command of General Behr, a Dutchman.

Colonel Mynne had thrown up some defensive works of turf and faggots at Newent, opposite the Gloucester entrance. The attack was made by the Parliamentarians soon after daybreak on the 13th of April, but we expected them and were prepared. Our infantry were drawn up with their matchlocks at the approaches from the Gloucester side. The cavalry assembled round the market-house, and many inhabitants capable of bearing arms were posted in places suitable for firing on the assailants.

The rector, Mr Wilse, was there, bravely encouraging our men, and in much danger from the cannon which played upon the church and his parsonage. General Behr sent a forlorn hope to attack our outworks. Behind these were five big guns which threw shot into the Royal Charles Inn, and did much damage to the church and steeple.[5] Soon there was a crash of chimneys and a heap of ruins round the Royal Charles, but few lives were lost, for the people of the town retired to the high ground of Stardens, which had been occupied by Sir John Winter.

The attack continued for three hours, when Colonel Mynne led two hundred men to the outworks, and the forlorn hope of the Parliamentarians was utterly routed. He then gave a signal to the cavalry to take the guns, and making a detour by the Ross entrance, we came upon the rebels' flank, when they gave way and their horse galloped for Gloucester, leaving the foot to take care of themselves. Many were slain in the Common Field, and at a place called to this day Woeful Hill.[6] In the afternoon a trumpeter rode over from General Massey, asking to be allowed to send carts to convey his wounded to Gloucester, at which we much rejoiced, there being but one chirurgeon at Newent. They abandoned two pieces of cannon in a muddy lane between the town and Woeful Hill.

By the end of April I was back again, guarding the bridge at Upton, and quartered at my own home. We found Bridget Nanfan at Hanley Castle, she and Isabel being engaged in a display of heraldry for the benefit of Giles and myself, as they were busy working our arms on two flags, with some token or resemblance showing the character and qualities of the bearers. Thus Bridget was not contented with working my arms *argent* a ratch hound *courant* between three hunting horns, but declared That my long legs deserved a shin-bone surmounted of another in cross, *argent*.

Isabel, too, would change Giles' coat altogether; as he was so fond of fighting, part of the shield should be blazoned *sable, gutte de sang*, interspersed with *gutte de larmes*. Thus we joked and laughed, though the *gutte de larmes* ran down the fair cheeks of those lassies when they were alone together, sobbing over their work; as they thought the time might come when the flags they wrought with loving fingers might prove our winding sheets.

We were now gratified by a visit from Lord Herbert, now Lord Glamorgan, who had been to see the new fuse invented by John Kelly. The old match was made of cotton or hemp, boiled in a strong solution of saltpetre, and generally hung at the girdle, whereas Kelly invented one steeped in moistened gunpowder, to be coiled round the arm or hat. Kelly's fuse was especially adapted for 'saker drakes', or light field carronades, which could be placed on towers of churches, or fired from the loopholes of a house or castle. They were equally useful for 'the leathern guns now come into fashion, and were very easy and light of carriage, for one horse could draw a piece which would carry a bullet of a pound and half weight, and do execution very far'.[7]

Very gallant looked my Lord of Glamorgan as he rode up to our drawbridge with half a score soldiers well mounted and armed, his rich plume nodding from his helmet, a crimson scarf around his waist richly fringed with silver, with boots of yellow leather reaching half-way up the thigh. Aunt Tabitha and Isabel accompanied me to receive this distinguished nobleman, but the former soon disappeared, and returned clad in her precious gown of silk instead of the quilted dimity. But before Aunt Tabitha arrayed herself in the silk dress which had lain in lavender surroundings several years, she paid a visit to the columbarium, and out of the pigeon holes took several doves which were consigned to the care of Isabel and the wenches.

The transformation of these pigeons into a pastie was soon accomplished, and so excellent was it that Lord Glamorgan asked for the written recipe, while in earnest converse over the delicacies which

appeared upon our table. My aunt was delighted, and she wrote out the
following:

> *With their heds down in the gravey,*
> *And their legs up through the crust,*
> *A chitterling to make it juicey,*
> *An egg or two, and eat you must.*

Early in May 1644, the King marched from Oxford to Reading, and
strange to say he occupied for one night Cowley House, the property of
his former enemy, Mr Hampden, in right of his wife. He was accompanied by the fighting antiquary, Richard Symonds, who 'on all
occasions had his note-book in his pocket to jot down coates of armes,
old shields, bishope's mitres, poetical inscriptions, coppys of verses,
fantastic quotations, family pedigrees', rather than the details of the
battles he saw and fought in. Thus his description of the King's march
from Cowley House occupies four lines; his account of the Vachell arms
in the 'dyning room windowes and the kytchen windowes' occupies
well nigh thirty.[8]

About the same time on 1st May 1644 a terrible tragedy was enacted
in our own neighbourhood, which was much commented on in the
news-letters.[9] Colonel Purefoy and a squadron of Roundhead horse
were quartered in Ledbury, making raids and assessments in all the
parishes round. They advanced one day as far as Hereford, and set fire
to a cottage within sight of the walls.

Returning by the village of Stoke Edith, some of the soldiers fell in
with the Vicar of the adjoining village of Tarrington, the Reverend
John Pralph, an old man of nearly eighty years of age, who was quietly
walking in the footpath between Stoke Church and St Edith's Well.
"Who are you for?" shouted the Roundheads. "For God and the King,"
replied the old gentleman; whereupon 'the barbarous rebel shot him
through the head with his pistol'.[10]

One publisher of a news-letter vindicated this outrage in terms which
would have disgraced a savage. "He was," said this scoundrel, "a reverend man, above fourscore years old, and was it not time, thinke you, to
sequester him out of this world? Had he not lived long enough to
corrupt both himselfe and a whole county! The Vicar's haires were
grown white with wearng the surplice so long, and with churching
women and singing before his congregation at Procession; this was one
of the reverend idolators belonging to the Common Prayer of this

kingdom, that great idol yet standing."[11] Such was the ferocious language indulged in by men filled with party hate and virulence.

Bitter retaliation by the Royalists soon followed. At the end of May, Prince Rupert marched upon Liverpool and Bolton, and at Bolton he was so enraged at seeing some of his followers put to death upon the city walls that he gave no quarter and a fearful slaughter ensued. [12]

It was well that the Queen was safe at Exeter, for by the middle of May, the Earl of Essex and Sir William Waller received instructions from the Parliament to combine operations and lay siege to Oxford. They marched with 20,000 foot and horse from Henley-on-Thames, so the King determined to evacuate the city which had been so long his refuge, and on the fifth of June arrived at Bourton-on-the-Water with some 6000 men and an immense number of coaches filled with ladies and their paraphernalia, glad to escape the dangers of a beleaguered town.

I was sent with Nanfan to meet the King and the Prince of Wales at Evesham. Evesham was an important place, and in the assessment made in 1636 was ranked among the nine highest rated corporate towns.[13] We passed by Fladbury, with its mother church to five or six hamlets, and its old and stately parsonage with windows full of armorial bearings. We saw, too, 'the parson's wife, a young woman, who was so far from pride as to be often seen carrying a milk-pail on her head', and thought how well it would be if other parsons' wives we knew of would follow her simplicity![14]

Again we rode by Evesham's battle-field, and I thought of one who died there for England's freedom.[15] But I had to give up dreaming and encounter the frowns of the townspeople, who were far from loyal.

At Evesham, Nanfan shared with me the chamber in which Leland slept, at the tavern above the bridge, said to have been a hostelrie since the days of Chaucer. Ere many hours had passed we learnt that Massey occupied Tewkesbury and was about to march on Evesham. Nanfan immediately rode forth to inform the King of this movement, and met the advanced guard of the Royalists at Wickhamford, the King being at Broadway.

His Majesty had been informed that Waller and his troops had reached Stow-in-the-Wold, but he knew nothing of Massey's advance from Gloucester. After a brief consultation it was determined not to enter Evesham, but to destroy an archway of the bridge, march by

Pershore and the left bank of the Avon, and blow up Pershore Bridge. We Worcester men then marched forward with Major Brydges, to occupy the Tewkesbury road and prepare the mine at the bridge.

The King, his army, and whole coach loads of ladies marshalled by Lord Cockayne, passed safely down the hill above the Avon at Pershore, and cleared the bridge without an accident. All were safe over, save Major Brydges and about thirty soldiers who had been preparing the mine, with some peasants who had been lending a hand at the laying of the gunpowder, when we were startled by a loud report. The man in charge of the fuse had fired it too soon, and the gallant Brydges, his men, and the unlucky peasants were either killed by the explosion or drowned in the river.[15] Such was the crowd of waggons, horses, coaches and troops in the narrow road to muddy Pershore, that little could be done towards saving those who were struggling in the foaming river. The King delayed his march until his officers pressed him to advance, as all had been done that was possible.

We escorted our King through the Sidbury gate into that ancient city which now wears the proud motto, *Floreat semper fidelis civitas*, amidst the roar of cannon, the sounds of music, and the cheers of the garrison and citizens. Ladies waved their kerchiefs, and emblazoned flags hung from every window. The clergy assembled with a loyal address, and the Governor, hat in hand, conducted his Majesty to the Bishop's Palace. For that night all seemed joyous and bright; but there was no rest for the King or us. We learnt that Waller was advancing on Evesham, and had proposed to Massey at Tewkesbury, and Lord Denbigh at Dudley Castle, to blockade his Majesty at Worcester.

The King's reverence for the services of the Established Church being well known to the citizens of Worcester, they exerted themselves to restore order in their Cathedral, and hid from view, as much as possible, the destruction caused by the Parliamentarians when their city was occupied by Lord Essex. Thus the King saw but little of the damage when he attended divine service in public on the eleventh of June, and it was during this service that he received despatches advising him to evacuate Worcester, unless he was prepared to abide a blockade.

As this was not to be thought of, we advanced up the Severn to Bewdley. The King was lodged in the mansion of Tickenhall, near the 'goodlie forest of Wyre', of which Drayton sings. Here amidst sylvan scenes we remained three days, and here the King wrote that fatal letter to Prince Rupert, ordering him to fight the battle of Marston Moor. The uncontrolled and arrogant courtiers of the 'thorough' type, advised the King one way, prudence counselled another, and the King halted between two opinions. At last it ended by his penning that letter, another step to ruin.

Waller's tactics were to prevent his Majesty and Prince Rupert from uniting their forces, he therefore hastened to move beyond the Royal army, and occupied Bridgnorth. The King, on his part, feared the junction of the forces under Waller, Massey, and the Earl of Denbigh. So, on the 15th of June we embarked our foot in barges and returned down the Severn to Worcester, leaving Waller to the northwards. From Worcester we marched to Evesham, where the Roundhead citizens had mended the bridge in order to receive Waller and his troops. For this we levied £200 on the evil inhabitants, and a thousand pairs of shoes for the use of our own jaded soldiers, and these commands 'without any long pause were submitted to and performed'.[16] The King took up his quarters for some days at the mansion of Mr Langstone.[17]

We rejoiced when we found ourselves on the breezy Cotswold hills above Broadway, and clear of the Avon and its broken bridges. The King then marched to Burford, on the western borders of Oxfordshire, and took up his quarters at the Priory, a house belonging to Mr Lenthall, Speaker of the House of Commons, who, without doubt, begrudged his Majesty the use of it.

After marching from place to place, intelligence reached the King that Waller and his army had taken up a position near Banbury, where the Castle was held by the rebellious Lord Saye and Sele. Banbury is a place Ben Jonson praised for its cakes and Sir William Davenant for its looms. I joined the Earl of Cleveland's brigade with some horse from Worcester on the morning of the 28th of June. He was stationed at Brackley on the left bank of the Cherwell, his Majesty and the rest of the army occupying Leigh Grounds, on the east of Banbury town.[18]

The morning of the 28th was misty, but when the fog cleared in the afternoon, Waller's forces were seen about three miles distant across the Cherwell, encamped upon Hanwell Common. His Majesty determined to offer battle and marched upon Crouch Hill, an important position the other side of Banbury. However, before our troops, over ten thousand in number, could defile through the town and across the narrow bridge, Waller hurried up from Hanwell and seized Crouch

Hill. The King on this withdrew his forces and passed the night in the fields between Grimsbury and Middleton Hills. Thus the Cherwell and the Castle of Banbury separated the two armies. On the 29th his Majesty marched northwards towards Daventry, Waller following on the other side of the Cherwell. Soon after the King had dined beneath a great ash tree near Wardington, Waller crossed Copredy Bridge, with 1500 horse, 1000 foot, and 11 pieces of cannon, while at the same time he sent 1000 horse to cross the Cherwell at a ford and attack our rear.

It was a day to be remembered by Cavaliers! Led by the Earl of Cleveland to his shout of "Hand and Sword!" we rode the rebels through and through. Lord Wilmot was down, shot in the arm, and had to surrender as prisoner when rescued by Giles Nanfan. Then the King ordered Lord Bernard Stuart to charge with the King's troop and Rupert's horse, and this completed the rout of the rebels. We took all their cannon, horses and harness, and thirty commanders and officers were our prisoners.

Among these was a Scot, who owed all he had in the world, 'even his bread and breeding', to the King's generosity.[19] Verily his Majesty had good reason to remember his countrymen! After his defeat Waller abandoned Copredy and withdrew to Bourton Hill.

On the evening of the 30th of June the King heard of the approach of 4000 Parliamentarians, so on the 1st of July he left Williamscot and marched 'with all his army, drums beating, colours flying, and trumpets sounding through Middleton Cheney to Dedington, where he slept at the Parsonage'.

It appeared to some of us, who were not in the royal councils, that the army was ever on the move without any definite plan. We marched the first week in July 1644, back again to Broadway and Evesham, many of the troops being quartered at Fladbury; then back through Broadway to Sudeley Castle, where the garrison fired at us; then to Coberly, where the King slept in a poor house.[20]

From this place I was sent with despatches to the Governor of Worcester, owing to the ill tidings which reached the King respecting the cruelty of the 'Saints' of Gloucester. Churches had been wrecked and men slaughtered within them, and brave Lady Winter was threatened with the fire and the sword. There had been a massacre in Newnham Church, and Colonel Congreve, Governor of Newnham, and Captain Wigmore, were murdered in cold blood at Dean Hall, on the summit of the hill above the Severn, when they should have received fair quarter.

Nor was this all. I had hardly reached Worcester when we heard of a circumstance which profoundly affected all English gentlemen. The Queen's accouchement had taken place at Exeter, and she had applied to the Earl of Essex to allow her to remove to Bath or Bristol for change of air, as the plague was now over, and the waters of Bath were considered so excellent for rheumatic invalids. Essex replied that 'it was his intention to escort her Majesty to London to answer before the Parliament for raising war against the King's subjects'. Some French writers declare that Essex 'set a price upon the Queen's head',[21] but I for one will never believe this of the Earl of Essex. Nevertheless, if the uncourteous reply was really sent to a lady in the condition of her Majesty, it was enough to raise the ire of every Cavalier.

Nor was it only Cavaliers who were indignant. In the first letter I received from Aunt Tabitha, after this history was bruited, she expressed herself as follows:

'What, my dr Nevew, is become of ye honor, ye shivalry, and ye manliness of Englishmen! It is enuff to make ye nites our forefathers to turn in their graves, armur and all. Bah! my Lord Essex, Bah!'

Chapter Sixteen

THE DEFEAT of Waller at Copredy Bridge was so complete that it broke the heart of his army and he had to retire to London. The King had marched into Somersetshire, and we heard of his being at Ilchester and Chard. I now received orders from the Governor of Worcester to carry despatches of moment and meet his Majesty on his road from Somersetshire to Oxford, at Hinton Waldrist, a village in Berkshire between Faringdon and Oxford.

I was to await the arrival of his Majesty at the Manor House, the residence of Sir Henry Marten. I avoided the towns on my journey as much as possible and rode by Coln St Aldwyn's to Faringdon, where I refreshed at Sir Robert Pye's house near the church. I had heard the Antiquary speak of the monuments here, so took the opportunity while my horse was baiting to visit 'the statues cutt of alablaster' of Unton and others.[1]

Hinton Waldrist is a *domus defensabilis* and a stronghold of some importance, occupying the site of a Norman Keep, surrounded by a deep moat, and with a great Edwardian barn for the gathering of corn. Near the drawbridge is a watch tower erected on a raised mound which commands a view of the surrounding country, from Woodstock on the north to the Cotswolds on the west, and away to the Chalk Downs of Berkshire on the south.

Sir Henry Marten received me with the welcome of a true Cavalier, and I remained with him three days expecting the arrival of his Majesty every hour. At last Sir Henry came to me in much tribulation and informed me I was to ride to Buckland, a village nearer Faringdon, where the King had arrived. He did not tell me the reason the King did not honour him by a visit.

I learnt, afterwards, that it was owing to the conduct of his son, Colonel Harry Marten, who, notwithstanding that the King had made a large grant of land to his father, had deserted the royal cause, and joined the Roundheads.[2]

Dame Marten was as unhappy as her husband at the sad disloyalty of her son, nevertheless she was not forgetful of her guests. Before I left she gave me some excellent advice, begging of me, at this season of the year, "To beware of superfluous drinking, but to eat heartily and abstain from fisick."

"Use not," she added, "to sleep much, especially in the afternoon, 'for that bringeth opilations, headache, agues, cathars, and all notorious distempers of the same kind'."[3]

I now left for Buckland, and at the turn to the village I met Lord Glamorgan riding slowly along with Dr Gaston in earnest conversation. Gaston seemed delighted to see me, and said the King was anxious for the Worcester despatches. Arrived at Buckland I found his Majesty seated in an arbour of the Rectory garden engaged in reading a number of papers.[4] He enquired how long I had been at Hinton Manor, and told me that Harry Marten, the rebel, maintained so close an espionage over all that went on at his father's house, that it was deemed inexpedient for him to go there.

The King had very few attendants with him, and I wondered what secret tactics were being concocted at this remote village among the wild Berkshire woods. Soon after Dr Gaston's return, his Majesty commanded him to proceed to Exeter, where Queen Henrietta required his services as scribe and secretary. He then commanded me to act as his equerry and accompany him to Oxford. Gaston handed over to me sundry satchells full of papers with especial admonition not to lose any. He was in excellent spirits, singing snatches as he packed up the despatches, such as:

> *Go teach your tenets of eternity to those that aged be,*
> *Do not persuade a loving maid there's any heaven but he.*
> *Come my Daphne, come away,*
> *Wee doe wast the cristall day.* [5]

When I enquired what had become of Lord Glamorgan, Gaston declared that he had returned to Raglan Castle to superintend a new water engine. The King remained at Oxford a few days and then returned to Somersetshire to his army. Meanwhile I was sent with some French papers to Bedford House, Exeter, where her Majesty resided since her accouchement.

I found the Queen in a room indifferently furnished. She lay, clad in a loose robe, with her babe by her side, upon a settee by the window, looking very beautiful, and gave me a smile of recognition as I approached and knelt by her side. The King's letter lay on her bosom and her eyes were overflowing, still she seemed brave, and in good spirits.

She questioned me much as to the appearance of his Majesty, how he looked and how he bore himself. "Dear heart!" she said, "Oh, Captain Forester, would that my beloved husband were here to look upon the face of this sweet flower." And truly the babe was a very cherub for rosy lips and pretty dimples.

The Queen then discoursed rapidly, as was her wont, on many subjects, and particularly on the storming and sack of Bolton. Her eyes sparkled as she spoke of the vengeance Prince Rupert had taken for his slaughtered soldiers whom the Puritans hung from the walls, and told me how the standards had been sent to Lathom House; also how the King had ordered his nephew to fight the rebels to the death in Yorkshire. The babe now whimpered, and her Majesty dismissed me, bidding me wait upon her by midday on the following morning.

I walked down the street, to the Clarence Tavern, when I was overtaken by Dr Gaston. He hailed me with his accustomed familiar manner and smiling face, and entered into conversation about his old father, whom he declared to be eminently loyal notwithstanding his oddity. He had named a bull-dog after King Charles and a squirrel after Prince Rupert.

He regretted that his revered parent had not been educated as a chirurgeon, as he was never so happy as when he was dissecting, anatomizing, probing, and scrutinising puppy dogs, mice, and any animal that could not bite, for the sake of deep inquiry into the beast's circulation. His experiments, too, extended to the brain, and he found that a pigeon with a thorn driven into its head gyrated for a length of time like a teetotum.

Dr Gaston then diverged into the discoveries of the future, due to these elaborate experiments, and how the impaling of millions of mice would hereafter enable man to save himself from the stomach ache. He enquired if the King had received the reply of Lord Essex to the Queen's request that she might be allowed to retire to Bath for the completion of her recovery, and declared that Essex with his whole army had reached Crediton, a few miles from Exeter – whereas he was really near Plymouth – and professed to think the Queen's position eminently dangerous, and to believe that Essex had set a price on her head.

I doubted both these statements and said so somewhat abruptly, when Gaston enquired if I did not think the Queen would be happier and safer in France. She was in a false position in England, hated by the Puritans, mistrusted by the Protestant Cavaliers, and a thorn in the side of the Jesuits, owing to her injudicious advocacy of their claims when they wanted to be let alone.

In reply to all this I said coldly, that with the Queen's courage and energy of character it was very unlikely she would desert the King. Dr Gaston smiled somewhat incredulously, shook me by the hand, recommended me to try the 'clouted' cream of Devonshire and Exeter pippins, and went his way to Bedford House.

Having refreshed myself and attended to my horse's comfort and that of Sampson, I roamed through Exeter for the purpose of making enquiries concerning the position of Lord Essex and his army and the probability of the town being invested. But the general opinion was that the only Parliamentarians within many miles of Exeter were a few scouts at Honiton, and that the garrison could hold out well, if the town were besieged, until relieved by the King, who was rapidly advancing, his guard being at Chard. The situation for the Queen was by no means critical or dangerous.

I then visited the Cathedral, and thought how the Antiquary would revel in the tombs of the Bishops, de Bohun, and Judge Dodderidge, with windows filled with the coats of arms of the Courtneys, and afterwards retired to the tavern.

Before daylight the next morning I was aroused by the host entering my chamber and telling me that a very small gentleman waited below stairs. Before I could finish dressing, Sir Geoffrey Hudson rushed into my bed-room gasping out, "She is gone, she is gone!" He then gave me the astounding news that the Queen had disappeared in the night, leaving her precious babe behind her. It is impossible to describe the state of alarm in which I found Lady Morton and the ladies and attendants at Bedford House, nor, amidst the wringing of hands, vociferations, tears, and sighs, was it easy to institute an inquiry into what had happened.

At last we succeeded in eliciting that Dr Gaston returned, after I had parted with him, full of reports of the march Essex on Exeter. He was already at Honiton and his advanced guard at Feniton. Thus the Queen, in her weak and nervous condition, had been driven well nigh to madness by the fear of the city being stormed, and that she should fall into the hands of the truculent soldiery. She left Bedford House soon after midnight, dressed as a serving maid, and accompanied only by Dr Gaston and her Confessor. For two days I searched the country round, accompanied by Sir Geoffrey Hudson, but to no purpose. The forsaken babe made sad lamentations for its lost mother, and sorrow and terror reigned at Bedford House. Nor was indignation altogether absent, especially among the ladies of the household.

At last a courier arrived with grateful tidings of the Queen's safety; she had reached Pendennis Castle, on the coast of Cornwall, after various hair-breadth escapes. For two whole days she had lain hidden in a wretched hut only three miles from Exeter gates. Her companions, although disguised – Gaston as a travelling tinker, and the priest as a dog doctor – had much ado to obtain provisions, and on one occasion the Queen listened to the discourse of some Roundhead scouts while she lay crouched under a heap of litter.[6]

The courier brought word that those of her Majesty's suite who chose to do so, might join her at Pendennis Castle. Eventually several set out robed in various disguises, but at Lady Morton's entreaty I remained at Bedford House to afford what protection was in my power to the infant Princess and her courageous and devoted nurse. The Queen did not remain long at Pendennis Castle; she took ship with her suite, all but Dr Gaston, whom she sent back to Exeter with a letter to the King.

But the sea was well nigh as dangerous as the land. The ship in which she sailed was attacked by a Parliamentarian cruiser as they neared the coast of France. The vessel was hit by shot, and a storm arising was nearly wrecked with all on board. They had to take to the long boat, and this was all but swamped as the drenched fugitives scrambled upon the shore of Henrietta's native country.

Within ten days after the Queen's flight, King Charles entered Exeter at the head of his army, and embraced his forsaken babe. He was long closeted with Dr Gaston, and what his Majesty thought of his Queen's flight I do not pretend to know or tell. I had my own opinions on the subject, and hold them still.

Before the King's arrival at Exeter we had heard of the total defeat of Prince Rupert at Marston Moor. The fatal letter written at Tickenhall had driven him into action when caution was necessary in the presence of a much larger army than his own. His cavalry got entangled in a morass and was well nigh annihilated. General Cromwell had lost his eldest son Oliver, only a few days before, in a skirmish near Knaresborough,[7] and both he and Fairfax shouted "No quarter". Upwards of four thousand bodies were buried in the Yorkshire bog, and Prince Rupert only saved himself by the speed of his horse. He lost, as well as his army, his faithful dog Boye, who was said to be the familiar of the bloody Prince, and to be shot-free and his skin impenetrable. Nevertheless, Boye died the death of a hero in the fatal charge on the Yorkshire heath.

When the King arrived he was weighed down with the tidings from Marston Moor, the loss of his beloved Queen, and the charge of his motherless child.

On the 27th July his Majesty rode forth to see Prince Maurice, attended by the Antiquary and others of Lord Bernard Stuart's troop. They stopped at Bradninch, where, notwithstanding it is a corporate town, 'all the houses are of clay, without any timber in the walls except the doors, roofs and windows, which is the fashion of the country'.[8] On the 28th his Majesty and the whole army marched to Crediton, 'a great lowsy town'.[9]

At Crediton the King slept, and the next day did me the honour of making me a Lieutenant- Colonel of Horse, commanding me to return to Worcestershire and supersede Colonel Vavasour as Governor of the district round Upton-on-Severn.

After a long and wearisome journey of nearly three days I reached Upton. I had to avoid Tewkesbury, which, as well as Gloucester, was now occupied by Parliamentarians. The sun was setting behind the Malverns, lighting up with his last rays the old tower of the church, the ever-flowing river, and the red cliffs of Ryall. The streets were full of soldiers marching with solemn tread towards the churchyard. As I rode to the Lion Tavern, I heard the voice of the Rector, Mr Woodforde, saying, "Earth to earth, ashes to ashes, dust to dust," as he committed a corpse to the grave. The hostler told me hurriedly that "a battle had been fought, one of our Worcester officers, Colonel Passey, had been killed, and now they were burying him by the Severn side."

Sir William Vavasour, formerly Governor of Hereford, was quartered at the Lion, and from him I learnt that a sharp encounter had taken place between the forces of General Massey and a body of Royalists under Colonel Mynne, the new Governor of Hereford, at the village of Redmarley, between Upton and Newent.

It appeared that Colonel Mynne, a brave soldier but ignorant of the country, and commanding a raw levy principally of Irish, had formed a plan for surprising Gloucester, as if Massey was a man to be caught slumbering. He had applied to Sir J. Gerrard at Worcester, for the aid of some Worcestershire horse, and requested they might be sent to meet him at Corse Lawn,[10] to wait there until he sent an aide-de-camp with orders.

Colonel Mynne, who was considered by the Roundheads 'a serious and active enemy and a perpetual terror to the country',[11] advanced from Ross, and overlooked Gloucester from the hills of Highnam and Lassington. Here his Irish brigade, 'finding that in Ireland nothing had been found more effectual to humble an enemy than the destruction of their standing grain',[12] proposed to set fire to some fields of waving corn, when a body of musketeers were seen crossing the Westgate bridge, and spies brought information that a large corps was marching from Tewkesbury and would join Massey at Over. On this Mynne fell back upon Staunton and Redmarley, and occupied the latter village for the night.

Redmarley is an ancient settlement; its mills and copses are mentioned in Domesday, while all around the hill platform, on which the village stands, are rich ryelands and deep hollow lanes, crossing each other and excavated in red sandy rock like unto sunny Devonshire. It is famous for its badgers and its bull-baits. The old church tower is a land-mark far and wide, and within the sacred walls rest the bones of George Shipside and Alice his wife. George was the loving brother-in-law of Bishop Ridley, who spoke words of comfort to the martyr as the flames surrounded him at Oxford, and Alice that 'sweet sister' to whom he penned his last letter.

Around the church and village Mynne encamped his men – 850 foot and 160 horse – and at day-break Massey attacked him with two divisions. The first corps Massey led himself, and crossed the river Leddon at High Leddon; the second was commanded by Colonel Edward Harley, and had occupied the ancient British Camp at Gadbury, in the parish of Eldersfield, the previous night. Thus when Mynne sent a trumpeter to Colonel Passey, who was at Corse Lawn with a corps of Royalists from Worcester, to beg of him to join their forces, the trumpeter was taken prisoner by the rebels.

The battle commenced with an attack by Massey with his Gloucester and Tewkesbury musketeers, and a desperate fight took place among the inclosures by the church, and later on among the gorse thickets on the platform above the hanging groves of Hazeldine. In the meantime the firing of guns and the shouts of the combatants were heard by Colonel Harley, who was in command of the detachment sent to Gadbury Camp; and he soon led his men by Staunton Mill and the Downs on to the platform whereon stands Redmarley Church.

Mynne was now placed between two fires, and his Irish legion gave way, but his Herefordshire soldiers rallied round him, and a hundred and seventy of his veterans died with their gallant General. I was told how my rival, Harley, 'distinguished himself particularly in this conflict', charging again and again at the head of his troop, and how he had 'received a severe wound in the arm'.[13]

Our Worcester Royalists were singularly unfortunate. Misled by spies, they remained at Corse Lawn, thinking that Mynne was on Corsewood Hill above the Lawn, and the messenger who was sent to summon them was taken prisoner by Colonel Harley. At last the sound of the guns at Redmarley told how the battle had begun, and Colonel Passey galloped in front of his troops, where the din of war re-echoed among the groves and woods. He fell in with Massey's rear-guard near the church, and was mortally wounded.[14] It was some time before our Worcester foot could reach Redmarley from Corse Lawn, and then they found the battle over, and the ground covered with the wounded and slain.

Out of heart at the loss of their Colonel, they did not encounter the victorious army of Massey, nor did they ever give a very satisfactory reason why they permitted the Governor of Gloucester to depart with his prisoners unassailed. The body of Colonel Mynne was taken to Gloucester and received honourable burial.[15] A few of the fallen soldiers were buried in the churchyard,[16] and a hundred and seventy where they fell. Poets have sung the deeds of 'Valiant Myn at Marley dead', and 'as one who did excel in honour and fidelity'. But with him died by the green slopes of Hazeldine many a loyal Herefordshire man, who, but for the war of brother against brother, would have been gathering this autumn day the golden grain of harvest.

After listening to the sad details of the defeat at Redmarley I was glad to retire for the night to Hanley Castle, and said nothing to Colonel Vavasour of my appointment as the Governor of the Upton district, thinking I would wait until the following morning. Aunt Tabitha and

Isabel both rushed to the drawbridge when they heard my well-known signal whistle, and it was day dawn before we had told each other all we had to relate. Aunt Tabitha was full of a fatal duel fought at Gloucester between two of Massey's officers, Majors Grey and Hammond,[17] in which the former was killed.

She attributed such quarrels to 'gross feeding, which breedeth gross blood and humours' and she also thought that some judgment must befall the Puritans, when the Parson at Hanley lost his cloth breeches, his fowls, and his copper saucepan on Sunday, while he was at church. Isabel was much dismayed at the death of Prince Rupert's dog at Marston Moor, and wept when she heard of the motherless babe at Exeter. She had heard of the fate of poor Boye from Old Gaston, who hated all dogs ever since he had been bitten by one, upon whom he was practising, by tying up his right femur with a tight ligature.

Weary with long-continued exertion, the sun had risen more than an hour before I looked forth from the casement in the tower above the drawbridge, at the old church over the lea. I was thinking of the happy Sundays of my youth, the bells summoning to prayer and praise, the congregation wending their way across meadows and by village lanes, and the kindly greetings between pastor, squire, and people, when Mary Bromley ran wildly across the drawbridge into the court-yard below my window, and I heard her say to Aunt Tabitha, who was feeding her poultry, "For God and mercy's sake, Madam, try and save my brother Dick!"

I ran down instantly, and found Mary in a fearful state of alarm, for her only brother had been taken prisoner under peculiar circumstances at Corse Lawn, and had been condemned by a court-martial held at Upton to be shot as a spy.

Mary was ignorant of my return to Hanley Castle, but as drowning men catch at straws, thought it possible that Aunt Tabitha, as sister to the King's Secretary, might have some influence with Vavasour. It appeared that the court-martial had tried her brother the afternoon of my return from Exeter, but I had been so taken up with the relation of the battle at Redmarley, that I had left without hearing any allusion to the court-martial. In a few minutes I was in the saddle, and galloping, as if for life, to Upton.

A flag with Sir William Vavasour's arms – a *fess dancette sable* – hung out of the window at the Lion, and there were several officers assem-bled in the court-yard of the inn, with a guard of soldiers at the entrance, which spoke of something unusual within. Sampson was among the soldiers of the guard, and when I inquired what was the matter, he told me that Captain Bromley had been condemned to be shot as a spy, having been taken prisoner at Corse Lawn, and convicted of being in company with the notorious spy, Captain Bound.

I immediately requested to be conducted to the chamber where the prisoner was confined, and to my great astonishment saw before me the young officer I had rescued from drowning in the Teme at the skirmish at Powick, and of whom I caught a hurried glimpse from the barber's shop, as he rode with Mary and Mr Bromley down the streets at Tewkesbury. Dick Bromley was leaning on a table with his head between his hands when I entered, but he recognized me in a moment, and, notwithstanding the anxiety of his present position, came forward with words of gratitude and greeting.

After some little explanation he entreated of me to spurn the idea that he could be guilty of acting the part for which he was condemned to death, and then gave me a very straightforward account how he was placed in the present dangerous dilemma.

General Massey, before he set out from Gloucester to attack Colonel Mynne at Redmarley, had sent out two reconnoitring parties, one by High Leddon, and another in the direction of Corse Lawn and Eldersfield. Bromley led the Corse Lawn expedition, and with him rode Captain Bound, now known to all the Royalist forces in our district as a notorious spy. No place was safe from the intrusion of this man or his emissaries. He was ever ready with some crafty disguise or other, and there was not a Royalist commander, if only he could catch him, who would not have hung him to the next tree.

But of all this Captain Bromley knew nothing. He had but lately arrived at Gloucester with orders from Lord Essex, and few among the Parliamentarians, save Massey himself, were acquainted with the sleuth- hound qualities of Bound. He was generally looked upon as a bold raider ever ready to volunteer on a dangerous expedition. Bromley therefore rejoiced to have him as a companion in his reconnoitring, as Bound was especially acquainted with the intricate roads by Chaceley, and the wild woodlands of Corse and Hasfield.

It was supposed that Mynne had marched towards Hasfield, and a dispute arose respecting a trackway through Corse Grove, when Bound appealed to a sketch of the country which he carried in his sword belt; and an adjournment was made to the hostel at Corse known as The Dragon, to examine the map, the scouts remaining outside. While thus engaged a trumpet was heard on the Lawn, a wide open common free from trees. Bound went to see by whom the blast was blown, and did not return.

He had only time to mount the Ghost and gallop off with the rest of the scouts, when the inn was surrounded by the Royalist troopers from Worcester. Dick Bromley was thus taken prisoner, and with him a number of Bound's papers. Among these was a drawing of the defences of Madresfield Court; a limning of the bridge at Upton, and the Church; a description of the defences at Castleditch, Birtsmorton Court, Strensham Court, and other places now occupied by the Royalists. But there was nothing to connect all this with Bound personally, so the papers were naturally believed to be the work and property of Captain Bromley.

It was without doubt a very awkward position. His father, Mr Bromley, was known to have had communication with Governor Massey, and all the Worcester men attributed the defeat at Redmarley to the system of espionage carried on by men from Upton or its neighbourhood. Bromley's explanations, and a previous knowledge of Bound's character and antecedents, so convinced me of his entire innocence that I immediately sought an interview with Colonel Vavasour.

Vavasour listened to me with soldier-like calmness and decision, but declared that it was impossible to accept Bromley's explanations in so grave a matter without a tittle of evidence to corroborate them. Spies had become the curse of the country, and Bromley had been caught red-handed with the most compromising papers in his possession. He had been fairly tried and was convicted of the most glaring and un-soldier-like espionage; an example must be made, and he must abide his fate.[18]

On this I produced the Commission of Lieutenant-Colonel which I had received from the King at Exeter, and informed Vavasour that he was no longer addressing a subaltern but his equal in rank; and I followed this up by handing him my appointment by the King as Governor of the Upton district, by which he was superseded in his command.

Like a true and hearty gentleman he arose and shook me by the hand, saying that my father, who was his old friend, would indeed rejoice at one so young having received such earnest of the King's trust and approval. He then signified his intention of resigning his command to me forthwith, and with it the responsibility involved in the prisoner, Captain Bromley. I then explained to Colonel Vavasour the part I felt certain Bound had taken in the matter, and how I was convinced that Dick Bromley was an officer and a gentleman, and no spy.

Colonel Vavasour then addressed the men, and I, assuming the command, released Bromley on his promise to surrender, if called upon, to be tried by a court-martial appointed by his Majesty, and a further promise that he would not again take up arms against his King during the present war. Having signed these articles he proceeded to Hamme Court, where his father lay ill, thankful for a happy escape from an inglorious end.

In the month of October was fought the second battle of Newbury, the place where Lord Falkland was killed a year before. The battle was fought on a Sunday, and the united forces of the army of the Parliament were engaged. General Cromwell and the Earl of Manchester quarrelled about the cavalry service, still the King was worsted and retired from the field of battle to Donnington Castle, where he watched the battle for some time, and then 'being persuaded by his Generals most earnestly', he 'marched with his regiment all night towards Bath and reached it by four o'clock next day, making fifty miles of it without rest'.[19]

The Parliamentarians had received such severe treatment that the King was not pursued, and eleven days later brought off his cannon and threw large supplies into Donnington Castle. In a skirmish before this Castle on the 9th of November 1644, in which both Prince Rupert and Prince Maurice were engaged, the King's horse was struck in the foot by a musket ball.[20]

At the close of this year General Cromwell made the celebrated speech in Parliament on the 9th of December which led to the Self-denying Ordinance, the 'New Model' of the army, and the resignations of their commissions by the Earls of Essex and Manchester. It was also marked by grievous requisitioning upon all the inhabitants within reach of all garrison towns. The very vegetables in the gardens were not spared to their hungry owners. "If the Lord had na' been on my side all the summer, for greens," said a poor woman to me, "I don't know what we should ha' done." Sometimes it was the Parliamentarians, some-times the Royalists who plundered, until farmers and villagers became desperate in their distress.

Nor did the soldiers hesitate to personally ill-treat those who dis-appointed them in their demands for money or provisions. Those who had been friends and neighbours became bitter and hostile enemies. Mr Cocks, of Castleditch, who had purchased the beautiful home of the Clintons among the pleasant woods of Eastnor, was besieged by troops from Gloucester commanded by his former friend Captain Hopton, one of the Hoptons of Canon Frome. Castleditch was not an easy place to take, it was so well protected by its moats and defences; still the old neighbour of former years so battered it with his cannon that Mr Cocks took refuge at Goldhills, a farm hard by, and the Roundheads seized his residence and filled it with troops.[21]

Wherever a house was considered defensible it was occupied by soldiers. The Royalists had taken Canon Frome and Captain Barrold commanded there. The Abbey House at Malvern had no defences, but Massey filled it with soldiers notwithstanding its proximity to Madres-field Court, occupied by Royalists.

Sometimes mansions capable of defence were filled with troops at the request of their owners. Thus Sir Giles Nanfan maintained a score of troopers under Captain Vincent Hasseli, and these were quartered in the adjoining villages of Pendock and Berrow. The Roundheads in Tewkesbury became bolder than ever, and seized Mr Richard Dowdeswell, one of our Commissioners of Array for Worcestershire, who was taken as prisoner to Warwick and thence to London. Every-where the long continuance of the war was producing harrowing scenes among the once happy homes of Englishmen, and both sides flattered themselves they were fighting the Lord's battles, as they struck down their enemies, for the sake of the Covenant, or for God and the King.

Meanwhile Prince Maurice was appointed Major General of all Royalist troops in the west of England, and I was summoned to Worcester to receive his orders.

Church Lane, Ledbury

Chapter Seventeen

NEW YEAR'S DAY was kept by the garrison and citizens of Worcester as a gift day, notwithstanding the war and the ominous times. Prince Maurice and his suite attended divine service in the Cathedral, and about mid-day hundreds of country men and women were admitted through the gates bearing gifts from relations to the soldiers, from tenants to their landlords, and from country friends to the citizens. Fat capons were, as in the days of Queen Elizabeth, still the usual gifts to landlords.[1] Ben Jonson's 'New Year's Gift Serving Man' was to be seen traversing the High Street and Foregate dressed, as in bygone years, 'in a blue coat with an orange, and a sprig of rosemary on his head, his hat full of brooches, with a collar of gingerbread, and a torch-bearer carrying a marchpane with a bottle of wine on either arm.'[2]

This New Year's Man also carried Worcester gloves to persons in authority, and some were filled with pistoles, as the lady once filled the New Year's gloves of Sir Thomas More with angels. Every person in the street bore an orange stuck full of cloves to hold forth and greet a passing acquaintance with the cry, "New Year's Day, God bless you."

I was not forgotten by friends below the Malverns; a stuffed boar's head arrived from Birtsmorton Court, geese and capons from Hanley Castle, enough to feed a regiment, and an immense pot of rue and rosemary salve from Aunt Tabitha. Isabel sent me a fine ribbon for my neck, and last but not least came a pair of gloves from Mary Bromley. I had not seen her since she was in such tribulation about her brother, and now she sent this New Year's gift with a few grateful lines. The gloves were worked in gold thread, like those which Queen Elizabeth took from her royal hands and presented to the Mayor of Worcester.

Amidst much feasting and jollity men's hearts were gladdened by the report that peace might be proclaimed any day, as Commissioners from the King were to meet Commissioners from the Parliament at Uxbridge. These hopes, however, did not last long, for we soon received intelligence of the execution of Archbishop Laud on the 16th of January. He was condemned by the Parliamentary leaders to be hanged, drawn, and quartered, but when the time came, the Saints who hunted him to the death, shrunk from inflicting these last tortures on his worn-out frame. The very judges who tried him refused to legalize the sentence, and he was beheaded. The execution of the Archbishop was an act of cruelty no partizan-ship can mitigate or excuse, and when the account of his death reached us at Worcester, we felt that peace was hopeless, and the struggle must continue to the bitter end.

Still the farce was carried on; the King's Commissioners met the deputies of the Parliament at Uxbridge on the 29th of January, and every one spoke very learnedly and disputed syllogistically, and after twenty days of debate and wrangling, nothing was settled, nothing was made clear, except that war must rage, and that Englishmen must kill their brother Englishmen in this bitter struggle over our common Christianity.

The New 'Noddle' Army, as we Cavaliers called it, assembled at Windsor under Sir Thomas Fairfax, a brave man, but so uncourteous in his demeanour, that the King named him the new brutish General of the Parliament. His Majesty's intention was to collect all the royalist troops and march with his combined forces upon London. He therefore sent Prince Maurice to Chester and Prince Rupert to Hereford and Worcester, where the latter published a Declaration setting forth the high authority of the King, without whom the Parliament was nil. No sooner was this done than Mr Ligon, of Madresfield, and Mr Nicholas Lechmere, of Severn End, met a number of Roundheads at Warwick and published a reply, enjoining all persons to forbear subscribing to the Declaration.[3] Mr Lechmere was a clever lawyer, and one of whom it might be said:

> *Here is an honest lawyer, wott you what,*
> *A thing for all ye world to wonder at.*

But like many others who joined the Parliamentarians, he had little idea to what conclusion they would come at last.

The withdrawal of our soldiers from Upton was a mistake, as may be understood from my aunt Tabitha's letter:

Handley Castle, All Fool's Day, 1645
Dr Nevew,
Bad times are come upon us since you took away the souldiers.
Captain bound has been to Upton and terrified Parson Woodforde with his threts and chamferings. He, with others you may guess of, went, in open day, to Upton Church, and broke the noses off the nobel nites who lie cross-legged in ye chancel. Then they came to

our Church and brake the heads of the Vergin Mary and the 12
Apostles in our grate east window. My Lord Cockayne sent Bridget
Nanfan a valentine, and says that if she won't 'fanne his warme desir',
hel 'woo the wynd an court the wilderness', and studdy some slow
but certain way to dye.' Says my Lord, but I suppose he is
fillusteringe.

> *'My woeful monument shall be a cell,*
> *The mourning of the purling brook my bell,*
> *And for my epitaph the rock shall groane*
> *Eternally; if any ask the stone*
> *What wretched thing doth in that conclave lye*
> *The hollow echo shall reply, "Tis I"*

On holding a council of war the King decided again to leave Oxford
and march to Worcester. As usual, spies conveyed information of the
Royalist movements and General Cromwell was sent to oppose their
march. This led to the fight at Islip Bridge in Oxfordshire. Cromwell
then laid siege to Bletchington House. Here Colonel Windebank, the
friend of John Kelly, Sir Giles Nanfan, Mr Gaston, senior, and other
royalist gentlemen, was in command, and unfortunately his young wife
and several other ladies were on a visit in the house.

Cromwell threatened to storm the place if it was not surrendered,
and Windebank, fearing to expose the ladies to the horrors of war,
marched out at midnight, leaving his arms, ammunition, and seventy
horses to the enemy. Alas! on arriving at Oxford, he was seized as a
prisoner, tried by a court-martial of Thoroughs, and sentenced to be
shot. Deaf to the entreaties of his broken-hearted wife, and of the ladies
for whose sake the surrender was made, the King permitted the sentence to be carried out. Windebank was set with his back against the
wall of Merton College, which had so long sheltered the Queen, and
shouting "God save the King!" gave the signal for his own death volley.

I had gone to Upton, and on paying a visit to John Kelly, found him,
with Old Gaston, examining a rare bird the latter had snared. As I
related the sad history of the death of Windebank, Kelly clutched an
oaken chair to prevent himself from falling. His cheeks became of an
ashy paleness as he asked in hollow tones, "Windebank shot dead, and
by the King's orders!"

"Dead" I replied, sadly and gloomily. He said not another word, but strode across the room, and seizing his Cavalier's hat, tore out the feather, and taking his sword he cast both into the Severn as it rippled past the door. Then I knew that John Kelly would never draw sword again for the cause of King Charles. Gaston's behaviour was a contrast to that of the Philosopher. He threw himself into an oaken chair and sat mumbling as if he had lost his senses; his face crimsoned as if he would have a fit of apoplexy, and then he arose and strode forth down Dun's Lane shaking his right hand on high as if denouncing vengeance from heaven. On his return home he hung his one-eyed bull-dog Charley.

The loss to his Majesty did not end here; when the circumstances of Windebank's death became known, more than a score of Royalist officers resigned their commissions and compounded with the Parliament. Lord Chandos never again appeared on the field of battle.

The number of spies now infesting Worcestershire was alarming. They were all supposed to be in the pay of the notorious Bound. At last I received a communication which gave hopes that we might apprehend this renegade himself. I sent Sampson, now a sergeant of horse, with half a score of musketeers, to guard the powder and fuses stored in the dungeon at Hanley Castle, with special orders to try to discover the haunts of Captain Bound. He soon fell in with Old Gaston, trapping coneys on Hanley Common, and knowing that he frequently saw the Spy, took the opportunity of inviting him to share a tankard of burnt posset at the tavern at Hanley quay.

Here Sampson listened patiently to a long disquisition on the rival claims of Michael Servetus, Father Paolo, and Dr Harvey, to the discovery of the circulation of the blood. He saved himself with difficulty from going to sleep, and ordered more burnt posset. This opened the heart of Old Gaston, he promised to present Sampson with a piping bullfinch, and to teach him how to entrap the nightingales in the month of May.

Another tankard, and he was still more communicative. He would not drink the health of the King after the death of Windebank, yet he mortally hated all Roundheads, and Bound in particular, but he owed the Spy a considerable sum of money and he had a mortgage on his farm. Then the burnt posset brought tears to his eyes, and he acknowledged that though he had a distinguished son, who was cipherer to the King, he occasionally communicated through Bound with Massey, and thus was enabled to pay the interest on the mortgage.

Sampson also gathered that Bound was now frequenting the small village taverns at Welland and Castlemorton for the purpose of making a raid upon Little Malvern Court, the residence of Mr Russell, a cousin of Sir William Russell, of Strensham. In the spirit of the times Mr Russell had been indicted before Mr Nicholas Lechmere as a Papist and recusant, and Bound considered that his plate and money would be useful to the Puritans.

I had made arrangement to go to Welland with a score of horse, but having received orders from Prince Rupert to remain in Worcester and see to the despatch of Major Pilkington with a squadron of horse to intercept a convoy going from Birmingham to Gloucester with powder, I entrusted the capture of Bound to Captain Morgan, a fiery, astute, little Welshman.

On receiving intimation that the Spy had again been seen prowling about the neighbourhood, Morgan and his followers started for Welland and Little Malvern at midnight. For three days they lingered in separate detachments among the wild commons and woodlands below the Malverns, but they saw no one save a few peasants and the Welland parson, the Rev. Howard Hamilton Snoper.

Mr Snoper was very civil to Captain Morgan, and proved an agreeable companion. He loved the woodlands surrounding his lonely vicarage and the birds frequenting the Welland glades. He had an absorbing passion for military books and saved all his money to buy them. He wore the most orthodox clerical garments and the broadest of bands; but he avoided theological discussion, and said he ought to have been born a soldier. He listened with interest to Morgan's account of the various battles he had fought, and any military details.

Mr Snoper was no ascetic, he liked his sack and burnt posset, and a good deal of it, while he smoked as much tobacco as von Prig. He had suffered from the depredations of Bound and his associates, and had lost his few sheep upon the common and all his chickens. One morning the reverend gentleman communicated to Captain Morgan, that he had received certain information that Bound had joined Massey's corps at Ledbury, on which Morgan led his troopers back to Worcester.

Mr Snoper addressed a letter to me, at which I was somewhat surprised, having no acquaintance with him. On opening the epistle I read as follows:

'Dr Dick, Don't send again 20 asses to catch an old lyon. Let heralds now say 'he beareth verdant an asses head rampant by the name of Forester'. I am, Dr Dick, your admiring friend,

BOB BOUND, *alias* SNOPER.

Postscriptum – Captain Morgan is a well-informed officer, and knows a grate deal about where your souldiers are; best respecs to him.

Both Morgan and myself were much mortified at this escapade and triumph of this impudent spy, yet this was not so disastrous as the expedition under Major Pilkington, who lost his life and that of several of his men, and did not intercept the convoy of powder and match that was sent to Gloucester.[4]

About this time I received a letter from my father at Oxford, from which it appeared that the Earl of Glamorgan had started for Ireland with the purpose of levying an army among the rebels who had perpetrated the massacres. This was opposed to the King's most solemn declaration that nothing should induce him to employ Irish Papists against his English subjects. The Queen in France and the Thoroughs in England advocated raising such a force, in defiance of the storm that would be certain to follow in all parts of the country.

During the deliberations at the council board, my father expressed himself strongly against the proposition. He thought it dishonest, after his Majesty's declaration to the contrary, and unworthy of a Monarch, to thus falsify his word. In consequence of this objection he was no longer summoned to the council, but was employed about the person of the Duke of York, while Dr Gaston took his place as private secretary, as well as the conductor of all the cipher correspondence. How far the King had compromised himself with Lord Glamorgan my father knew not, but he was very anxious respecting his Majesty's ultimate determination.[5]

We learnt at Worcester that General Massey occupied Ledbury in force and threatened Hereford, which latter place Prince Rupert had just left on his way to Shrewsbury and Chester. It was therefore determined to send Captain Forwards, as Giles Nanfan was now called, to carry the in- formation to the Prince as he halted at Leominster, and he would doubtless retrace his steps and drive Massey back to his stronghold at Gloucester.

I then marched with two hundred horse for Canon Frome, a fortified mansion a few miles from Ledbury, once the home of the gallant Sir Edward Hopton, Yeoman of the Stirrup to King Charles I, but now garrisoned for the King with a hundred and twenty men under Colonel Barroll, who held the place for two years against several attacks by the Parliamentarians. The council at Worcester thought that Barroll might spare some men to assist in expelling Massey from Ledbury.

We crossed the Malverns by moonlight, at the pass of the Wych, and the sun rose as we passed by the great oaks in the park at Canon Frome and appeared before the moated stronghold of the Hoptons. Here we broke our fast and received a soldier's welcome from Captain Barroll. At eight o'clock Giles Nanfan rode up with the news that Prince Rupert had retraced his steps, and our orders were to meet him at Bosbury.

The Bishops of Hereford used to frequent Bosbury as good hunting quarters, and portions of their ruined palace still remained. Our gallant Cavalier General was breakfasting in what was left of the refectory,[6] and quaffing the cider for which Bosbury is famous. Lord Astley and Lord Loughborough with other officers were following his example in Harford Manor House, and well nigh filled the panelled room with the armorial bearings. Others were refreshing at Bosbury House, the property of Sir Walter Pye of Faringdon, who was destined afterwards to be besieged in his own house near that town by his Roundhead son. A flag, with the coat of Harford, *sable* two bends *argent* on a chevron *azure*, told us that a scion of the family was among the regiments, although the Manor House was deserted.

The beat of the drum and the fanfare of the trumpet startled the cuckoo in the woodlands and orchards as we followed our princely leader to Ledbury on that glorious April morning. The spring sunshine lighted up the golden gorse, and the nightingale warbled in the woods and thickets as the dairy-maids crossed the paddocks to call the kine with their sonorous 'kai-yu-kai'. Giles Nanfan rode by my side, devoutly hoping we might be spared the slaughter of some of our old neighbours, as Higgins of Eastnor, or Hopton the Parliamentarian.

Ledbury lies pleasantly on the left bank of the Leddon, and above it rise the wooded rocky hills of Dog Hill and the Frith, while on the right, a little more than a mile distant, is the famous Roman encampment, Wall Hills. The town consists of one long street leading from the Hereford and Leominster roads to the Gloucester highway, crossed at right angles by another shorter street on the road leading from Ross to Malvern. The old church, with its detached tower and fine spire, stands a little distance from the town, and above is the Upper Hall, the residence of Squire Skipp, a grandson of the first Protestant Bishop of Hereford. A market house, said to have been erected in the time of King Stephen, stands in a wide irregular market-place, much used in bygone days for baiting bulls, bears, and Redmarley badgers. Close to the cross street is the New House,[7] a modern structure belonging to a good Royalist, Captain Skinner.

Massey was engaged in holding a court-martial upon one of Prince Rupert's soldiers, whom he intended to hang as a spy, when he was startled by our trumpets as we entered the Homend on the Hereford Road. No time was lost by the Governor of Gloucester in endeavouring to raise a barricade of carts and baggage waggons across the Homend, where the street leads to the market-place.

Lord Ashley and Colonel Washington were ordered to force this barricade with their foot soldiers, that we might act with our cavalry.[8] They cleared a passage in gallant style after a short half hour's struggle. Lord Loughborough's troop of horse now charged, and we followed close behind. Five bullets passed through Prince Rupert's clothes and struck his armour, but he escaped unwounded. It was a fearful struggle in the open space, with no attempt at strategy, and my horse, shot through the forehead, fell dead, and I fell with him, hopelessly entangled for the time with the gear and stirrups. I was partly stunned, and found myself lying on the ground with Captain Forwards bestriding me, and knocking down the Parliamentarians as they approached, by tremendous sweeps with the rammer of a cannon. Then came a rush of our men and I was on my legs again.

A party of Roundheads had been raiding and requisitioning both at the Lower and Upper Hall, and the sound of heavy firing made us aware of a sharp contest in the direction of the Church. I therefore called upon some men to follow me and ran up the Church Lane, when, on the entrance to the churchyard, I encountered Colonel Edward Harley. He recognized me in an instant and awaited my attack with imperturbable coolness.

I soon found that he was an excellent swordsman and was consequently on my guard. Nevertheless he seemed weak and exhausted, and I was not aware that he had not recovered from a gun-shot wound received at Redmarley. His sword was soon beaten down, and one stroke over the head would for ever have deprived me of my rival. But the thought rushed through my brain, that the death blow would go to the heart of Mary Bromley, so, staying my hand, I brought the point of my sword to a salute. Colonel Harley recognized the gesture with a smile and at once surrendered as my prisoner. This I would not allow and begged of him to take horse and save himself, when, giving me a look of astonished gratitude, he calmly walked down the Church Lane.

Fierce fighting was now going on in the churchyard, and a number of the Roundheads fled for shelter to the Church itself.[9] Hoping to prevent bloodshed within the sacred edifice, I entered with a score of Royalists and proclaimed quarter in a loud voice to all who would lay down their arms, so the Roundheads withdrew within the large chancel and into the beautiful chapel of St Catherine. An officer of the Parliament now came forward offering to surrender, and we discussed the terms briefly, as we stood by the side of that mysterious tomb of some royal lady; that monument of ancient days bearing the arms of England, but which neither by time or date, reveals the secret as to the corpse which rests beneath it.[10]

A furious contest now raged in High Street and Southend. Prince Rupert and Massey engaged in a hand-to-hand conflict, and both had their horses shot under them.[11] The struggle continued in the narrow alley called Back Lane and in Bishop Street, and a number of the Roundheads took refuge in the Lower Hall, where they were slaughtered to a man. Here fell Major Backhouse, and Captain Kyrle of Hom House.

At last the Parliamentarians gave way, and the infantry fled to the neighbouring woods for shelter. Massey, mounting a trooper's horse, galloped down the Gloucester road, followed by as many horse as could clear the town, and Colonel Harley escaped with him. Giles Nanfan rode in pursuit, and chased the rebels for four miles.

It was a sorry sight when the fight was over; Englishmen rolling in blood on the ground and clutching the dust in their agony. Opposite the Market Place sat Honeywood Yates of Bromesberrow, supporting the head of his brother, who was apparently dying. The tears streamed down the cheeks of poor Honeywood as he tried to pour some wine into the closed lips of the wounded man, whom he had himself struck down in the melee at the barricade. Fortunately the wound was not mortal, and I helped to carry him into the Plume of Feathers, but it was some time before Honeywood recovered from the deadly sickness that came over him when he believed he was a fratricide.

One hundred of the rebels were killed, and many more would have been put to death, but Prince Rupert rode up and down the town and commanded to give quarter. The Prince passed the night at the New House and marched the following day for Ludlow. I was ordered to return to Worcester, and before I left Ledbury Prince Rupert informed me that the King was about to leave Oxford and march northwards to wipe out the blot of Marston Moor. He ordered me to impress upon our Worcestershire Commissioners of Array the necessity of recruiting for men and money.

Letters from my father at Oxford led me to suspect that the preparations for the coming campaign were far too much discussed by the courtiers and even the generals of the army. The Queen, in Paris, insisted on being informed of all that was going on in England, and participating in all the most secret affairs; Dr Gaston, therefore, was constantly employed in sending letters from the King, written in cipher, which exercised the ingenuity of the poet Cowley to decipher, and were then bruited through the French court. This was carried to such an extent that the King wrote a letter of expostulation to Lord Jermyn,[12] the Queen's principal adviser, but not a line was ever received from her Majesty which evinced any desire that the war should terminate save by slaughter and conquest.

In the mean time, a letter from my aunt at Hanley Castle was sent by special messenger to inform me that Bound and the Gloucester Roundheads had been bolder than ever. Bushley Park, the residence of Mr Dowdeswell, had been ransacked, also Corse Court, Pull Court, and the dwelling-house of Mr Cower at Combhill. Above all, Captain Bound had laid an information of witchcraft against Nurse Stubbs before Squire Bromley.

This, my aunt declared, was because he coveted a strip of land which belonged to the poor widow, the land-marks of which he had more than once removed, as it adjoined some land of his own in the Upton meadows. Aunt Tabitha entreated for my presence, or that of Giles Nanfan, with a squadron of horse, when, as she said, there was little doubt that Bound 'would scuttle out of Upton, like an astonied coney'.

In consequence of this letter I obtained permission from the Governor of Worcester to send some troopers to occupy Upton, and to accompany them and inquire into the state of affairs described by Aunt Tabitha, while Captain Forwards, now raised to the rank of Lieutenant Colonel for his gallantry at Ledbury, was sent with a regiment to occupy Bromsgrove.

We left Worcester at night; a bright moon shone upon the yellow gorse and fine old trees round Madresfield as we crossed the Old Hills, the waters of the Severn glistened in the moonlight on our left, and the Malverns loomed darkly on our right, while nightingales trilled in every grove. As we rode on the sun arose, the sky-lark soared on high, and the peasants appeared at their cottage doors in Hanley village as we reached the green slope above the moats of the Castle, the waters of which gleamed like burnished gold, while Isabel's garden appeared gay with spring flowers on this the first of May 1645.

Early as it was, my sweet sister was surrounded with village children, who had reared a May-pole the night before, and were now suspending garlands of wild flowers. The Puritans prevented the rearing of a May-pole at Hanley Cross, so Isabel set up one of her own among the Castle ruins. Aunt Tabitha was feeding her fowls, but at the sound of our trumpet before the drawbridge, the May-day revellers were left to their own devices, and my loving relatives rushed to bid me welcome. While Aunt Tabitha hastened to make arrangements for breaking our fast, Isabel walked with me in the gardens and by the moat, and listened with heightened colour and dewy eyes as I told her of Ledbury fight, and how I owed my life to the sway of the gun rammer of Captain Forwards, which he had seized when his horse was killed under him and his sword broken.

After a short delay I conducted the squadron into Upton and paid a visit to John Kelly, wishing to learn more respecting Nurse Stubbs' alleged witchcraft. I found him busily engaged with a new puffing engine, in the company of Casper Katloff, the Marquis of Worcester's secretary, who like himself was a philosopher and a mechanician. I looked with amazement at the machine as it lifted an iron rod by the aid of fire and water, and thought that if Nurse Stubbs was a witch, here assuredly were two wizards.

Kelly questioned me anxiously respecting the King's new secretary, Dr Gaston, and evidently looked upon the appointment with considerable apprehension. With respect to the witchcraft with which Captain

Bound had accused Nurse Stubbs, it was a serious matter. No magistrate could refuse to grant a warrant for the apprehension of a witch, and the public were too ready to believe any accusation of the kind against an old or infirm person, or one who led a retired and isolated life.

His Majesty James I had himself investigated the evidence against Dr Fian, who was charged with raising the storm the King encountered on his return from Denmark, and inflicted the horrible torture of the boots and then burnt him alive.[13] Moreover, at this time a learned Prebend of Worcester, the Rev. Joseph Glanville, was engaged in writing a work on Witches – now celebrated all the world over – which treats of the familiar spirits who assist such hags in their wicked designs.[14]

Bound declared that Nurse Stubbs had baptized a cat, and tied four joints of a dead man to her feet, and the cat was called Rutterkin, and mounted on her shoulders and sucked her under the ears. This cat had been seen to vanish up the chimney with a flash of fire and return in the shape of an owl, and Stubbs had been heard to say, "Bound, that cursed Bound," three times in her sleep. The result was that two pigs and a calf died at Soler's Orchard, and Hell Cat had fallen lame without any injury. Of all this Bound made oath before Mr Bromley, who had no choice but to issue a summons for Hannah to appear for trial. It was a case similar to that of the Lincoln witches, who were condemned to death by Judge Hobbert, and suffered accordingly.

The law passed in the time of James I against witchcraft was very stringent, and the witch-finder was a public officer. So notwithstanding that Nurse Stubbs was well known in the neighbourhood, and also Bound's hankering after her strip of land, there soon assembled a mob before her door ready to howl out the terrible cry of "Witch, Witch!" and to expose the victim to the ordeal of water by tying her hand and foot and tossing her into the Severn. And this without doubt would have happened had not brave Mary Bromley, hearing the hootings and shouts of the excited crowd, taken her old nurse under her protection, and linking her arm within her own, dared the bargemen and butchers to touch her at their peril.

Bound, who had sent the mob to Nurse Stubbs' dwelling in Dun's Lane, took care not to go himself, and on my arrival with the troopers he 'scuttled away' from Upton, as Aunt Tabitha prophesied, and the crowd dispersed. Bound did not appear before Mr Bromley to support his accusation, but for weeks after there was much cutting of witch elms and hanging of boughs within the houses and over the doors. Some travelled all the way to the Forest of Wyre for sprigs of the great sorb tree, or to the slopes of Malvern for boughs of the rowan ash.[15]

Mary was in such a state of excitement that I thought it necessary to escort her homewards, when I found her sadly apprehensive respecting the failing health of her father. The sorrows of the times were wearing and tearing at his kindly heart. He was zealous for his faith, but was wise enough to comprehend that over-intensity of zeal often leads to the persecution of those who differ from us; and he had lived long enough to see every truth, religious and philosophic, which his fore-fathers accepted, shaken to its very foundation by religious and political fanaticism. Nay, more, he saw that his own relations, such as General Cromwell, would endeavour to root out the Catholic faith and the Anglican Church, not by moral persuasion and example, but by the fire and the sword. Even now they sought the Bible for its damnatory clauses and dwelt on those alone.

Mary and I talked of these things, for her heart was full, and we stood for some moments looking at the sun as it set behind the Malvern Hills, and wondering if we were the same persons, and England was the same land, as in the days when we were boy and girl together.

Our meditations were roughly broken by the clarion sound of trumpets, and we saw Captain Berkeley ride down the Red Hill at the head of a squadron of horse. I recognized his device on his flag, *gules* a chevron between ten crosses. Another trumpet, as if in answer, rung out in the streets of Upton, so taking a hasty farewell of Mary I hurried back to the town, and there found the streets full of troops and Prince Rupert himself in command. He was on his road to Worcester, and brought the news that King Charles was marching on Evesham at the head of ten thousand men. Oxford was about to be invested by Fairfax, and his Majesty thought it better to retire towards the western counties.

Chapter Eighteen

THE PRINCE OF WALES was now sent to Bristol in order that he might cheer the garrison, and keep up communication with the west. Prince Rupert advised his Majesty to march northwards and join the triumphant Montrose in an attack upon the Scottish rebels, who were besieging Pontefract Castle, but the King determined to relieve Chester, which was beleaguered by Colonel Brereton. On the 12th May the King reached Droitwich, where he penned a letter to his Queen, and on the 16th he slept at Lord Ward's house, near Dudley.[1]

Giles Nanfan joined the Royal forces with a Worcester troop at Bromsgrove, and marched with the King to Chester, which was relieved on May the 20th. At this crisis, when Prince Rupert again pressed the march northwards, news reached the King that the House of Commons had appointed Cromwell lieutenant-general, and that Oxford, where the Duke of York was left behind, was closely besieged by Fairfax. This vehemently excited the fears and wrath of Lord Cockayne, the ladies, and all the Court party.

The relief of Oxford was considered absolutely necessary. The advice of Prince Rupert to join the forces of Montrose was set at nought, and the King marched back again on the road to Oxford. On the last night of May he took the important city of Leicester by assault, 'a terrible night and still more terrible daybreak',[2] for although the storming was carried out with great courage, there was much unnecessary bloodshed and plundering of the innocent inhabitants of the town.

The King's prospects now looked so bright that he wrote a letter to the Queen saying that 'without being over sanguine, his affairs since the rebellion had never been in so fair and hopeful a way'. Indeed so little fear had he of any attack by the Parliamentarians that when at Daventry on the 12th of June he amused himself with hunting in the country.[3] His troops were foraging in all directions when my father brought him tidings that Fairfax was approaching.

On the night of Saturday, the 14th June, I had an extraordinary dream! Of late years, owing to his constant attendance upon the King, my father and I had been much separated, but I never forgot the beneficent, firm character, the high honour, and the buoyant cheerfulness of my sire. A Churchman and a Royalist, he was at the same time liberal in his religious views, and never indulged in that insolence which condemns all conceptions of the Almighty save its own. He had no faith in the infallibility of *human* 'creed concocters', but was a firm believer in the simplicity of the Christianity of Jesus; while he abhorred what some preachers taught of the Father of Jesus, ascribing to Him actions worthy only of a savage, or thanking Him, in their Bible phraseology, for the blood and slaughter of their own countrymen.

A few weeks before I had received a letter in which he mourned for much he could not change, and evidently feared that the King was halting between two opinions; but his last words were, 'We must do our duty!'.

Fatigued with a long day's foraging with scouts across the Malvern Hills, I slept soundly on my humble pallet at the Earl's Post. My dreams were of other days, and in the spirit, I was with my father as in days of old, riding side by side among the woodlands and glades below the Malverns. I heard him again warning, as age warns youth, against that expediency which trims 'twixt vice and virtue, and hovers between truth and falsehood.

We had ridden up the Red Earls Dingle between Swineyard Hill and Little Malvern Priory, and were gazing upon the woodland hills of beautiful Herefordshire and the distant mountains of Monmouth and Brecon, when a shout of *duty*, which seemed to reverberate like the pealing of thunder through rocks, and glens, and valleys, startled me, and then my father suddenly disappeared and I was left alone upon the crest of the Malverns. I awoke, my heart palpitating and with drops of perspiration on my brow, but the bugle-call in the street told I had overslept the waking hour, and I was soon dressed and among my men in the High Street of Worcester.

Three days later, half-a-score worn, wounded, and wearied Royalists rode up to the Northgate of the city, and among them was Giles Nanfan, no longer looking the fiery Captain Forwards who charged right up to the standard of Massey at Ledbury. His head was tied up in bloody bandages and his right arm hung useless in a sling. He came from the wreck of the King's army at Naseby, and I knew from the expression of his countenance as our eyes met that my own loved father was among those who had fallen fighting for their King. On the night his spirit passed away I was awoke by that clarion call of *duty*.

It is not necessary to enter into the details of that stern battle. On the wide, open moorlands which surround the hamlet of Naseby, where every autumn the plough turns up the bleaching bones of horse and rider; where the herbage grows rank with the blood of Englishmen; where Shakespeare's Avon rises on one slope, and the Nene and Welland of the Fen country on another; there was fought the three hours' fight which ended in the utter rout of King Charles' army. The field word of our Royalists was "God and Queen Mary", that of the Roundheads "God and our strength".

Fortune for a while favoured the King. Ireton was wounded in the face, Skippon was down and supposed to be dead, and Prince Rupert's cavalry fought their way to the rebels' camp. "One charge more and we shall win the day," shouted the King, but Cromwell with his Ironsides had thrown himself between the now separated cavalry and infantry, and presently both horse and foot fled in disorder. The King escaped by riding hard to Leicester and Ashby-de-la-Zouch, but he left a field covered with the dead, five thousand prisoners; above a hundred colours; his baggage; several coaches full of ladies of quality; and his private cabinet[4] of letters and papers.

The number of Irish women who followed the King's army much incensed the Parliamentarians, for above a hundred of these hags were found on the field, with long skean knives about a foot in length for butchering the wounded. After the battle some leniency was shown to the Royalist officers who were taken prisoners, and many, who gave their parole not to serve again during the war, were allowed to retire to their own homes. Among these was Giles Nanfan, who after an interview with General Cromwell, was permitted to superintend the burial of my father's body and those of other officers, who fell where the King's guard made their final stand. Giles brought me a bean blossom, which my father wore in his hat, with his feather and his broken sword.

In after times we visited his grave together; it lies among the scattered trees, on the slope of Dust Hill[5] in front of Naseby village, and side by side with many a soldier's grave.

I was soon summoned by the call of *duty*! I wished heartily to go to Hanley Castle to comfort those who were sorrowing for the dead, but I was ordered by Colonel Washington to carry the sad news of the defeat of Naseby to the strongholds on the Wye, and then to join the King who had taken refuge at Hereford. All I could do, therefore, was to write to Mary Bromley and ask her to be good to our mourners, and to

John Kelly to watch over their welfare. That night I reached Ross, which had seen many changes during the war.

Prince Maurice was there with a large army in 1643, and a few weeks later it was plundered by Waller on his way to the siege of Hereford. In 1644, Colonel Mynne turned the church-yard into a military camp, and a sharp fight took place on Wilton Bridge between his troops and those of Massey. At Ross I fell in with the loyal and brave Rector of Goodrich, the Reverend Mr Swift,[6] who advised me to keep clear of Walford Court, as it was the residence of that stony-hearted rebel, Colonel Robert Kyrle,[7] who, a traitor double-dyed, betrayed Monmouth to our foes, and, later on, assisted Colonel Birch in the attack upon some of his own kinsmen at the siege of Goodrich Castle.

It was Mr Swift who sold an estate at Bridstow to raise money for the King, and saved the broad pieces from plunder by Kyrle's troopers by stitching them inside his clerical breeches. Following Mr Swift's advice I rode by Wilton Bridge and Wilton Castle. The arch of the bridge next Ross had been destroyed by the orders of Colonel Rudhall of Rudhall, to check the march of the Parliamentarians, but timber was laid across the gap and I crossed without difficulty.

On my right was Wilton Castle rising above the Wye among great oaks and elms. In former times it had its day; it was built by King Stephen in 1141, and was the stronghold of the De Longchamps and the De Greys, when it passed to Brydges, that bold Lieutenant of the Tower, who ventured to dispute the warrant for executing the Princess Elizabeth, and thus saved her life. But the present owner, Sir John Brydges, was 'neither flesh nor fowl, neither a King's man or a Roundhead'.

He was one of those who attempted to walk on both sides of a street at the same time, and so fell at last into the gutter.[8] No one could behold the grand towers of Goodrich Castle as they rose above the Wye, without feeling that it was a most important fortress to hold for the King. Once a stronghold of the de Clares in 1203, and then of the Talbots in 1331, it was now the property of the Countess of Kent. The Roundheads had it for a time; but now it was held for the King by that bold loyalist, Colonel Henry Lingen.

With Colonel Lingen were other Herefordshire loyalists, Sir Walter Pye, of the Mynde, Captain Berington, the Cornwalls, and the Bodenhams, all good Herefordshire men and true. Flanked by round towers at the angles, and surrounded on the landward side by a deep moat hewn out of the red sandstone, a single drawbridge spanned the gulf across which I was conducted to the Castle. Soldiers occupied the towers above the bridge, from which boiling water and molten lead could be poured upon any assailants, and the royal standard drooped from the Lady's Tower as if in dejection for the tidings of which I was the bearer. The Norman Keep was manned by brave and stalwart men, who afterwards proved to be stern defenders. Colonel Lingen received me in the Edwardian hall, whose timbers were of Irish oak, without knott or knarle, and, as we met, the last rays of the setting sun poured in through the great Earl's windows.[9]

Lingen had heard nothing of the defeat at Naseby, or that the veil of death was now drawn over many a heart he knew once blithe and gay. He listened in silence with pale cheek and quivering lip, but his loyalty rose higher than before, and he immediately prepared to set out for Hereford and share the fallen fortunes of his King. When night set in, messengers were despatched to Monmouth, Raglan, and Chepstow to entreat the governors to levy provisions, scour the country for recruits, and man their walls. While within the Castle, the Royalist officers held a midnight council and determined to defy any attempt to blockade by vigorous sallies.

Leaving the command for a time to Sir Walter Pye, Colonel Lingen set out the next day for Hereford, and I accompanied him. We passed by Pengethly, the seat of Sir Edward Powell, baronet, a judge of the Court of Requests, but we only saw his portrait by Vandyke,[10] hanging in the timbered hall, for the aged owner had been driven away by the plague at Ross and the troublous times to reside in London. Colonel Lingen, however, ordered the steward, Grubbe, to send timber and cattle forthwith for the King's service to Goodrich Castle.[11]

The ride from Pengethly to Hereford by Harewood, with its oaks and orchards, is one of rich and varied scenery, while grand was the view of the Black Mountains and the rich valleys of Herefordshire as we gazed across the Mynde Park, the residence of Sir Waiter Pye, upon the blue hills of Monmouthshire and Brecon. Then came the view of Hereford city, its Cathedral and its Castle, which, as says Master Leland, had been 'one of the fayrist, largest, and strongest in all England'. Founded by Harold the Saxon, many an English king had crossed its drawbridge and occupied its keep. But even in the days of Leland in

1520, the Castle was declining. The drawbridge was 'cleane down and the whole castell tended towards ruine', so now it was too dilapidated to be of service to King Charles, although a company of soldiers was quartered within its ruinous walls.

The defences of the city were much the same as in the time of Leland. The walls in circumference were a goodly mile. The gates were six in number and fifteen embattled towers projected from the walls, having embrasures in the shape of crosses in the centre and sides. A great ditch, supplied with water by a brook, encompassed the whole town, save where it was defended by the Wye.[12] As we rode to Wye Bridge gate, the Castle Keep and Cathedral spire rose into view, and ancient Hereford looked a right strong city. Within its walls were soldiers of good reputation, many gentlemen of honour and quality, besides loyal citizens well armed.

The King was lodged at the Bishop's Palace and was less cast down than I expected to find him, being still sanguine that Providence would interfere in his behalf, though the sad and exciting events of his daily life were leaving their marks on his pale and anxious countenance.

His Majesty was pleased to appoint me his personal Equerry, telling me to serve him as did my loyal father. After my audience I sought for lodgings in Castle Street, when I met Dr Gaston and my Lord Cockayne. Gaston had discarded the parson's cassock, gown, and bands, and affected the dress of a country gentleman and cavalier. He smiled and bowed with his usual nonchalance, and none could have imagined that he lived amidst jarring discords, or had witnessed the rout at Naseby. Lord Cockayne's manner was more subdued than usual, and well it might be, for he was one of those whose advice prevailed above that of the gallant Rupert, and his azure banner with the three cocks gules had been trampled in the dust.

The disaster at Naseby was now becoming known even in remote districts, and it was almost impossible to obtain recruits. It was like asking sailors to volunteer for a sinking ship. Men were pressed into the service, but soon ran away, and some country gentlemen who had accepted officers commissions, failed to report themselves at head quarters.

At a meeting on Widemarsh Common the King summoned all his loyal subjects to assist him with money and recruits with but little avail, although multitudes flocked in from the country hoping to gain a glimpse of his Majesty.[15] A discussion now arose whether the King should accept the invitation of the Marquess of Worcester to Raglan Castle. The Marquess was an English Catholic, one of those, among many county families in England, who clung through good and evil to the ancient faith.

They loved their native land far too well to become Roman Catholics, like those Jesuits who thought no means too foul to win subjects to the Church of the Pope. A few English Catholics had been made tools and dupes of Jesuits, such as Garnet, Parsons, Fisher and Greenaway, about the time of the Gunpowder Plot, and now it had become the fashion to treat Catholic gentlemen and men of honour as if they were Jesuit priests, and the Puritan drew no line between English gentlemen and the scum employed by the Society of Jesus and the gold of Spain.

Many an English Catholic was stung to frenzy at being termed a 'Roman', as if he were a foreigner likely to profane the land of his birth. But it was of no avail! The time was rapidly coming when the very name of Catholic was regarded as the symbol of moral poisoning, so some of the Protestant gentlemen of Herefordshire objected to his Majesty visiting Raglan Castle on religious grounds, and declared that such a move would be most unpopular.

A council met in the Library of Hereford Cathedral, and it was amusing to see Dr Gaston trimming with the Catholic gentlemen one moment and the Protestant leaders another. Upon all he smiled, and all he flattered; but as the Herefordshire gentlemen had not a Jesuit intriguer amongst them they soon gave way, and the Marquess of Worcester's invitation was accepted and preparations made for our departure.

As Dr Gaston was busy writing, the King sent me to a small room adjoining the Library for a despatch box. Here to my surprise I found Old Gaston, the Secretary's father, the King's box wide open before him, into which he quickly thrust a paper he was evidently perusing. He showed no sign of shame or emotion, but pretended to be watching the last struggles of an unhappy mouse which he had somehow captured, and was smothering with scorched paper and burning wax, while he remarked learnedly upon "opilations, circulation, and pulsations".

His son now rushed into the room, and glancing nervously at me, muttered something about being sent by the King, seized the despatch box, closed it with a snap and returned to the conference in the

Library. Old Gaston proceeded to examine the defunct mouse and to skin it.

On June the 30th, the King's body-guard was sent forward to Ewyas Harold on the road to Abergavenny, where they encamped among the ruins of the Castle. We followed next day, and the Governor of Hereford, Colonel Barnabas Scudamore, attended his Majesty. We rode among deep, red sandstone lanes, to the wild region of Grosmont, above the sparkling Monnow. Grosmont is famous for the ruins of its Castle, now clad with ivy and the habitation of owls. It was besieged by the last King of Wales, the bold Llewelyn, and well nigh surrendered when it was relieved by Henry III.

The King dined at Mr Pritchard's house near unto Grosmont, and there he knighted Colonel Lingen, afterwards the staunch defendant of Goodrich Castle.[14] On the 3rd of July we reached Raggland height, and its 'famous castle fine',[15] surrounded by outworks, bastions, hornworks and trenches, and the royal standard flying from the citadel Melyn y Gwent. The owner, the Marquess of Worcester, was now an aged man, the living shadow of a past renown, but he had raised 1500 foot and 500 horse for the service of his King. He met his Majesty on the drawbridge in front of the great entrance, and delivered up the keys of his fortress. The garrison under arms were drawn up in the great court, where stood the fountain trim of the poet Churchyard in the shape of a marble horse.

The establishment was princely; there were grooms of the chambers, a master of horse, ushers, masters of the armoury, huntsmen and fal-coners, twelve grooms for war horses, and an hundred and fifty inferior domestics. High festivities followed on the reception of his Majesty, and no one could have imagined that desperate civil war was rife through-out the land, or that some present had recently fled, helter-skelter, from the field of Naseby.

Nor did some of the noblemen, gentlemen, and guests appear to realize that a dire storm was gathering around them. They cursed and swore as they played bowls, invoking the name of the Most High on the pitching of a quoit or the bound of a tennis ball. At last they brought upon themselves the rebuke of the Marquess, who said, when certain officers were boasting of the external defences they had helped to strengthen, "Aye, Sirs, but you have left the main place open and unfortified; you have made no fortification against Heaven, for there is

such swearing and drunkenness amongst you that I fear me that from
thence will come your greatest enemy, and you have made no provision
against him."

Located in one of the turrets of the Castle I found Casper Katloff, the
German whom I had met at John Kelly's. He showed me the great
waterworks and took me to his workshop, where the models and machines, the pride and delight of the Marquess and Lord Glamorgan, were
arranged. There were 'models of semaphores, engines whereby to raise
ships for repair, cross-bows to shoot two quarrels at once, keys to fasten
all the drawers of a cabinet at one locking, a cannon that could be shot
six times in a minute, invisible ink for secret writing', and a hundred
more things, all since described in my Lord Glamorgan's book, *A
Century of Inventions*. Among these strange mechanisms was also the fire
and water engine from the Waterside, which Aunt Tabitha describes as
'the Spitter and Fitter'.

In a room not far from Casper Katloft's, Dr Gaston had his writing
materials. I now saw more of the Secretary, and was often completely
puzzled. Always good tempered and full of fun, he often startled me by
the unscrupulous things he said, as if to try my sincerity. As the King's
equerry I was sent continually to his room, but I never entered it without having the impression that he was trying to hide or cover over the
manuscript he was translating into cipher. He professed to take a strong
interest in or Protestant Anglican Church, but I constantly heard him
speaking to his Majesty as if recommending trust and confidence in the
Church of Rome.

I had ever been brought up in chivalrous ideas of the fidelity and
inherent goodness of women. Gaston declared that no woman's opinion
upon religious questions could ever be entertained by any sensible man,
and that no one of the sex was ever tolerant of any form of religion
which did not happen to be her own.

Gaston, senior, was another puzzle! I had seen this man at the hospitable boards of Sir Giles Nanfan, or the Governor of Worcester, as a
Royalist, and now I knew that he could condescend to cater for information for the Puritans and Captain Bound. When at home, one day he
would be eating and drinking at the expense of Parson Woodforde,
especially when salmon or lampreys were in season; the next he was
with the Catholic Priest at Hanley, whom he once nearly killed through
persuading him to live upon boiled couch grass through an entire Lent,

inasmuch as he wished to see the effect upon his constitution. Now he was constantly fussing in and out of his son's room.

After the great festivities at Raglan Castle, the King and the Marquess of Worcester held long conferences. The Secretary was always present at these consultations, and took unusual pains to employ me in fetching papers and parchments from a distant part of the great buildings. I soon learnt that the employment of the Irish Catholics under Lord Glamorgan was the subject of discussion, and that the only objection the King had to sanction the raising of an Irish army was that he had pledged his kingly word that he would *not* do so.

After these conferences, there was a good deal of writing or dictation on the part of the King, and after he left the room old Gaston assisted his son in transcribing them into cipher. Often and often did I hope that his Majesty was careful to see that his Secretary wrote neither more nor less than he dictated.

Dr Gaston's respected father occupied a very anomalous position. He was for ever on the watch lest his son should be interrupted, and, in the interim, amused himself by catching flies and putting them into spiders' webs. I observed that he carefully avoided meeting the King, and if he saw him pass his eyes glittered like a ferret's before attacking a rat.

I now attended his Majesty to several towns in the neighbourhood in the hopes of rallying troops to the royal standard. We went to Ruperra, the seat of Mr Morgan, where the King slept; and then on to Abergavenny, where the Roundheads had burnt the Castle.[16] Here we heard of the destruction and slighting of Kilpeck Castle in Herefordshire.

On Tuesday, July 29, his Majesty, attended by the Duke of Richmond, the Earl of Lichfield, and his regiment of Guards, went from Ruperra to Cardiff, and 'in the afternoon attended a rendezvous of the inhabitants of Glamorganshire'.[17] At Cardiff we heard that 21,000 Scots, under the Earl of Leven, were marching upon Hereford, and had occupied Ledbury and from thence laid siege to Canon Frome. Soon after came the tidings of the foul massacre of Captain Barroll, the brave commander, and seventy of the garrison in cold blood. Then arose the question that if the Parliament thought fit to employ Presbyterians to glut themselves with the slaughter of the English, why should the King hesitate to employ his Catholic subjects in Ireland to defend him?

We now received tidings that Hereford was closely invested, with anxious requests from Sir Barnabas Scudamore for speedy relief. In reply his Majesty wrote to Sir Barnabas complaining of 'the deficient Herefordshire levies, of remissness in apprehending deserters, the principal of whom should have been and are ordered to be executed'.[17]

Notwithstanding the perilous situation in which all Royalists were now placed, the King had still unbounded faith that God would not suffer rebels to prosper, and he wrote from Cardiff to Prince Rupert at Bristol, telling him 'not in any way to hearken after treaties', and declaring his 'positive resolution not to accept less than what was offered in his name at Uxbridge'.[18]

Alas, Royalists now on all sides, with the exception of a few mad spirits among the Thoroughs, deplored with Prince Rupert, that his Majesty had not accepted the Uxbridge negotiations. It was now too late! The King determined to leave Cardiff. The Welsh refused to move for the relief of Hereford, and it was recommended by some that the King should march with his little army to join the Earl of Montrose and Lord Digby in the north, while Gaston advocated the King sailing for Ireland and putting himself at the head of the Irish Papists. The situation was perilous in the extreme; the councils divided; the King and most of his followers were disheartened and dismayed; but Dr Gaston was smiling and jovial as ever.

Chapter Nineteen

TIDINGS now reached us that General Cromwell was about to march on Cardiff with six thousand men. All that remained of the King's forces in the west of England were the troops under the cruel and dissolute Lord Goring; those under the gallant Lord Hopton; the garrison of Bristol with Prince Rupert in command; and a few strong places and fortified towns such as Hereford and Chester – loyal Chester.

Owing to the rumours that Cromwell was about to attack Cardiff, the King determined to march to Brecknock. His force consisted of three thousand horse and a few hundreds of foot, newly levied in the counties of Monmouth and Glamorgan, with which he hoped to join Montrose and Lord Digby on the Scottish border. On the 3rd of August the cavalry rode forth for Brecknock; the King with his body-guard, and the foot soldiers to follow on the morrow.

The King was lodged in Cardiff Castle, a stronghold built by Robert Fitzroy, the first Earl of Gloucester. His Majesty was in the Keep, where also lodged Lord Cockayne, Dr Gaston, and myself. The body-guard occupied the angle turrets, and their commander, Captain Pritchard, slept in the Black Tower, above the dungeon. In this dungeon, Duke Robert of Normandy was confined for more than thirty long years, and there his eyes were seared out by the command of his learned and loving brother, Henry I.

The night before we left Cardiff for Brecknock, we experienced an omen of threatening danger, the same terrible warning which preceded the loss of the White Ship, when King Henry's only son, Prince William, sank beneath the avenging waves, and which to this day is said to portend a catastrophe to a reigning monarch.

Captain Pritchard, on the night in question, heard first the sighing and wailing of some shivering spirit; then piercing shrieks as of a strong man in his agony at the torture of the heated irons. Then appeared a head monstrous to look upon, with eyeless sockets shining through the darkness; the pale lips moving strangely, as if denouncing, at a brother's hands, 'such foul wrong, such damned treatment'.

The Captain of the Guard, unable to endure this longer, rushed into the court-yard, where he met others who had heard the weird sounds and, when the troops assembled in the morning, the events of the night were discussed and believed by all, although Dr Gaston declared that Pritchard was a dreamer who had supped on periwinkles.

On our way to Brecknock, we passed Castell Coch, or Redcastle, once the stronghold of Ivon Bach, and then we halted at the extensive ruins of Caerphilly. Besieged and much injured by Owen Glendower in 1400, this great fortress, with its vast extent of moats and meres, walls and towers, had never been repaired, and was now only garrisoned by a few soldiers as outposts, who looked as wild as the moorlands by which they were surrounded. It was the last refuge of the unhappy Edward II. before his murder at Berkeley Castle. Another sad omen for the King!

The march from Caerphilly to Brecknock was over a wild, hilly, moorland district, until we reached the beautiful vale of Usk and the dirty Welsh town which is the capital of the county. Few of the inhabitants could speak English, and our suppers consisted chiefly of a hard, tasteless cheese, known to the Englishman as 'skim dick', with a thin beer called currooda.

The King was entertained by Sir Hubert Price[1] at the Priory House, and now appeared to feel the full danger of his position. From Brecknock he wrote in a letter to the Prince of Wales, 'Charles, it is now time that I should prepare for the worst'. Brecknock Castle, too, had its omen for the sad and hunted monarch. A fine fortress built in the time of the Red King, the inhabitants destroyed all but the Ely Tower, and rased the strong town walls to avoid the troops being quartered there. When looking forth from the Ely Keep upon the lofty Vans and sparkling Usk below, his Majesty was told how, in this very turret, was concocted the scheme between the Bishop of Ely and the Duke of Buckingham which led to the downfall and death of Richard III.

He probably thought, as he looked back upon the past, that much of his misfortune and of his people's anger was due to the advice of his own Duke of Buckingham. Cardiff, Caerphilly, Brecknock, all had their ill omens on this luckless journey.

In vain the accomplished Slingsby tried to shed a brighter halo over the royal prospects, by reverting to the war achievements of Bernard Newmarch, and how the great Conqueror hurled back the tide of civil war from Northumbria to the wilds of Wales; or the Antiquary related how the waters of Lynn Savaddan[2] rolled over a sunken city, and the skulls of its inhabitants came up on the lines of the fishermen. The King was sad and silent, and there was little of hope among his followers, who, nevertheless, were prepared to follow him to the death. From Brecknock we marched across the waste, untrodden route to Old Radnor. Our guide between Welsh Hay and Talgarth was Sir Henry Williams of Gwernyfed, where the King dined and slept. Sir Henry conducted us by safe but cruel ways, distressing to jaded, ill-clothed, and hungry soldiers.

The weary King set us an example of patience and endurance, for he never uttered a word of complaint. We passed a great peat bog known as the Rhosgoch, which our guide declared was once frequented by the beaver, but we saw only a dull black morass, where the peewits called eternally, 'bewitch, bewitch', and the heather bleater rose with tortuous flight.

At a place among the mountains called Blaencerdi, the King asked for a cup of cold water, and a pretty farmer's maiden gave him a mug of milk. We then rode by Cwm Ceste to Radnor. Of this journey Sir Henry Slingsby has written in his diary, 'In our quarters we had little accommodation; but of all the places we came to, the best was Old Radnor, where the King lay in a poor low chamber, and my Lord of Lindsay and others by the kitchen fire on hay.'

No better, either, were we accommodated for victuals, which makes me remember this passage, viz., that the King was at his supper, eating a pullet and a piece of cheese. The room without was full, but the men's stomachs empty for want of meat. The good wife, troubled with continual calling upon her for victuals, and having it seems but that one cheese, comes into the room where the King was, and very soberly asks if the King had done with the cheese, for the gentlemen without desired it'.[3]

From Old Radnor we marched by Presteign and Wigmore Castle, the once proud home of Ralph de Mortimer, but now a melancholy deject-ed prospect of stately ruins rising above a poor village situated among rugged rocks and wild ravines. Sir Robert Harley, of Brampton Bryan, was born here, but he and his brave lady, Lady Brilliana, dismantled the fortress in 1643 as they could not spare men for its defence. Alas! what ravages had this unhappy war caused in this neighbourhood in a few short years.

After the sad death of Lady Briliana Harley, and the raising of the first siege of Brampton Castle in October 1643, Sir Michael Woodhouse, Governor of Ludlow, having been successful in the attack on Hopton

Castle, again besieged Brampton Castle. The high-hearted and courage-
ous Lady Brilliana was cold in the grave, nevertheless a gallant defence
was made until defence was no longer possible. Three of Sir Robert
Harley's little children were taken prisoners, and the destruction of the
Castle was added to that of the church, the village, and the farm houses.
'All became as waste places and even as the shadow of death'.[4]

Croft Castle too had been wrecked soon after the death of Sir William
Croft, whom I had seen fighting for his royal master on the field of
Edgehill. A few months earlier, and Croft would have heartily welcomed the King, but he fell mortally wounded in the month of June 1645,
near Stokesay Castle, by the banks of the sparkling Onny. Of him the
poet said: *Then Croft was slain, they conquered Herefordshire.* [5]

His house was destroyed by the Royalists 'lest the Parliament should
garrison it',[6] so neither at Croft Castle or Wigmore Castle was there any
hope of refreshments for our wearied troops. The King, therefore, took
up his quarters at Wigmore Grange, where the milch kine and stores of
sheep belonging to Mr Cockerham furnished good provender for
hungry soldiers.

From Wigmore we marched to Ludlow, and here the King commanded me to prepare for a journey to Yorkshire with despatches for
Lord Digby, who had gone there with a force of royalists to reinforce
the Earl of Montrose. Lord Digby was a brave but rash soldier, and
committed himself as a diplomatist by entering into a secret correspondence with the Pope's secretary at Rome.

The King had long conversations with Dr Gaston respecting a secret
despatch written to Lord Digby in invisible ink. This was to be stitched
inside one of my stockings, and another set of papers prepared, which,
if I had the ill-luck to be taken prisoner, would convey no information
to the enemy. Thanks to Gaston, I was kept in ignorance of the contents
of the despatch, but I knew the secret of the ink, and I suspected that it
related to the expedition of Lord Glamorgan. The secretary informed
me that the phrase 'we'll shuffle the cards' was understood among those
royalists who carried on a correspondence with the Queen's Court in
France, and might be used if necessary to show I was trusted by the
King.

I could not pass through Shrewsbury, and Chester was beleaguered; I
arrived at Whitchurch and found the whole of Cheshire subject to Sir
William Brereton and the Roundheads, I therefore proceeded to Tar-

porley, having the commands of the King to see Sir Rowland Egerton, of Oulton, a constant loyalist, and to whom his Majesty had written to assist in 'the defence of his person, the Protestant religion, and the laws of the land'.[7]

The next day, passing through the wild forest of Delamere, consisting of woodlands intermingled with wild wastes of heather and gorse, I had reached a point in the old Roman road from Chester, near to the ancient encampment of Eddisbury, when a squadron of Parliamentarian cavalry appeared in the distance, their corslets and skull caps glancing in the sun. For a moment the hope crossed my mind that I might not be observed; but that hope was soon dispelled, for the troop halted, and I had to take the chance of escape by galloping away at full speed or face the matter out. As my horse was better suited for a long journey than a race, I rode on quietly and saluted the leader.

The Captain of the troop, for such appeared to be his rank, was a gaunt, powerful man, in the demure attire affected by the Puritans; he wore a high-crowned hat, while his helmet hung at his saddle-bow. I hoped to pass as a peaceful traveller, when to my disgust he thus addressed me:

"Well met, Colonel Forester, we have been waiting for you some time, and began to be afraid you had escaped us. I am Sir William Brereton, and I request you, in the name of the Parliament of England, to hand over to me, first your arms; secondly, the despatches you are carrying from the King; and lastly, as you have the credit of being a gentleman, if you will give me your word of honour that you will not attempt to escape, I will not place you under arrest, and we will ride together to Chester."

It was to no purpose being ruffled, and Sir William spoke so calmly, I felt the wisest plan would be to meet him as if about to transact the business of one gentleman with another. I therefore handed my arms to an individual, whose countenance was nearly concealed by an enormous hat, and started as I recognized the blazing eye of Captain Bound. I then took the belt from my waist which contained the papers from his Majesty to Lord Digby, but not the secret despatch within my hose, and I gave my word of honour not to attempt to escape.

On our road to Chester I had an opportunity of observing this Roundhead General. He was grave and tern, but courteous in his demeanour, and to all appearance an unlikely man to order the execution of prisoners in cold blood, although he had lately hung thirteen of Prince Rupert's own regiment, under the pretence that they were Irish Papists. The Prince took vengeance by hanging thirteen Cheshire Puritans in Sir Vincent Corbet's park, and thus one act of cruelty led to another.

I felt in no mood for conversation as I rode gloomily along, but was naturally very anxious to discover how my journey had become known to the enemy, and having recognized Bound, I felt sure he it was to whom I was indebted for my capture. I tried Sir William Brereton by alluding to the fact of his having a well known spy in his troop, but he took no notice of the remark, and changed the subject by speaking of the charge made against his Majesty of sending for Irish Papists to reinforce his army, which I indignantly denied, and Brereton, I thought, smiled incredulously.

When we arrived before Chester, the Roundheads were in possession of all the suburbs without the walls, and Colonel Poyntz had his quarters at a place called Boughton, on the south east of the city. It overlooks the river Dee, and here one Marsh was burned in 1555, for preaching against the Pope and Papists. The General apologized for taking me to a poor place, but hoped to find me better house-room in Chester in a few days. I asked if I might entertain some hopes of a speedy exchange, but he declared that Prince Rupert had no prisoner they cared to have back again. He would write for orders to the Parliament, and in the meantime I might remain at large, but restricted to localities within two miles from the city.

The garrison inside Chester had been reduced to great distress, but the loyalty of the Chester people was such that assault after assault had been repelled. Having given my parole that I would not attempt to escape, I was anxious to find some one to whom I could entrust the letter in invisible ink from the King to Lord Digby. I had pledged myself not to attempt any communication with the garrison or royalists in Chester, but I considered I was free to employ a messenger outside the walls if I could find one.

Day after day passed wearily away, and for want of a better occupation, I often watched the proceedings of the fishermen as they plied their nets for salmon, for they met with an easy sale and good prices from the Parliamentarians outside the walls. The head fisherman was a short muscular man, about forty years of age; he spoke in our

Worcestershire dialect, and his voice seemed familiar to me, but he gave no sign of recognition when he offered me an 'opple', saying that it was good for the 'digester'.

The booming of cannon was heard in the distance. "There goes Merry Nellie!" said the fisherman, and I learnt on inquiry that Merry Nellie was a big cannon used by the Roundheads in besieging Beeston Castle. The net was now hauled ashore, and I made a bargain for a small salmon to take back to my quarters. "Crying you mercy," said the fisherman, "can you shuffle the card."

This royalist signal told to me by Gaston, and known only to a select few, proved that I had met with a staunch Royalist, who might be trusted to convey the King's secret letter to Lord Digby. Not to appear over-anxious before the other fishermen, I renewed the conversation about Beeston Castle, and then asked my new acquaintance to send the fish to my lodgings, thus informing him where I was staying. He proposed to bring it himself and I went my way. Night came and the fisherman sent the salmon, but did not appear himself.

Weeks passed away, but I received no information respecting the movements of the Royal army. The siege of Chester was being pressed by Sir William Brereton and Colonel Poyntz with vigour, when to my surprise, the trumpets of Langdale's regiment announced that his Majesty had arrived to relieve Chester.

It was more than trying to witness the entrance of his Majesty into the beleaguered city, and to recognize Lord Lichfield, Sir Marmaduke Langdale, Colonel Manley and others, as they rode at the head of their troops, while I remained a mere looker-on. It would have been easy to escape, but I should not have been my father's son had I attempted it.

The battle of Rowton Heath was fought on the following day; the Royalists found themselves between two fires, and were defeated. The Parliamentarians occupied the suburbs of Chester, and Poyntz with another division advanced from the west. Six hundred of our troopers were slain, and with them Lord Lichfield.

The King witnessed the battle from the Phoenix Tower, and by his side stood Sir John Byron, the Governor of Chester, who afterwards distinguished himself by his splendid defence of the ancient city for twenty long weeks. The next day his Majesty escaped to Denbigh, where more ill news reached him in the defeat of Montrose at Philiphaugh.

After the disaster of Rowton Heath, it seemed to me more important than ever that I should send the King's secret letter to Lord Digby. Sir William Brereton held out little hope of my effecting an exchange, and proposed to send me with other prisoners to London. While I was musing on my unhappy situation, I received a visit from the fisherman, who brought me a present of eels and invited me to witness another draught of the nets in the Lee. An expression in his face intimated that he would say more if we were alone, so I walked with him to the river side, beyond which I had pledged my word not to go. I inquired if he was a true Royalist, and he replied by a significant nod. I then asked if he would render his Majesty a most important service?

Again he nodded, and I proposed that he should convey a letter to Doncaster and be munificently rewarded. His countenance lighted up and he appeared delighted at the opportunity of doing good service. "We'll 'shuffle the cards'," he said, and undertook to go on board a fishing smack that night and sail for Liverpool; the remainder of the journey he would travel on horseback. I was delighted at my success, and arranged to meet him in the evening with the secret packet. I then described to him the personal appearance of Lord Digby, with a caution to surrender the King's letter to him only.

We parted, and I retraced my steps, full of anxiety, towards my lodgings, when recollecting that it would be well to give my new acquaintance a present of money, I ran back to the banks of the Dee. The fisherman was half way across the river in a boat, and in the prow sat, facing me and nursing a great cat, Old Gaston, who had disappeared from Raglan Castle, and who, so said his son, had been sent on an important mission by his Majesty.

Evening came, and the loyal fisherman made his appearance. I inquired about the Secretary's father, but he declared that he never saw him before, and merely rowed him across the river for a small consideration. He thought he had been buying a Manx cat from a Cheshire boatman, and seemed mightily amused that it had no tail. I then gave him the letter, and saw him row in his wherry to the fishing boat which was to take him to Liverpool.

The Parliamentarians had now possession of all the suburbs, and the siege was pressed closer than ever. Sir William Brereton proposed that I should enter the city with the offer of treaty to surrender, as there was now no hope of relief, and he would willingly spare the citizens and garrison the horrors which are certain to occur after a place has been taken by storm. I willingly acceded, and was admitted by the east gate,[8] which men say was erected by the Romans.

Sir John Byron, to whom I was conducted, called a council to consider the terms offered by the besiegers, but they would not listen to them, and garrison and citizens continued to fight most bravely for more than two months after the King's flight to Denbigh. It was reported that Byron daily expected Irish troops and Lord Glamorgan. As I remained two days within this ancient city, I visited the tower from which the King watched the battle, and realized for the first time how completely the place was beset on all sides. The Governor pointed out to me the direction of the Castle of Hawarden, which the brave Captain Sandford had taken from the rebels, and which still held out for the King. He also showed me the works he was now strengthening, which afterwards enabled the garrison to repel the assault made in several places at once.

Rejoicing in my heart that Sir John Byron and his gallant friends were still determined to hold out, I returned to Sir William Brereton at his quarters at Doddleston Hall. Immediately on my arrival I was put under arrest and taken to a farm-house near at hand, on the charge of being a spy. I could not learn any particulars of the accusation. "You will know soon enough," was all that I could extract from the surly Roundhead who was in command of the soldiers who effected the arrest.

All that night I was kept as a prisoner in a badly furnished chamber, and the following day I was marched off to Doddleston Hall, and ushered into the presence of Sir William Brereton, Colonel Poyntz, Sir George Booth, and other officers. Standing aside was the fisherman, and now I felt sure that this man had betrayed me, and carried the King's instructions to Lord Digby to Brereton. Looking sternly at me, and without making any salutation on my entrance, Sir William said, "I regret, Sir, that one of the King's officers should so far have forgotten the honour of a gentleman as to have attempted to deceive one who trusted him. I was fool enough to take your parole, and you gave me, as the despatches you bore, a set of rubbish, while at the same time you carried the secret information of a spy hidden in your garments. A court-martial has been held upon your conduct, and a judgment pronounced, that you be hung as a convicted spy within four-and-twenty hours."

Startled and agitated at such an intimation, I was still enabled to bear myself with dignity, and replied calmly that I was no spy, and that he who dared to call me so, lied foully. I was a Lieutenant-Colonel in his Majesty's service, and had the distinction, since the death of my respected father, of serving as his Majesty's equerry.

He selected me to bear some despatches and a private letter, and I had not the remotest idea what that letter or despatches contained. The letter I considered I had a perfect right to conceal, and a right to convey, in the best way I could, to the nobleman for whom it was intended.

To this Sir William Brereton did not vouchsafe a word, and I saw plainly I was a doomed man. He then ordered the sergeant-at-arms to remove the prisoner to the place from whence he came, and seeing that further expostulation was useless, I resigned myself to my fate with as much dignity as I could muster.

I shall not attempt to convey any idea of my sensations as I was taken back to the farm-house on that September morning. The sun shone brightly and lit up the autumn tints and this earth seemed much more beautiful just as I was leaving it.

It was hard to die so young and so ignominiously; still, I felt that I was going to be sacrificed for the cause for which my beloved father died; and was it not a better land to which he had already gone – unlike this world of enmities, bitter strife, and religious animosities, so unhallowed that not even the grave can quench their angry flames?

The thought of my aunt and Isabel in their unprotected state, saddened me still more. Could I but have a chance to procure writing materials, I would pen a line to Mr Bromley and John Kelly; both would be kind to them for the sake of days gone by, and Mary, I thought, would sometimes sorrow for my hard fate; but the soldier who acted as a sentinel with loaded musket, would listen to no request, and the people of the house were forbidden to hold any communication with me.

Thus the weary hours passed away and my allotted time for life was shortening when Colonel Poyntz appeared. He had an abrupt manner, but there was a kindliness in his eye very different from the expression of Brereton. He told me that he had communicated with his brother officers who constituted the court-martial, and that if I would disclose the secret and enable them to read the King's apparently blank letter, my life would be spared; at present all they had was a piece of blank paper!

My heart bounded within me at this announcement. I knew that the letter was written in an invisible ink, and by holding the paper before a fire the writing could be read easily, and I rejoiced that the secret injunctions to Lord Digby had not been divulged. My reply to Colonel Poynts was, as before, that I was utterly ignorant of the contents of his Majesty's despatches, and that if he and Sir William Brereton chose to murder me in cold blood it was not possible for me to prevent it. I told him Sir William Brereton's name would be handed down to posterity as the Cheshire Butcher. Colonel Poyntz replied that the men hung by Brereton were Irish Papists, and met with their deserts. He then left me to my thoughts and the prospect before me of only a few hours to live.

Chapter Twenty

COLONEL POYNTZ had gone an hour when the Fisherman made his appearance, much to my annoyance and disgust, for if there is one reptile I hate more than another it is a traitor.

"So you won't tell 'em, Colonel," he said, "how to read that letter! I would if I was you!" I sternly requested him to be gone and leave me to my own meditations.

"I knows as how you knows how to read that letter," he replied, "and I advises you to tell 'em how to do't." I stared at him in astonishment but without making any reply. "Why, says you to me," he continued, "when you gaed me the letter, says you, tell my Lord Digby if he has any difficulty in reading the 'pistle to just . . .' and then you stops as dead as a hammer, and all as Captain Bound and all of 'em can do – and the Captain can read Gaston's conundrums – can't help 'em to the pith of that ere letter. They have soaked un, and iled un, and sprinkled un over with all sorts of juices, and he won't come out."

"So that scoundrel Bound has had to do with this traitor's work," I almost involuntarily broke out.

"Don't use hard names, Colonel," said the Fisherman, "it does no good and only riles a body. Captain Bound and me belongs to the inwesti- gating corpse of the Parliament, you and Dr Gaston to the King's corpse, only we inwestigates better than you do, that's all."

I informed him that the King had no 'investigating corps', as he was pleased to term it, and disdained to employ a set of scoundrel spies. "Hard names again, Colonel," he persisted; "what do you call Dr Gaston! Now he beats our Captain, he do, for of all the lying, hypocritical . . ." Here the sentry entered, and I begged of him, as a man and a Christian, to relieve me of the presence of one who sadly interfered with the little time I had left to me in this world. Upon this the soldier ordered the fellow to move out, and he departed shaking his head and saying, "Better tell 'em how to read un."

Shortly after this interview with my betrayer, Colonel Poyntz re- turned and reported that another meeting of the court-martial had been held at his particular request. "There is much difference of opinion, Colonel Forester," he said, "as to the amount of espionage of which you have been convicted. Sir William Brereton considers that you should have surrendered to him the secret letter of which you were the bearer, and that in attempting to bribe one of our men you broke the rules of honourable warfare."

I, with the rest of my brother officers, looking upon the fact that you knew nothing of the contents of the King's private letter, of which we can make nothing save the superscription, have given you the benefit of the doubt; and if you will sign a document declaring, on your faith and honour as a Christian gentleman, that you will not again serve King Charles in arms and as a soldier during the present war, you are free to leave Chester."

I had no choice but to consent, and thanking Colonel Poyntz for saving me from being murdered, I signed the proposed document, and gave my *parole d'honneur* not again to appear in arms against the Parliament during the present war. The next morning my horse was sent down to the cottage, and a pass to Hereford through the ranks of the enemy.

At Hereford I learnt from Sir Barnabas Scudamore how active the King had been since I left him at Ludlow. With his cavalry, under Sir Marmaduke Langdale, he had made many rapid marches, but instead of effecting a junction with Montrose, he turned back and relieved Hereford from the Scottish besiegers, while Langdale's horses went into Wales. The King then hoped to relieve Chester, and again taking to mountain paths marched westward to join Langdale and his Welsh levies. They met in the wild region of Dorston Castle,[1] at the head of the Golden Valley, where the Druidical Arthur's Stone tells of a race who lived before the Flood. The fortress has long been in ruins, nevertheless here the King sheltered, and the next day marched to Holm Lacy, the seat of the Lord Viscount Scudamore.

Then came the march from Hereford by Presteign, Newtown, and Chirk Castle to Chester, and the defeat at Rowton Heath. I now for the first time heard of the loss of Bristol, and how from Hereford the King had written an indignant letter to Prince Rupert desiring him to seek his subsistence somewhere beyond sea. Alas! his Majesty would not see or understand the conviction which all royalists felt – and Prince Rupert was among the number – that resistance was useless, and that every life now lost was a life wasted.

This was not all! I had to learn of ill tidings and adversity. Soon after the defeat of the King at Chester, Lord Digby was attacked and beaten by a Parliamentarian force in Yorkshire. He escaped and fled to

Ireland, but his portfolio was captured containing papers of a most compromising character, which the Parliament had investigated,. There were letters from the King in cipher of which they had found the key; secret negotiations between the Queen and the Irish Papists; a treaty for bringing the Duke of Lorraine with a foreign army into England; and above all, what was most calculated to enrage the whole English people, Royalists as well as Parliamentarians, a plan to ask 'his Holiness the Pope' for pecuniary aid to send an army of invasion to the British shores![2]

Such schemes as these incensed the nation beyond all control. Thus through the plans of wild enthusiasts and schemers, and the intrigues of foreign Jesuits, the King had to bear the imputation of plans which were beyond a doubt dangerous and traitorous to the nation at large. Nor was his Majesty long in feeling this. After Lord Digby's disaster in Yorkshire, the King crossed the Trent and went to Newark. The Papistical correspondence Lord Digby had been carrying on was discussed at Newark, and Prince Rupert and Prince Maurice were so disgusted at the secret negotiations found in his portfolio, that they parted from his Majesty in great anger. Prince Rupert, indeed, did not hesitate to say, "Lord Digby is the man that has caused all these distractions among us."[3]

The King did not remain long at Newark, for General Poyntz and his army were approaching to beset it. He therefore once more sought refuge in Oxford, and thither I determined to follow him and report in person the cause of my failure to deliver his letter.

At the end of October in 1645, after so much had befallen me, I crossed the Malverns at the Wind's Point. The woodlands above and around the old church at Little Malvern were bright with the red leaves of the wild cherry, the rich gold of the horse chestnut, and the bronzed foliage of the oak. The scarlet berries of the mountain ash attracted the white throated blackbird, and banks covered with black elderberries reminded me of Aunt Tabitha's winter possets.

A few swallows might yet be seen flitting above the gorse on the green slopes, while there was a murmur of winds through the woods and long shadows of the hills were projected across the plains below. I heard the sharp notes of the felt, in October a sure sign of an early winter, and observed a flight of wild geese high over head on their way to the Severn marshes. The autumnal face of nature is but a sermon admonishing us short-lived human beings that we too must fade as a leaf the wind has taken away.

I reached the wide open heath at the turn of the Ledbury high road towards Upton, and looked for the familiar sight of Hanley Castle Keep towering above the trees of the vale, but I could not descry the well known tower, so rode on, as mayhap some lingering oaks of the Chase interfered with the view, until I came to the little hill beyond Hook brakes and common. But what a sight was there! The old Keep, which for hundreds of years had been the resort of England's proudest barons and the home of the daughter of one of England's greatest kings, was levelled with the ground. There was not one stone left upon another!

I reined up my horse and sat aghast for some minutes at the utter destruction before me. Then thoughts of the fate of Isabel and my Aunt Tabitha rushed across my mind, and half distracted I rode up to a crowd of country people who were wandering among the heaps of rubbish for what they could recover from the ruins. Two of the flanking towers, standing as if in mockery, were all that was left of Hanley Castle.

Some of the peasants recognized me, and from them I learnt by degrees the cause of the destruction which had befallen our old and loved home. Captain Bound had persuaded a party of Parliamentarians, after his return from Chester, to ransack the place for plunder. My aunt kept the drawbridge up, sounded the big bell, and made much show of defence with our old domestics, but no one in Upton, save John Kelly, now ventured to interfere with the sack of a royalist's domicile.

The raiders, led by Bound, crossed the moat on timber, and soon found that the defence of the place was a mere sham. They insulted my aunt, and declared they would pitch her headlong into the moat if she did not produce the plate and money; but at this juncture Kelly and brave old Parson Woodforde made their appearance. Bound was very superstitious, and terribly afraid of the astrologer and his complications, so did not oppose his taking Aunt Tabitha and Isabel to the Waterside.

Then the raiders held a market, and brought out all the stools, tables, chairs and other furniture, and sold them to the country people and Upton Roundheads for ready coin. Even the corn in the horse bins they put up for auction. Bound appropriated the silver plate and sent off Isabel's wardrobe to Seller's Orchard, and then some of his crew went into the dungeon below the Keep.

How it happened must remain unknown until the Judgment-day; but they must have let a spark fall among the stores of gunpowder, for in a moment, as the concourse outside in the great court-yard were buying, selling, and jeering, and not a few sorrowing, there was a dead, thudding sound, and the great Keep, which was five stories high and thirty feet broad, was shattered from base to summit, and fell, like the tower of Babel, burying all within it in hopeless ruin.

Such was the end of the frequent residence of King Edward's daughter and her husband the famous Red Earl; and the home of Isabel Despencer; the birth-place of the Duke of Warwick, and the King-maker's wife. This catastrophe sobered the drunken soldiers who were conducting the sale of our household goods, and they hurried off to Tewkesbury from whence they came. Bound accompanied them, declaring that the accident was no fault of his, but a solemn visitation of Almighty God upon the home of malignants, and an earnest of his fiery wrath against us. Three days had elapsed since the catastrophe, yet the courts and premises were crowded with people.

After listening to the sad tale and surveying for a while the ruins, I rode away to Upton, and soon learnt, by the cold reception I met with from mine host of the White Lion, how fallen was the royalist cause in his estimation. The very women in the streets, who formerly stood at their doors and said "Good morrow" or "Good even" with a smile, now turned their backs as I wandered down the street. However it was not all dark, for no sooner did I mount the stone steps which lead to the Waterside than John Kelly was wringing my arm off, and Isabel hanging round my neck, while Aunt Tabitha was mumbling away at my left hand, weeping, and kissing it at the same time.

Under the circumstances in which I was placed at Chester and Hereford, I had found it impossible to send a letter, and they feared I had fallen at Rowton Heath. We had all much to tell and much to hear, plans to make for the future, difficulties to be faced, and it was well nigh daylight before I lay down to rest on a little couch in Kelly's museum of curiosities, with a half-a-dozen skulls staring me in the face, and six or seven stuffed serpents hovering over the head of the bed.

As luckily my aunt's little fortune was untouched, enough was left for the maintenance of Isabel and herself, with strict economy. Kelly insisted upon their occupying his dwelling until they could make arrangements to retire to some quiet spot and avoid the ill-natured world, which ever looks askance upon humbled and fallen fortunes. I was rejoiced to find that nothing could exceed the kindness of the Bromleys. Mr Bromley was in failing health.

An amiable and good man, such raids carried on by his own party, which he had no means of controlling or preventing; the sorrows of his country, and the ruin of many nobles round him – such as our own, that of Sir William Russell, and many country gentlemen with whom he had been intimate in his youth – were all too much for a sensitive heart like his, and, notwithstanding the victories his party were winning, he was rapidly passing away to that land where so many a victim of this war had preceded him.

Mary had been like a sister to Isabel, and Madam Bromley, notwithstanding her husband's illness, entreated them to make Hamme Court their home until better times, and society was more settled. But Aunt Tabitha could not endure the idea of a Forester sheltering at the house of a Roundhead, and I fear did not meet the kindness in the way it was meant.

I now, for the first time in my life, was in want of money. We had several hundreds of gold pieces, and several securities on land, placed for safety in a niche in the dungeon beneath the ruins of the Keep, but it was impossible to get at a single coin or parchment without enormous labour, and for aught I knew the niche itself was blown to atoms. Here again our friend Kelly met the difficulty. He would replenish my funds, and would employ men to move the rubbish above our treasure; in short, he was our very friend in need, the *amicus certus in re incerta*.

It was now my duty to wait upon the King. He was in distress, and so much the more was I bound in honour to offer him my poor services. I could no longer serve him as a soldier, as my word was pledged, but I could attend upon his person, or at all events show that I was devoted to his cause. This was what my father would have done, and neither Kelly or my aunt said a word to dissuade me. Isabel moped and wept, but she never asked me to turn back from the plough to which I had put my hand, or desert the cause for which our father died.

I would fain have seen Mary Bromley once again before my departure, but she was much confined in her sick father's room. She was a rich man's daughter, I a broken Cavalier dependent upon a friend for the means to join the King my master. The ruined equerry of a ruined King; the fallen Keep; the dead bodies beneath the debris; the fortune left by my father for the support of my sister and myself lost beneath the wreck of our home – alas, all these were emblems of my present condition! So I gave up all idea of seeking an interview with Mary, and bidding farewell to the little party at the Waterside, mounted my horse, and proceeded on my journey to Oxford.

My road lay through Evesham, Tewkesbury being full of Parliament-arians, and I was passing Earl's Croome on the road to Pershore, when I overtook Mr Bromley, who was taking the air in a French chair, borne by his own domestics, and by his side walked his daughter Mary and Colonel Edward Harley. I was shocked to see the change in the fine old English gentleman, and stammered out something, I know not what. Mary blushed when our eyes met, and I could tell from the demeanour of both father and daughter that they sorrowed for our dead, our shattered hearth, and deep misfortunes.

Tears rolled down Mary's pale cheek, as she looked upon the face of the companion of her youth, now wan enough with grief. Colonel Harley accosted me, and I drew up with something of hauteur, and waited to hear what he had to say. His voice was gentle as that of a woman, when he thanked me for saving his life, as he chose to call it, in the struggle at Ledbury.

"I have told Mr Bromley," he said, "and his fair daughter, of a Forester's generosity, and of conduct worthy of the days of our fore-fathers, the knights of old. Nor shall I be contented," he resumed, "until you have received the thanks of one dearer still; even of her who is to become my wife, and to whom Mary will be bridesmaid."

In those few words, what a load was taken off my heart! I did not venture to speak, but I looked again at Mary, and shaking Colonel Harley heartily by the hand, rode on, on my way towards Evesham. When I reached the summit of the hill above the great common of Defford, I turned to look back upon the Malverns and the home of my youth. I could see where the great oak rose by Hamme Court and Southend, and my heart felt more joyous than in the days before our ruin. Dark clouds hung over the horizon, but to the darkest there was a silver lining telling that God's sunshine would again arise to bless the earth; and why then should I despair, if, with a brave heart and honest purpose, I might look forward to a time when He, 'who makes His winds to blow, and rain to fall on high and low', might 'turn our clouds to sunshine'.

Arrived at Oxford, I was shocked beyond expression at the change. Loyalty was no longer the watchword, and the Puritans ruled with a high hand. As rats leave a ship doomed to shipwreck, so did many of the King's followers disappear from the scene of action. Dr Gaston had impressed upon his Majesty the advantages of sending him to France on a mission to the Queen, for some awkward inquiries were being made respecting the King's cipher. The Antiquary departed to Paris and Rome, leaving 'four bookes of marches bound in leather' under the care of his sister, and hundreds of Royalists followed his example. Before leaving England he sent Aunt Tabitha a famous recipe:

> For the Belly Ake: Brimstone beaten to a powder, black sope to make
> a paste, and give him the quantity of a hen egg. Stirr him and keep
> him warme.[4]

I was much struck with the demeanour of his Majesty, and the grandeur of his equanimity. 'Not all the waters in the rough rude sea can wash the balm from an anointed King', was true of King Charles I and his patience. With Sir Henry Slingsby, after the defeat at Chester, I wondered at:

> '. . . ye admirable temper of ye King, whose constancy was such that
> no perils could move him to astonishment, but still he set ye same
> face and settled countenance upon what adverse fortune soever befell
> him, and neither was exalted in prosperity nor dejected in adversity.[5]

It is not easy to foresee what future historians will say of the character of his Majesty. Many will wrench and distort every word and action for party purposes, and many will form wrong opinions through party prejudice. With much unaffected piety, the King was ever surrounded by casuists, who quenched the power of detecting the germs of evil, and who were ever ready to sacrifice honesty in zeal for royalty and the Church. No cold retrospect will explain to a future generation how the King was tempted by his love for his Queen to tamper with his royal word, and now and then to act in a spirit of expediency, which was inconsistent with the royal honour. A conscientious man, conscience was sometimes blunted by his association with those who had none. Thus he would enter upon a wrong course without knowing it, while he often acted in public politics as he would never have done in private life.

The flight of the birds I saw at Little Malvern in October prophesied truly of the coming winter, and the 6th of December of this year 1645 was remarkable for the setting in of a severe frost. We now heard of the surprisal of Hereford by Colonel Birch, whose subtlety was so profound that on the 18th of December he overpowered the guard at Bishop's Gate on the east of the city, led in a powerful corps, and Hereford was captured before the citizens were out of their beds.

Sir Barnabas Scudamore, Sir Henry Lingen, and others escaped across the frozen Wye and got safe to Ross. The Parliament rejoiced greatly at this *coup-de-main*, and ordered a public thanksgiving for special mercies at the end of this highly prosperous year. From Upton I received intelligence that the services of the Church had been badly attended, but that Giles Nanfan was continually there on Sundays, going with Isabel. He had become fascinated by the preaching of Parson Woodforde, and seldom swore, at least within the hearing of Isabel. The Puritans now called our Church service 'mass and popery', and report said that a petition was to be sent to Parliament to appoint an able, preaching, gospel-teaching and godly Minister, in place of good old Mr Woodforde. They also petitioned the magistrates to put in force the order of Parliament prohibiting the use of the Prayer book under penalties of imprisonment.

A large party waited on Mr Bromley, who was too ill to see them; then they went with their hair cropped, in steeple-crowned hats, and bands a foot long, to wait on Mr Lechmere at Severn End. The cautious lawyer received them with pious courtesy. The best cider was handed round in large silver flagons, Mr Lechmere making many promises to his Puritan brethren. They departed well pleased with their host, his cider, and themselves, being assured that ere long an orthodox, godly minister, and a Boanerges in the pulpit would fill the place of the 'papistical parson Woodforde'.

Strangest of all was the intelligence that Captain Bound had been to Church! Hannah Stubbs was dead, and Bound visited her upon her death-bed, and came away much affected at the interview. He declared that mutual forgiveness had been interchanged, and that she had left him the disputed bit of land, and the right of assart. Scandal said that he put the pen into the right hand of the corpse for a sham signature. Still, Captain Bound had been to Church.

The Western Front, Severn End

219

Chapter Twenty One

THE OPENING of the year 1646 was not more favourable to the cause of the King than the close of the fatal '45. His Majesty had for some time been corresponding with the Generals of the Scottish army. Notwithstanding their religious differences he felt assured of their generous sympathy in his fallen fortunes. Was he not like them a Scotsman born and bred? Hospitality was a sacred duty with the northern races, he had but to ask that and he was safe! His noble-hearted countrymen would surely never break the bruised reed; so King Charles determined to go to Newark and deliver himself up to his magnanimous Scottish subjects.

On the 27th day of April, Generals Fairfax and Cromwell reached Newbury, within a day's march of Oxford, and at midnight the King prepared for his flight. His beard was cut off by Mr Ashburnham, and he rode out of Oxford by Magdalen Bridge, disguised as a groom, behind Ashburnham, with a groom's cloak strapped round his waist. After many wanderings our Monarch reached the Scottish camp before Newark, and 'many lords came to wait upon his Majesty with professions of joy on finding he had so far honoured their army'.[1]

The Prince of Wales had been sent to Pendennis Castle in loyal Cornwall, and the King, fearing to send a despatch even in cipher, commanded me to do my utmost to convey to the Prince, by word of mouth, his Majesty's intentions respecting the Scots, and his determination to avoid the Irish Papists. After much consultation with some loyal Oxford residents, I decided to travel as an Oxford merchant connected with the fish trade, and thus secured a pass from General Fairfax.

I left the city three days after the King departed for Newark, carrying no papers and riding a good horse which the Marquess of Worcester had given to the King. I wore a steeple-crowned hat of fair dimensions, and took the precaution before I left Oxford to learn a little fish parlance, and the price of dried herrings per ton and load. Halting at Exeter for a day's rest, I reached Plymouth and afterwards Pendennis Castle without more than ordinary adventure.

I had some difficulty in gaining admittance to the Castle, as the aged Governor, Sir John Arundel, having the Prince of Wales within the walls, would not allow me to enter until the Prince himself came down to the barbican and recognized my features. The Prince occupied Henry the Eighth's Tower, which had been much enlarged and strengthened by Queen Elizabeth, and passed much of his time in fishing off the rocky headlands.

The garrison of Pendennis Castle numbered several hundred men, and from its position overawed the whole neighbourhood, so the Prince was comparatively safe from Fairfax and his Roundheads. I found his Royal Highness much altered since I saw him at the siege of Gloucester. He was tall for his age, swarthy, with large black eyes, and bore himself with grace and dignity; and he had already assumed the genial, good tempered address which distinguished him throughout life, and blinded so many to faults which were inexcusable. He and his brother, the Duke of York, had encountered so much of trial and buffeting, that both were manly, self-confident, and courageous beyond their years.

Sir John Arundel, the Governor, now near ninety years of age, had frequented the Court of the great Elizabeth and breakfasted with Sir Walter Raleigh at Arvenach. He loved to tell how he had quaffed a glass with Shakspeare at the Mermaid, and enjoyed 'Cynthia's revels, before snuffling Roundheads and hypocritical Puritans interfered with honest players'.

From time to time came reports that we were to be besieged by Fairfax. "Let him come," said the game old Governor, "we'll singe that rebel's whiskers yet!" But Fairfax was occupied before Oxford, and by the middle of June tidings reached us of the surrender of that city which had gone through so much for his Majesty. The Duke of York was sent to the Palace of St James', and Prince Rupert and Prince Maurice sailed to France.

Soon after we received bad news from Worcestershire. The country gentlemen now despaired of rallying the fortunes of the King, and every Royalist was treated with contumely by his Puritan neighbour. The clergy hardly dared show their faces at the country towns, and were everywhere subjected to plunder and insult. The Royalist garrison at Madresfield surrendered ignominiously, and Captain Ashton, the Governor, was reported 'to have swallowed a golden hook'. At Worcester, Colonel Washington held out until his powder ran short, and there was every prospect of famine. At last he yielded to the entreaties of many ladies who had gone to the city as a refuge, and surrendered to Colonel Birch and General Whalley in the middle of

July 1646. Our Puritanical neighbours, Mr Nicholas Lechmere and Colonel William Ligon, were nominated on the Parliamentary Committee.

The Prince of Wales was now become anxious about his own position and, weary with incarceration within the walls of Pendennis, varied only by an occasional fishing foray to the rocks of Kosemullion and Maenglas. I had written to Aunt Tabitha and John Kelly, through a sea captain trading to Bristol, asking for home tidings. It was therefore with no small delight that I beheld the well-known face of John Kelly on board a Bristol sloop which arrived in Falmouth harbour.

He had received my letter, and, notwithstanding his determination never again to draw sword for the King, came to urge the Prince of Wales to leave England without delay. Goodrich Castle had been surrendered by Lingen on the 10th of August, after a long and tedious siege; and nine days later the venerable Marquess of Worcester had marched out of Raglan Castle, with all the honours of war, having held out until the powder was reduced to the last barrel. But it was not only the downfall of his state and the ruin of his home this fine old chieftain sorrowed for. There was a tale John Kelly had to tell which overshadowed the affection this staunchest of Royalists once felt for his King.

The Prince of Wales was much interested in the fate of the venerable Marquess, whose devotion to his father had been so marked, and enquired particularly and earnestly how he bore his losses and the wreck of magnificent Raglan Castle. Kelly hesitated, the blood rushed to his forehead, and I saw by his countenance there was something terribly wrong. At last he replied, "The true old nobleman, your Royal Highness, lives up to the motto of his family, *mutare vel timere sperno*." No more passed upon the subject in the presence of the Prince but as soon as we were alone, Kelly inquired in an excited manner, quite unusual to one of such philosophic temperament, if I knew anything of the King's instructions to Lord Glamorgan.

The King, he reminded me, had pledged his royal word at Oxford, and publicly taken the Sacrament at Oxford on that pledge, that he would never connive at Popery. But Lord Glamorgan had raised five thousand men and led them to Waterford, for the purpose of assisting Lord Byron at Chester, on the express understanding that the Catholic religion would be countenanced by the King in Ireland!

The Parliament had in their possession what appeared to be secret treaties authorizing Glamorgan to make the largest promises upon condition of the Irish taking up arms in his behalf. Yet Charles declared to the Parliament 'on the faith of a Christian', that all the warrants bearing his name which had been found in the baggage of the Archbishop of Tuam, slain in a skirmish near Sligo, and in Lord Digby's portfolio, 'were mere forgeries!'

Here was a position for Lord Glamorgan! Who forged the documents? The aged Marquess of Worcester was most indignant and well nigh broken-hearted, and declared vehemently that his son had acted up to the King's express commands.[2] I was startled at these declarations of John Kelly. It was impossible to believe the King capable of such cowardice and black-hearted treachery. I had my suspicions, but I had no proof and held my tongue.

Soon afterwards the Marquess of Antrim arrived at Falmouth, with a store of ammunition and eight or ten pieces of cannon. He came with the approbation of the Queen, and sailed with two frigates which he had taken from the Spaniards. We also now learnt that the King was at Newcastle, endeavouring to make terms with the Scottish Presbyterians.

After much consultation the Prince of Wales determined to leave Pendennis Castle, and invited me to accompany him as his equerry, which, as I had received no summons from his Majesty, I determined to do. We therefore took our departure in the Spanish frigates, sailing first to the Scilly Islands and then to Jersey, finally reaching the coast of France, on the 18th of September 1646.

The change from war-tormented England to the gay life of Paris and the Court of the Queen Regent and the young King Louis, was something startling. We found the Queen of England at St Germain's, surrounded by priests and Jesuits. She had not seen her eldest son since in terror and sorrow she stole away from Exeter and left her new-born babe to the care of strangers. But Henrietta Maria had met with much sympathy in her native country; the Queen Regent of France had received her as a sister, and allowed her a good and sufficient income.

When we first reached Paris, 'the Queen of England appeared with all the splendour of royal equipage, she had a full number of ladies, of maids of honour, of running footmen, coaches and guards'.[3] Her treasurer and adviser was Lord Jermyn, an old man of near seventy years of age, and the poet Cowley was his secretary and decipherer.

The poet Waller also was at the Queen's Court, and Sir John Denham, and my Lord Cockayne, who found his way across the seas after the defeat before Chester. Here, too, was the ever smiling and obsequious Dr Gaston, who preferred the French court to the Scottish camp, and had again so contrived to smile himself into the good graces of our Queen, that she employed him to translate all the letters she received in cipher.

Soon after we arrived in the grand city, the Queen Regent, and her young son the King, invited our Queen and the Prince of Wales to Fontainbleau, and I had the honour to attend. I was astonished, and Lord Cockayne delighted, at the attention paid to ceremonials. The gay courtiers and vivacious French ladies would converse for hours upon the arrangement of a headdress, and the colour and disposal of ribbons, while the two Queens occupied days in arranging matters of precedence and who should occupy a stool, a fauteuil, or a chair.

The etiquette of hospitality required a long apology, before the young King of France could take precedence of the Prince of Wales when they danced a brawl.[4] When the Prince went into a drawing-room, he must sit on a stool not on a chair, and when either of the Queens arose he could not sit at all. As for the attendants upon the royal personages, the men aped the manners and ways of women; they would pose for half an hour supporting their inane countenances upon the tip of a forefinger, and gazing at a *fleur-de-lis* or a rose, as if life was intended to be passed in concocting sonnets, or the adoration of *bric-a-brac*.

To Prince Rupert and all real men, this was utterly distasteful, but the ladies of the Court encouraged it and so did the Jesuit priests. The former loved the essences these effeminate creatures carried about their persons; the latter had a sneaking sympathy with everything which struck at the root of true manliness.

The Prince of Wales developed early that adoration of the fair sex which was his bane through life. He soon fell in love, or fancied he did, with Mademoiselle Montpensier, a haughty beauty the Queen would have liked him to marry and, young as he was, she was flattered by his devoted attention.

The Prince evinced much readiness of wit and repartee, and possessed already great power in hiding his views and opinions under a cloak of bonhomie and good temper. He would converse with Father

Cyprian and the Abbé Montaigne, and listen to profound dissertations on their Church and faith with great gravity, but on their departure he was ever ready with some witty remark on men and manners, priests and women.

I soon found I was not fitted to be a French courtier. No soldier was! I continually carried my nose at the wrong angle; was too broad in the shoulders and always posing the wrong leg. Then I wore yellow ribbons when I should have worn blue; in short, I despised myself and the whole affair, and I entreated the Prince to provide himself with another equerry, who could undertake the grimacing of a fop, and allow me to act as his secretary and escape from the court and its ceremonials.

The Prince laughed heartily at my expostulations, but refused to dispense with my services, and promised to give me certain signs when I was at a loss to know what was required of me. He said that I must accompany him clad in rich and gay attire to the betrothal of Mademoiselle de Themines, and attend him at a masked ball which was to succeed the signing of the marriage articles. I was to wear carnation trimmings, very sweet scent of lavender, and anoint my hair. Then I was to find an interpreter, my French being scanty, and hire a pair of dominoes; loose garments which can be worn over other apparel, and be laid aside at pleasure, a convenient dress for those who wished to remain incognito for a time, or perhaps for the whole of an entertainment.

With the aid of a guide and interpreter, I found a costumier near the Louvre, and having selected a blue domino of royal colour for the Prince and a sober grey for myself, was leaving, when a strange-looking figure accompanied by one of the Queen of England's pages shambled into the costumier's. There was no mistaking the oscillations of his nose or the colour thereof; it was Old Gaston. He appeared to be glad to see me, said he was come for a habit for his son, and offered to show me a tame tortoise and a French magpie. I asked him if he still possessed a Manx cat, and fancied his nose grew redder.

Our Queen was bent upon her son looking his best in the eyes of Mademoiselle Montpensier, so herself arranged the ornaments of his dress and the colour of the rosettes to his shoes. She quite approved of the blue domino. The Prince, however, intended to have some fun, and wear my grey domino instead of the blue one originally intended.

The Queen, he declared, was certain to divulge to the whole Court the colour of his domino and thus spoil his sport. He entreated me on no account to make myself known until the time came for throwing aside the dominoes and unmasking.

As we drove to the Louvre the Prince said to me, "Forester, lend me that rose you bear, and take my lily, and should a mask address you with the word 'Rufus', remember that your reply must be 'Newcastle'. Imitate my voice, as far as you may, and say 'Gad Zooks'. Then learn all you can, and keep what you hear for my private ear and your own bosom, and if any lady should . . ."

What was to follow I know not, for we were just arriving at the grand entrance, but it seemed to me that, for a youth seventeen, the Prince of Wales was somewhat over-ready for intrigue.

With the exception of the two Queens, every guest was masked and shrouded until a signal should be given to appear in the magnificent Court dresses worn at this celebrated ball. I watched the novel scene before me with interest, forgetful that I was attired in a blue domino until a lady spoke to me in a low tone in French. All I understood was "La Reine, La Reine," and I could only say in reply, "Gad Zooks!" She repeated the message, if message it was, and again I said, "Gad Zooks!"

Here the fair one was interrupted by a tall domino addressing me with the word 'Rufus', and no sooner had I replied "Newcastle," than my arm was seized and I was conducted to a recess by no less a person than Prince Rupert, who supposed that I was his nephew.

I hated being thus placed in the position of a spy, but there was no help for it. "Charlie," said his Royal Highness, "since we last met, your royal mother has arrived at a strange determination. She has been holding council with Abbé Montaigne, that fellow Gaston, Father Cyprian, and I know not who besides, and she has determined to send a messenger to your father to entreat him to abandon the Episcopal Church of England."

All I could say was "Gad Zooks!" but I was so completely taken by surprise that I had difficulty in suppressing my agitation. "Do not let it be supposed, Charlie," continued Prince Rupert, "that you, of all of us, approve such a step! Let it be quite understood that you will have nothing to do with this matter." Here, fortunately for me, he turned away and mingled with the crowd, and I breathed more freely.

I had taken particular notice of the 'habit', as Old Gaston called it,

which he had selected for his son the Secretary. It was a sober grey
domino, but with a purple cape behind. I had seen this domino passing
from time to time and the wearer continually entering into conversation
with some lady. At last, as he was passing me, and carrying an enormous bouquet of flowers, I tried the effect of a deep-toned, sonorous,
"We'll shuffle the cards," and the consequence was the fall of the
bouquet and no small evidences of surprise. I passed on quickly, and
before the bouquet was recovered took shelter in one of the many
recesses.

I was in no slight trepidation! What would happen when all the
dominoes were laid aside, and it was seen that the azure blue was not
worn by the Prince of Wales, but enveloped the form of his humble
equerry! Presently I recognized my own grey domino with the rose
fastened to it. How heartily did I wish I was wearing it! The Prince of
Wales was conversing with some Court beauty he had discovered, and
he took the rose and gave it her, saying:

> *Go lovely rose,*
> *Tell her that wastes her time and me,*
> *That now she knows,*
> *When I resemble her to thee*
> *How sweet and fair she seems to be.*[5]

I was much relieved when the Prince came up to me and proposed that
we should exchange garments. He led the way to a retiring room and I
got rid of the azure attire. He laughed heartily at my adventure with
Prince Rupert, and said, "I know I can trust you, Forester, as my father
trusted yours. I have had my fun for to-night, and to-morrow we will
discuss this phantasy of my mother's."

Soon the trumpets sounded and all masks were laid aside. It is
impossible to tell of all the splendours of that ball, the dresses, the
beauty, the *toute ensemble*. Among the most conspicuous figures was my
Lord Cockayne, who substituted ribbons and spangles for diamonds,
which had become scarce with our Cavalier nobility. The most
honoured lady was Mademoiselle de Montpensier. 'She was placed on a
throne in the middle of the room, and the young King of France and
the Prince of Wales seated themselves at her feet'.[6]

I do not think it was to Mademoiselle the Prince gave my rose, but he
paid her every attention when the dominoes were laid aside. Indeed we

had to follow her coach after the ball to the porter's lodge of her hotel, and halt there until the haughty beauty had entered for the night. The account given of this touching gallantry by Mademoiselle herself is that 'it made a great noise in the world that winter, and she felt not the least embarrassed, as she had an idea of marrying the Emperor'.

In the grey dawn of morning I assisted the Prince to disrobe; he then told me that he had received intimation that Sir W. Davenant was to be sent from Paris on a private message from the Queen to his Majesty, and he wished me to request Dr Gaston to attend at his lodgings by mid-day.

With my mind full of suspicion that Gaston had tampered with the despatches of the King, in the case of Lord Glamorgan, I had to send him with his pens and parchments to the apartments of the Prince of Wales. In the conversation which ensued, Gaston recommended that the King should be advised to dissemble about religious matters. Such advice was in direct contradiction to that ever given by my honest and straight forward father. Yet here was an Anglican clergyman recommending falseness where above all things I had been told to be true.

While Gaston was smiling and talking, and rubbing his fat hands, Prince Rupert entered with Sir William Davenant. He seemed surprised to see me, and I blushed with shame at the trick I had innocently played him at the ball. He then turned to Dr Gaston and inquired peremptorily if he had sent verbatim the last communication from her Majesty to the King at Newcastle. The reply of the Secretary to the haughty questions of Prince Rupert was good-tempered and genial, but not straight forward, and he made a round-about speech like that of General Cromwell when delivering a religious dissertation.

This kind of answer did not suit the plain soldier, as he intimated in somewhat powerful language, but nothing more could he extract from the Secretary to the Queen. Prince Rupert now informed us that the Queen had yielded to the advice of the Jesuits, and decided to send a letter to his Majesty to say that 'she had resolved, if her opinion respecting the abandonment of the Episcopal Church of England was not taken, to retire into a convent and never see the King's face again'.[7] The rendering of the message into cipher was strenuously opposed by Prince Rupert, who proposed that Sir William Davenant should carry the message by word of mouth.

I saw the Queen's Secretary flinch, but he smiled as sweetly as ever, and declared at once for Prince Rupert's proposition. Thus it was arranged that Sir William Davenant should travel to England charged with a personal message from the Queen, and leave immediately for the coast. The meeting then broke up, and Davenant and Gaston returned to St Germain's.

As soon as they were all gone, the Prince of Wales remarked, "Gad Zooks, Forester, I believe all my mother's sorrows have turned her brain. She forgets all her promises to my father, wants me to conform to the ritual of the Romish Church, and believes that all our calamities are owing to our belonging to a Cabal of Heresy, as she is pleased to term the Church of England. Now this will never do! You and I know the mind of the people of England better than this; and that nothing can be more fatal to the hopes of my father or myself than to be supposed to be tampering with Rome."

To this I had but one reply, which was that I believed the right plan, and the only right plan, was to tamper with nothing, but to act up to one's own convictions in all honour and honesty. Indeed, I felt indignant that a mere youth, for such Prince Charles then was, should be already the victim of those who advised him to dissemble until they had quenched all feeling of truth and honour under the incubus of expediency. It was expedient for a wife to dissemble to her husband; for a King to dissemble to his people; for a child to dissemble to the mother that bore him! I hoped and trusted that the gracious young Prince would avoid such desecration of a man-like character, but I did not think it would be by following the advice of such as Dr Gaston.

Soon after the departure of Sir William Davenant for an interview with the King, we had an example of what a brave woman can do in an emergency. Lady Morton, in whose charge at Exeter the Queen had left her little daughter Henrietta, when she was but a fortnight old, escaped from England and the clutches of the Parliamentarians, and reached Paris in safety. In order to effect this, she disguised herself as the wife of a French servant, and dressed the little Princess in rags, like a beggar boy, and called her Pierre, that name being somewhat like the sound by which the little child would call herself Princess if she were asked her name.

Lady Morton herself wore a hump of a bundle of linen and walked from Oatlands to Dover with the child on her back, pretending that she was her little boy. She then crossed the sea from Dover to Calais in a common boat, and arrived safely in Paris.[8] Such a romantic adventure caused a great sensation in Paris, and the joy of the meeting between mother and child was the theme of poets and of song. Lord Cockayne wrote a ballad of extraordinary length, but the beauties of his verse have not been transmitted to posterity. Edmund Waller was more successful, when he selected for his subject the fidelity of the beautiful Lady Morton, and his poem was presented to Queen Henrietta on New Year's Day 1647. This verse yet lives.[9]

Christmas came, but with it no meeting of dear old friends and true, no gathering of children round the hearth, no yule log, no mummers, or Lord of Misrule, no waits, no jollity. Nothing marked the day of the Nativity save the bells tinkling for mass, and shorn priests moving to and fro in the streets. Christmas Day 1646 was nevertheless a day stamped on my memory, for I received a packet of letters, the perusal of which brought back old times, and though much of sorrow and disaster was contained therein, there were gleams of sunshine among the clouds.

The tidings from Upton related how good Parson Woodforde was forbidden to officiate in the parish church of which he had been pastor for years. A new rector was appointed, and our old friend was turned adrift upon the world.[9] The Parliament had issued an edict making the use of our liturgy penal, and forbidding the administration of the sacraments of the Church according to the rubric. Examples were known where clergymen ejected from their livings for malignancy had entered the army as volunteers, and had been killed in action.[10] Isabel wrote of the desecration of churches, of domestic bereavement, and bitter poverty among families who were known to us, and whose only fault was loyalty to their King.

Mr Bromley died soon after I left Pendennis Castle, and a letter from Mary gave a description of her father's last hours. She told how he had prayed most earnestly that God would grant peace to our distracted country, and had sent a kindly message and a hope for God's blessing to Dick Forester, 'whom he should never behold again'. Mary said that she and her mother seldom let a day pass by without seeing Aunt Tabitha and Isabel, and had not forgotten our old servants and domestics in their cottages at Hanley. She wrote to me as 'Dear Richard' instead of 'Dr Col. Forester', and that cheered my heart in exile. Verily a kindly word from a gracious woman is honey to the afflicted soul!

John Kelly sent me good tidings of the health of my aunt and sister, still his guests at the cottage by the Severn. He and Madam Bromley had set the Upton bargemen to remove the debris of the keep at Hanley Castle, and had recovered most of our money, as told by Aunt Tabitha in the following epistle:

Dear Nevew, I hope this will find you well in helth as it leaves us at present. You will be glad to hear that sum of our goods have been digged out of the ould castell. There is the grate fire shoul, tongs, and popker. Also the pictur of the goos with ye 9 gulls, but above all, the Lord be thankit, ye gold Jacobuses. Do nettles grow in Paris? If so, drink lots of nettle broth in March, and eat muggins in May.

Yr. loving Ant, TABITHA FORESTER

Chapter Twenty Two

THE OPENING ceremonies of the new year of 1647 contrast greatly with those of the first Janiveer in old England. All the inhabitants were engaged for some time previous in preparing presents for the great *jour de fête*, the presents were of a kind Sampson would have declared to be 'a nation queer lot'.

The Prince of Wales commenced the day with a visit to his royal mother, and I attended as the bearer of an enormous box of confections made of sugar, called *bonbons*. Every one connected with the royal family of France was expected to make a present to the young King, and the Earl of Cockayne, being attached to the court of the Queen of England, knelt before his juvenile Majesty and presented him with a gridiron of barley sugar and a stuffed cockatoo.

The Prince of Wales purchased a sweet cupid, the size of a young child, as a gift for Mademoiselle Montpensier, and I was employed in rouging its cheeks and tinting its nose for several hours.

Paris seemed full of sugar; there were temples and pagodas, carrots and churches, hats, musical instruments and saucepans all of sugar; but to my mind a pair of good fat capons, a haunch of venison, or even a bunch of Aunt Tabitha's hog's puddings, would have been of far more worth than all the *bonbons*. Yet it was only men who gave these luscious souvenirs, the ladies contented themselves with receiving, bestowing only sweet smiles and honied words in return.

Dancing concluded the festivities of the day at the Court, and next morning the Prince and his attendants arose with ghastly countenances, the effect of the *bonbons* and the sour wines, which are not to compare with our Worcestershire cider. The fair lady to whom the Prince had shown so much gallantry, left cupid all night in an open balcony, much to the detriment of his hair and complexion.

The next day Lord Cockayne called upon the Prince of Wales to inform him that the Queen Regent and his Mother had appointed him to a *fauteuil*, and that stools would not be required for the future. He was also to be permitted to hold the flambeau the next time Mademoiselle Montpensier arranged her hair for a court party.[1]

As the year thus opened amidst fêtes and music, balls and discussions about precedence, there came the astounding news that the Scots had sold their King for £200,000 to the Parliament. Charles had entreated to be allowed to go to his native Scotland with honour and freedom, but the Parliament of Scotland preferred the money to their honour, and on the 16th day of January 1647, the Commissioners received the person of the King. The Scottish army then recrossed the borders, and his Majesty was taken to Holmby House, not far from the field of Naseby, and kept a prisoner. He asked in vain to be allowed to have a chaplain of the Anglican Church, but the Presbyterians were anxious that he should listen to the Covenanters and profit by their sermons, which lasted for hours and ever insulted the royal captive.

For some time the Earl of Cockayne swore the treason of the Scots to be impossible, for he was a grandson on his mother's side of the Earl of Cockpen. But the Queen was not surprised; she declared that this could never have happened had the King gone to the Catholics of Ireland. The Jesuits were now in great hopes the King would throw himself into the arms of 'the only true Church'. He was very susceptible to those weaknesses of human nature on which women practise, and there was no doubt of the vast influence of the Queen over her husband.

In the meantime Sir William Davenant returned from England, and announced that the King was bitterly grieved at his wife's proposed plan of retiring into a convent, and regarded it as a personal desertion in his calamity, but he remained firm to the Church of England.

I watched the effect of these tidings upon Dr Gaston. In the presence of the Prince of Wales and Prince Rupert he spoke of his Majesty's high sense of honour, and that he was an example for the moral admiration of mankind. But when they left I saw him at the table with frowning brows and clenched teeth; the fat hands grasping his chair, and anger glittering in his eyes, while he vented his rage on his father's cockatoo.

It was now manifest that the Presbyterians, in sending back the Scottish army across the borders, had dug a grave for the burial of their own hopes and power. They fully intended to crush out the Independents, the Vanes, Ireton, Cromwell and others, who had led the Parliamentarian troops to victory after victory.

The present army was to be disbanded and a new one raised upon the Presbyterian model, in which General Massey, the hero of Gloucester siege, was to bear high command. Large bodies of the force of General Fairfax and of Cromwell's Ironsides were to be shipped off to Ireland, separated from their officers, while Cromwell and other Independent generals were to be sent to the Tower.[2] The arrangements were admirable from a Presbyterian point of view; but an insuperable difficulty arose from the troops refusing to cross the Irish Sea, declining to be separated from their old officers, breaking up their cantonments at Nottingham, and marching upon London.

In Paris we exiles formed hopes that these dissensions would end well for the King, and for a time Mademoiselle de Montpensier treated the Prince of Wales with less contempt, and allowed him to compliment her upon her 'fine figure, her noble mien, her fair complexion, and the beauty of her flaxen hair'.[5] But the tempest which had burst over England was now sending its dark, death clouds over Paris, and while the English Parliamentarians were quarrelling among themselves, the French citizens began to hold those stormy meetings which were to end in the civil war of the Fronde.

At this time the position of the Prince of Wales was most unfortunate. The Queen exercised her authority over him, and required the submission she exacted from his father. He was never able to lay his hand upon a dozen pistoles without borrowing, and was surrounded by political intriguers and Jesuitical agents, devoid alike of honour and honesty, and who sometimes even dared to advocate the assassination of the enemies of royalty.

Queen Henrietta Maria thought it necessary to announce publicly that the newly recovered babe of Exeter should be brought up in the Romish faith as the 'child of benediction', while report said that she was tampering with the Prince of Wales, and persuading him to attend Roman Catholic functions. This was reported by spies to the Parliament and did infinite harm to the cause of the King. Again, Dr Gaston and other advisers advocated the doctrine of expediency to the young Prince, especially in matters of religion, so that he soon began to take the downward path of dissimulation and deceit. A worse school than Paris for a youth like the Prince of Wales could hardly be found, nor a worse adviser than his own mother for the future King of England and his Protestant subjects.

It was the middle of November and I was thinking over Aunt Tabitha's advice, that 'the best fysick this month is good exercise, warmth, wholesom meat and drink, and to be sure to go dry of the feet',[4] when I was summoned to attend the Prince of Wales on a ride in the wild woods of the Bois de Boulogne. On my return, to my quarters I found my old friend and comrade, Giles Nanfan, availing himself of whatever provisions, which were scant enough, the domestic could find in the cupboard. The sorrows of the times had told upon Giles, who looked ten years older since last we met. Grey hairs were already silvering the dark brown clusters, and there was the weary look of sadness which protracted misfortune ever brings.

Sir Giles Nanfan had refused to accept the negative oath and covenant, and his whole property was laid under sequestration; an inventory was taken of all his personal estate and goods, and a Gloucester attorney was sent to take possession and levy monies. Sir Giles, on account of his age and infirmities, was not sent to London, but was allowed to withdraw with Dame Nanfan to a small farm-house they possessed in the parish of Berrow, situated below the Ragged Stone Hill of the South Malverns. On the Ragged Stone and Midsummer peaks I had often wandered, in happier days, with Bridget and her brother, and discoursed on the weird shadow of the one, and the bold hill camp of the other.

Sir Giles had not long been laid in the grave, when Captain Hasseli, who had deserted the Royal cause and joined the Parliamentarian banner of John Yates of Bromesberrow, again renewed his attentions to Bridget Nanfan. Although false to his king he was true to his love, and succeeded in persuading her that he acted like hundreds of others when provoked by the tyranny of the King. Windebank, who was shot at Oxford, was Hasseli's great friend. "His murder, for murder it was," said Hasseli, "had sent scores of Royalists into the ranks of the Parliamentarians." But Giles Nanfan had sworn solemnly that the first time he ever met the renegade he would inflict personal chastisement upon him, and he sternly forbade his sister to speak to him again.

Having ridden to Birtsmorton Court to meet the agent sent by the sequestrators, Giles walked on to the farm-house occupied by his mother and sister by the Ragged Stone dell. In an arbour formed by a clipped yew in the garden hedge, he heard the voice of Bridget in tones of expostulation, and on entering he found the recreant Hasseli. Burning with ire he seized his former friend by the collar, and dragged him forth with blows and curses, while Bridget ran screaming to the house. Swords were quickly drawn, and the brother and lover adjourned to a meadow hard by. Hasseli was no match for one of the best swordsmen in England, and in a few moments he lay gasping on the grass with Nanfan's rapier driven through his heart.[5]

Giles' fortitude broke down as he described to me his sister's anguish at this catastrophe! He had raised what money he could for the support of his mother and sister, and left England to join the Prince of Wales and the court in France. Soon after the arrival of Giles we received intelligence of the overthrow of the Presbyterian party by the Independents; the government was in the hands of the latter, and Fairfax, Ireton and Cromwell, were their chosen generals. The active leaders of the Presbyterian faction had to disappear. Massey fled to the Hague, others to France, and some were shut up in the Tower.

The King was removed to Windsor, and then to Oatlands and Hampton Court, from whence the Queen was informed that he was in constant communication with the generals of the army; that Cromwell, especially, had shown much sympathy with his misfortunes, and obtained leave for the royal children to visit their father. Moreover, it was rumoured that Fairfax was to be Mayor of the Palace, Cromwell to be Earl of Essex with a Garter, and Ireton, Lord General of Ireland.

No sooner was this negotiation of the King with the Independent generals reported in Paris, than the Queen and the Jesuits became alarmed for the Romish religion. The priests flocked to the Court of the Queen of England, and many were the expostulations and invectives of the Abbé Montaigne, Father Phillips the Queen's Confessor, and Dr Gaston the Secretary, who declared that the Anglican Churchman detested Independents as cordially as did the Catholics, that the King would be compelled to turn Independent and wear a steeple hat and bands, and would have to renounce Bishops for ever and sign a document for the expulsion of all Papists.

Mr Gaston, senior, had become quite an institution about our Queen's Court. He fed her dogs and plumed her parrots, and his shambling figure might constantly be seen lingering about the royal chambers. To my utter astonishment I heard that he was chosen as a messenger to London with despatches for the Generals, and, as the Prince of Wales hinted, with a secret letter from the Queen to the King. He was also to take a saddle for Lady Carlisle as a present from Henrietta Maria. Accordingly in a few days this strange diplomatist started with his despatches, six poll parrots, and the saddle.

It appears that Gaston rested at the Blue Boar in Holborn, where he indulged in his favourite burnt posset, and, according to his own tale, the saddle disappeared. Some say that he told the Parliamentarians how to rip the lining. Of a surety they intercepted the Queen's secret letter to the King, and Generals Cromwell, Ireton, and Fairfax learned from it that, notwithstanding their apparent peaceful negotiations with the King, he had decreed their doom if ever he regained his power.

The intercepted letter betrayed the fact that the Queen advised his Majesty to make every concession that was expedient for the present, but when the right time came, 'to reward the rogues with a hempen cord instead of a silken garter'. After this the Generals broke off all negotiations with the King, and Cromwell is said to have declared that he would never again enter into his presence. Old Gaston never returned, and report said that when the searchers found the secret letter, there was attached a label on which was written 'Windebank'.

Soon after this episode of the Queen's letter, the King planned a flight from Hampton Court, but the roads were bad, the weather stormy, and he and his followers lost their way in the forest. Charles then determined to seek the hospitality of Colonel Hammond, Governor of the Isle of Wight, but Hammond refused to receive him save as a prisoner. In the mean time the Army Council met at Ware in Hertfordshire, and the abolition of monarchy in England was settled by the soldiery, who were ready to mutiny against any general or officer who objected. General Cromwell's life was threatened on suspicion of smuggling away the King. On the 14th of December the Parliament sent propositions for the King to sign, but when they were presented to his Majesty he refused his consent.

This intelligence reached Paris by slow degrees, but the tidings received were too often perverted, and frequently both the Queen and the Prince of Wales were deceived by their own followers. I still found it difficult to discourse in the French language, and seldom ventured to commit myself in conversation, though I generally understood what was said by others. Dr Gaston was not aware of this, and would often speak most unreservedly, in my presence, to the Abbé Montaigne, and I observed that he agreed to all Popish propositions with a studied humility of deportment.

The year 1648 commenced with many complications. The Generals of the army in England found it necessary to comply with the wishes of the soldiery or be considered as traitors to the Republican cause. An important debate took place in Parliament on the 3rd of January, on the occasion of the King's refusal to entertain the propositions presented to him, and General Cromwell was reported to have said that it was useless to expect any good from a man whose heart God had hardened. The result of this debate was that the House voted that they would make no more addresses to the King, and would receive nothing from him.

At this time the war of the Fronde broke out in Paris, and all the resources of the French Government were overthrown, while the royal family of France bid fair to become as destitute and distressed as that of England.

King Charles was a close prisoner in Carisbrook Castle, but his second son, James, Duke of York, escaped from his imprisonment in May. He put on a woman's dress, and sought refuge in a house in London, where he remained some days, habited in female apparel. He then embarked with a single attendant on board a vessel bound for Holland. A portion of the English fleet had forsaken the Commonwealth and taken refuge at Helvoetsluys. Prince James went on board one of the English vessels and hoisted his flag as Lord High Admiral, to the great joy of the English sailors.

On the arrival of this welcome news, the Prince of Wales announced his intention of leaving Paris and joining his brother, to the great satisfaction of Giles and myself, who were heartily weary of the life in Paris. It was bad enough to have to pose at the Louvre, or listen to the chatter of the French courtiers, but now it was impossible to obtain sufficient money from Queen Henrietta for the daily food placed on the Prince's table. Things went on from bad to worse, and the Queen could not pay the adherents of the Prince of Wales; her income being stopped from the Queen Regent of France, who was reduced to the greatest straits in consequence of the civil war of the Fronde.

At the end of June we left Paris for Holland, and it was well we departed then, for by the middle of July the royal family of France were forced to seek shelter outside the walls of their capital from their infuriated subjects. On the departure of the Prince of Wales, the Queen, his mother, retired to the convent of the Carmelites, and Dr Gaston took up his quarters near at hand in order to conduct the deciphering of her correspondence. The Prince had impressed upon him the necessity of keeping him informed of any events in England, as it was probable the Queen's means of communication would be superior to his own.

While these events were happening with us exiles, the Scots announced that they had not given up monarchy, and the King concluded a secret treaty with the Scottish Parliamentary Commissioners to confirm the Covenant and suppress the Independents, Levellers, and Agitators. Forty thousand men were voted by the Scottish Parliament, and we heard of risings in various parts of England and Wales, under old Royalist leaders.

The Cavalier exiles in France and Holland declared themselves ready to join a force under the Prince of Orange, King Charles' son-in-law, for the invasion of England, and the crisis was so great that the officers of the Republican army met at Windsor, where they listened to sermons, and 'held discussions with prayer and fasting for four or five days together'. Their alarm, however, soon gave place to redoubled exertion to contend with this Royalist revival, and with such success that every vessel from England brought us accounts of the defeat of the Malignants, as the Roundheads delighted to call us.

Letters from home told of the sorrow which had befallen all those who had fought for the Royal cause. Eardisley Castle, the ancient home of the Baskervilles, had been burnt to the ground and Sir Humphrey Baskerville reduced to poverty. The estate of Sir Walter Pye of the Mynde, was mercilessly confiscated, and its loyal owner wanted bread; while in Worcestershire, unhappy Royalists hung about the doors of committee rooms, waiting in vain to get their 'compositions' assessed, and borrowing from day to day the means to purchase food.

After the siege of Pembroke, General Cromwell had been 'hunting up malignants' at Gloucester, from whence he wrote for three thousand pair of shoes, and had been much feasted on sugared plums by Gloucester Roundheads. Aunt Tabitha expressed a wish that she had the soleing of those shoes, and was not complimentary in her expressions respecting Mr Bromley's 'poor cousin'.

The Prince of Wales now determined to communicate if possible with his father, and aid his escape from a country where only persecution and insult awaited him. Preparations were therefore made in July for the fleet at the Hague to sail for England. Before we sailed for the Downs, the Prince endeavoured to obtain the latest intelligence received by his mother from her unhappy husband; but no messenger arrived from the Queen, and no despatches from Gaston, thus we were absolutely ignorant whether the King was still at Carisbrook Castle, or had been removed elsewhere. In consequence of this failure of information, our cruising in the Downs came to nothing.

The Independents now determined to remove the King from Carisbrook Castle. It was laid to his charge that he had not only signed a secret treaty with the Scottish Presbyterians, but had written to Lord Ormonde urging him to take the field with an Irish Catholic army.[6] On the last day of November, therefore, Colonel Cobbett was sent with a squadron of horse to seize his Majesty, and convey him to the close prison of Hurst Castle, a desolate block-house projecting into the sea. A staunch Royalist, Colonel Edward Cooke of Highnam, a brother of the Parliamentarian Sir Robert who was killed before Worcester, entreated the King to fly, but he refused, having pledged his royal word not to attempt to escape.[7]

A few days after the removal of the King to Hurst Castle on the 6th of December, one hundred and fifty members of the House of Commons were retained in custody and excluded from their duties by three regiments of horse under the command of Colonel Pride. This transaction was called Pride's Purge, and it was reported that General Cromwell planned the purge, but when next day he received the thanks of the remaining members, he declared that he had not been acquainted with this design, yet since it was done he was glad of it, and would endeavour to maintain it. Thus the army was no longer the servant of the nation, but its master.

A news-letter was sent us to the Hague, in which the King was described as asking after his daughter Elizabeth, and the reply was, 'The Princess Elizabeth is very melancholy'.

"And well she may be," answered the King, "when she hears the death her old father is coming to." These ominous words deeply affected the Prince of Wales, and after a consultation with the Duke of York, he determined to despatch Colonel Cromwell, a cousin of the General's, and myself, with a *carte blanche*, to which his signature was attached, and by which he bound himself to any terms the Parliament might demand, if only his father's life might be spared.[8]

Duplicates of this *carte blanche* were to be taken to the principal generals of this now omnipotent army. These generals were Fairfax, Lambert, and Cromwell. After a rough passage we reached London early in the first week of the year 1649, which will be remembered by Englishmen through all time. As the vessel drew near the quay, the waters of the Thames were crowded with watermen, shouting "Boat, your honour, boat!" while fine barges conveying London aldermen passed rapidly to and fro. As General Cromwell had lodgings in Westminster, I took a wherry to the stairs, and then found the streets so foul and miry that I was glad to hire one of the sedan chairs, now become common conveyances, to carry me to his abode.

The House of Commons had appointed a High Court of Justice for the trial of the King. Among one hundred and thirty-five Commissioners were the Generals Fairfax, Lambert, and Cromwell, with Bradshaw, Harrison, Pride and other political agitators, who were far more inimical to the King than were the generals of the army.

General Cromwell had lately arrived in London from the siege of Pontefract Castle, and I found him in common lodgings, for at this time he had no regular residence in London, nor had he assumed that high political importance in the state which many royalists now attribute to him, confounding his position then with what it was after the victories of Dunbar and Worcester two years afterwards, when he was far more powerful for good or evil than in 1649.

When I succeeded in obtaining an interview, he was engaged with a pile of papers, but recognized me instantly and received me with his usual blunt courtesy. I presented him with the *carte blanche* from the Prince of Wales and in a few words explained its purport. The General then seated himself opposite to me, and with a stern expression of countenance and still sterner manner said, "Why should young Charles Stuart send this paper to me? Who am I that he should suppose I have power to interfere with the Commissioners of the High Court of Justice?" I replied that copies of the paper were sent to Generals Fairfax and Lambert, as well as himself, as being all popular with the powerful army.

"The Generals of the Army, Colonel Forester," said Cromwell, "are the servants of the People of England, and the Parliament has declared that Charles Stuart, King of England, has traitorously and maliciously levied war against the present Parliament and the people therein represented. We Generals have no right, even if we had the power, which we have not, to fill up any *carte blanche* or make any terms with the King, or any members of his family, without the sanction of the Commons of England." This was spoken in a stern, decided tone, as if there was no appeal. I remembered Mary Brimley's account of her cousin, that he was naturally compassionate towards objects in distress, and that he was very tender towards sufferers,[9] so I appealed to the

General and spoke of the broken-down monarch reduced to the last extremity of sorrow; of the Queen and her bitter grief, and now in actual poverty in Paris; of the little Henrietta, so lately restored to her mother's arms; of the innocent children, the Princess Elizabeth and the Duke of Gloucester, still in London; until my voice failed, tears filled my eyes, and, I could not help it, rolled down my cheeks.

General Cromwell seemed touched, and giving me time to recover myself, rose from his chair and paced up and down the room. He then said, "Colonel Forester, God is my witness, that there is not a Cavalier in all England who has less personal ill-will to Charles Stuart than I have. When he was at Hampton Court but lately, I endeavoured to appeal to his better feelings and to induce him to look upon his kingly office less as a despot than he has hitherto done. I took my honest-hearted wife into his presence and together we obtained from the Parliament leave for his children to visit him. How has he repaid me! His wife wrote to him to make me his dupe first, and hang me afterwards. Pleasant letter that for my wife to read and ponder on! But let that pass!"

At this crisis of the conversation we were interrupted by Cromwell being summoned into the ante-room; he desired me to remain until his return, and handed me a packet of papers telling me to make myself acquainted with their contents. I found they were copies, written in a firm bold hand, of the King's correspondence, arranged in order and labelled 'On the word of a King'.

As I read these letters my cheek flushed with shame that the King could be charged with the treachery indicated therein. At the same time I saw but one means of explanation, one loop-hole by which to escape from the moral conviction of his double dealing. I recollected the power possessed by the translator into cipher of much of the King's correspondence, and his Majesty's solemn asseveration, 'on the faith of a Christian', that the letters to Lord Glamorgan were forgeries. I remembered the expediency doctrine of the Jesuits, by whom the Queen was surrounded, and which had so lately been urged by her Majesty in the case of General Cromwell himself.

When the General returned, he said, "I perceive that you have read that sad history of treachery to friends and of double-dealing with the people. What say you now to the word of a King? We have been told that Kings are made in God's own image, what think you of this likeness of the Creator?"

I hastened to assure him that I could not deem it possible that the King was guilty of the overwhelming deceit indicated in the letters attributed to him. There was some horrible mistake! His Majesty was highly religious, continually engaged in prayer and church services. Such falsehood and treachery were altogether contrary to his character!

"You think then, Sir," said Cromwell sternly, "that the warrants bearing his name, found in the baggage of the Catholic Archbishop of Tuam, who was slain in a skirmish near Sligo, were absolute forgeries?"[10]

"I replied that I had great doubt of the good faith of an agent employed to translate his Majesty's letters into cipher, and that I would rather believe King Charles' word 'on the faith of a Christian' than the oaths of all the Jesuits under the sun.

"You are not the only person who believes in the honour of a King," said the General. "It is impossible for me to foresee the result of this trial, but rest assured that if Charles Stuart is condemned to banishment from the realm, or it may be to death, not all the generals in the army can save him! I had a narrow escape of falling a victim to Harrison's dragoons because they chose to consider I had been too friendly at Hampton Court, and should Charles be condemned by the Commissioners of Parliament, and Fairfax and I made an effort to save him, they would hang us as high as Haman. But one thing I will promise you; obtain for me evidence that the King's letters were tampered with, or the cipher changed to what he did not intend, and I will take care that these forgeries are properly represented to the Commissioners, and they will, without doubt, have their due effect at the coming trial."

I now felt that the only hope was to return to Paris to see the Queen and Gaston, and induce the latter to confess that he had interfered with his Majesty's letters and tampered with the cipher. There was absolutely no other explanation. And for this explanation my soul yearned, for there is nothing more sad than the discovery of meanness in a great man, or the want of honour in a woman you have trusted.

When I reached Paris it was besieged by the Fronde, and for some days I found it impossible to effect an entrance. I found the Queen almost destitute of the necessaries of life, and for many days during bitter cold weather, she had kept the little Princess Henrietta in bed all day, because they had no fire.[11]

This was no time to enter into disquisitions with the royal lady concerning Jesuitical correspondence, and I sought an interview with Dr Gaston. The Queen had not seen him for some days, but at last I learnt from the Abbé Montaigne that he had joined the Jesuits and was summoned to Rome. From that moment I felt that the fate of the King was sealed. The so-called Anglican clergyman had doubtless long been a member of the Order which spread its ramifications so wide and so deep, and which was ruining the Catholic religion in the eyes of all men who believed that there was virtue in truth and godliness in honesty.

I had heard my revered father say, with respect to the Gunpowder Plot, that it was a plot of apostates and converts, not of Catholics. That scheme of wholesale murder was born of English Protestants converted to Jesuitism. Fathers Garnet, Parsons, and Owen were once Protestants. Guy Fawkes, Winter, Catesby, and Wright had been Protestant boys. The Littletons were members of an old Catholic family, but they never knew the full wickedness of the plot. Sir Everard Digby was a convert; so was Lord Monteagle. Coughton and Hendlip Hall, the resort and hiding place of Jesuit priests, were the abodes of fanatics the Jesuits had trained to be the disgrace of the Church they had entered and the curse of every honourable Catholic in the realm. Never, until the Judgment day, will be known in full the ramifications of Jesuitical conspiracy with which King Charles I was surrounded from the time he married Henrietta Maria of France.

Chapter Twenty Three

KING CHARLES' death is generally attributed to Oliver Cromwell. There is little doubt that, at last, he was one of the chief promoters, but it would assuredly have been carried out without his consent, for, until after the battle of Worcester, he was not of sufficient importance in the army itself or in the state to have opposed the determination of the army then so powerful.

At the time of the King's execution Paris was so closely besieged that the Queen of England was beleaguered in the Louvre, and the Queen Regent of France was shut up for safety in the fortress of St Germain's. Henrietta Maria with her little daughter, then only four years of age; endured the severest privations, and her servants wandered from house to house in search of food, until the Cardinal de Retz made an appeal to the Parliament of Paris and asked whether they would permit the daughter of their Henri Quatre to be reduced to such dire distress.

Thus the middle of February 1649 arrived before it was whispered at the Louvre that King Charles had been murdered by his own subjects. Men thought it possible that he might be imprisoned, or banished the kingdom, but the idea of *death* entered into the mind of no one. The horrible rumour spread like a dark sea fog, and we crowded round Lord Jermyn in hopes he might tell us something which would lend a light in the blackness. He knew the truth; but the Queen remained in ignorance until James, Duke of York, contrived to pass the environments of the besiegers and suddenly appeared at the Louvre dressed in all the trappings of mourning and bereavement.

I need not dwell upon the scene of sorrow when the calamitous tidings were revealed to her Majesty by the Pére Cyprian Gamache, who has told in eloquent language of the anguish of the afflicted Queen.[1] She must have thought sometimes in her inmost heart that her advice, expressed wishes, adverse religion, and fatal letters, helped to drag her devoted husband to the scaffold.

I was naturally curious to learn how far General Cromwell was personally concerned with the King's death, and heard that his name was the third upon the list of those who signed the death warrant. Among others was the name of Harry Marten, of Hinton Waldrist. It is recorded by my old comrade, Antiquary Symonds, that General Cromwell, desiring to view the King's body as it lay in the coffin, forced the lid open in order that he might look once more upon the face of him whom he had learned to regard as the curse of England.[2]

How little did he think then that the crown of martyrdom had been given to that cold brow; of the bitter enemies to Puritanism who would rise up in every part of Europe; of the reaction to monarchy in a few short years; of the horrors of the death that awaited some of his own comrades; of the deep desire for vengeance which would end in rifling his own tomb, exposing his own 'noisome body' upon the gallows tree, and hoisting his fleshless skull upon a spike at Westminster.

When I rejoined King Charles II at the Hague, he had been recognized by the States of Holland as King of England, and all the exiled Cavaliers rallied around their youthful monarch. Among them came Lord Loughborough, who led us in the charge upon the barricades at the battle of Ledbury. Strange to say, also, it was Lord Loughborough who brought General Massey to the young King and introduced him as a future subject and soldier.

This was indeed a singular turn in fortune's wheel. The hero of the siege of Gloucester, the leader of a score of battles against the troops of King Charles I, was now ready to swear devoted allegiance to his son. Massey, with all the active heads of the Presbyterian party, had been driven into exile by his quondam friends the Independents, and was one of those who was shocked at the execution of King Charles.

Indeed, this is true of all Presbyterians. They did not look upon the slaughter of their King as belonging to the 'providencies, mercies, and judgments' of Almighty God; but as the outcoming of 'carnal counsels and 'downright human blood-thirstyness'.

Thus, soon after we met our old enemy at the Hague, Massey was fighting to the death for the restoration of Charles II to the throne of his fathers. The young King would willingly have remained at the Hague, had not the Council of State in England insisted on his removal, so Queen Henrietta wrote to her son to join her in France.

Accordingly we reached the French capital in the middle of July 1649. The first interview between the widowed mother and her son took place at St Germain's, but as the civil war in France was now drawing to a close, she returned with him to her abode at the Louvre.

On the 18th of August the Queen Regent, and her young son Louis XIV, made their triumphal entry into Paris, and the young King of England was there in deep mourning for his father.[3] He was thus formally recognized at the Court of France.

In the mean time the fatal blow which had been struck in England was about to convulse our unhappy country again. The wretched remnant of the House of Commons, the Rump, could not claim to represent the people, for the people were not represented, but the country was governed by a Council of State. Lord Fairfax was Lord General at the head of the army, and Generals Cromwell, Ireton, Harrison, and Lambert, were under his command.

An act was passed prohibiting the proclaiming of any person to be King of England by sound of trumpet. But another trumpet sent its clarion notes throughout all Christendom, and this was the publication of Eikon Basilike; the secret outpourings and prayers of the slaughtered King during his imprisonments.

In a few months it passed through many editions, and Charles Stuart became Saint Charles and the White King to thousands. I sometimes wonder, when the hand that holds this grey goose quill shall have crumbled into dust, how future ages will look upon the character of the unhappy Monarch, who lived in times bitterly hostile to Church and King. Will he be numbered, in the great hereafter, as the truly pious, God-fearing monarch we Cavaliers believe him to have been, or as the hypocritical, deceitful tyrant he was pronounced by the Council of State?

It is not easy to describe the effect of the Eikon Basilike. It drove Scotland wild with the remembrance that they had sold the King into the hands of his executioners. The Marquess of Ormonde, then in Paris at the Court of Queen Henrietta, was entreated by the Irish to return to Dublin and head an army who would fight for their young King and take vengeance on the Regicides. Chancellor Hyde was to proceed to Spain to implore assistance. Prince Rupert with his royalist ships would show the world that the blood of the Martyr should be avenged; and the Prince of Orange promised both men and money.

For a time it seemed that the chivalry of the Cavaliers would overcome the thraldom of the Puritans. But Queen Henrietta doubted the success of the policy which demanded that her son should proceed either to Ireland or Scotland to assert his rights. She knew jealousy would be excited among his adherents in England; she mistrusted the Scots, as well she might; and although her heart warmed towards her fellow Catholics in Ireland, she knew the disordered state of the country, and the terrible anger of all English Protestants if her son should head an army of Papists.

Then the priests and the Jesuits put their fingers into the dish, and no sooner had the Marquess of Ormonde gone to Ireland and endeavoured to engage the Irish Catholics to support the King, than the Pope's Nuncio organized a conspiracy in Ulster to oppose Ormonde. Charles now determined to proceed to Jersey and await the Scottish proposals. He had ever been brave, and now declared that it was far better for a King to die in such an enterprise than to wear away life in shameful indolence. The Scottish Parliament had proclaimed Charles II as soon as they had heard of his father's death, and now was ready to welcome him if only he would sign their Covenant.

Meanwhile the English Puritans and Independents determined to send an army to Ireland, and General Cromwell was Commander and Lord Lieutenant, with Ireton, his son-in-law, as second in command. It was therefore thought better not to attempt an expedition to Ireland. Thus the remainder of 1649 passed away in making preparations to land in Scotland.

More than once, when I was sent from Jersey with despatches to Queen Henrietta at the Louvre, it was evident how she hated the Scottish Covenant; still it was thought expedient by her Majesty's advisers that her son should dissemble and sign anything, and accept everything, with mental reserve, if only it conduced to establish him on the throne.

In the mean time Cromwell landed in Ireland, 'I determined,' as he himself wrote, 'to carry on a great work against the barbarous and blood-thirsty Irish.'

"You," he said, in an address to the Irish themselves, "unprovoked, put the English to the most unheard-of and most barbarous massacre, without respect of sex or age, that ever the sun beheld."

Thus before the month of September was ended, we heard of the slaughter at Drogheda on the 3rd of September 1649, and in October of that of Wexford; for Cromwell gave no quarter, declaring it to be 'a righteous judgment of God upon barbarous wretches who imbued their hands in so much innocent blood'. Before the close of the year 1649, Ireland was well nigh crushed under the iron heel of the invaders, as every one who differed in religious opinion from the Puritans was punished with confiscation, slavery, or death.

King Charles II now caused a Declaration to be issued, addressed to all his loving subjects, in which he intimated that he was firmly resolved, by the assistance of Almighty God, to be the avenger of his father's innocent blood, and this was issued from Castle Elizabeth, Jersey on the 31st of october 1649. After this manifesto we returned to the Hague. King Charles was now in his twentieth year, and on the 1st of January 1650, he received a letter from his royal mother reminding him of the extraordinary presage which appeared in the heavens at his birth, and how he was not to be daunted, if for a time his royalty was eclipsed, for although the sun was eclipsed at his birth, there was observed a new star appearing at mid-day, and this was an emblem of his future greatness and glory.[4]

The Scottish Commissioners arrived at Breda, a place in the Netherlands much protected by marshes and ditches, in the month of March 1650, bearing with them a handsomely bound copy of the Covenants. And here the expediency tactics of the young monarch commenced. He signed a treaty accepting every thing that was asked, declared his deep sorrow for the sins of his father in tampering with Catholics, and the sins of his mother, who was a Catholic still, and promised to sign the Covenant itself on his arrival in Scotland. Thus commenced a system of dissimulation and duplicity which continued throughout his life.

The opening of the campaign in Scotland was most disastrous. In the spring of this year 1650, after an interview with the King, the chivalrous Marquess of Montrose and the Earl of Kinnoul crossed over from the Hague to the Orkneys for the purpose of rallying the loyal Highlanders to the royal standard. It is almost incredible, nevertheless it is true, that the jealousy of the Earl of Argyle and the Kirk Presbyterians destroyed the most faithful royalist in all Scotland.

General Strachan was sent by the Kirk leaders, who invited the young King to Scotland, to destroy one of his most devoted followers. Montrose was unexpectedly attacked by a large force at the pass of Invercarron. He fled and took refuge with an old and trusted friend, who betrayed him to the Covenanters; they carried him to Edinburgh, and there hanged their young King's best friend and bravest soldier. A bad beginning, and an omen of the coming eclipse was this slaughter of the devoted Montrose, the true Royalist and Cavalier, through the enmity of his own countrymen, the Earl of Argyle and other Scottish Presbyterians.

It was now evident that the Scots, however anxious they might be to restore the monarchy, were determined to maintain Presbyterianism, so, hard as the terms were to digest, the young King accommodated his conscience, yielding to the advice of his Council, he accepted offers of the Scots.

In the month of June we all embarked at Scheveling, the Dutch Admiral, the famous von Tromp, accompanying the young King to the ship which was to convey us to Scotland. We entered the Moray Firth on a bright summer's day and soon after landed in the Firth of Cromarty.

The scenery of the North of Scotland contrasted strangely with that of the streets and hotels of Paris, or the flat, dismal country around the Hague, of which we were heartily tired. A long wall of dark brown precipices, crested by thickets of gorse and firs, runs along the edge of the Firth, and in this two great rocks called the Sutors, mark the entrance to the bay, like mighty turrets of some gigantic fortress. No sooner had our vessel passed this portal of Nature than we found ourselves in a quiet bay, on the western shore of which was a little fishing town, backed by hanging woods, sloping promontories, and in the distance a line of blue Scottish mountains.

On a low hill, behind the town, stood the ancient Castle of Cromarty, 'a mossy time-worn building, rising to the height of six stories, battle-mented at the top, and roofed with grey stone'.[5] The first person to welcome the young King when he set foot upon the land of his fore-fathers, was Sir Thomas Urquhart, a Cavalier 'who would have fought for the crown if it had been hung upon a bramble bush', but a strange mixture of the soldier, the patriot, and the pedant.

In the rude quarters of this old Castle of Cromarty the King abode several days, and his evenings were enlivened by long dissertations upon his host's elaborate memoir on 'The True Pedigree and lineal descent of the ancient and honourable family of Urquhart, beginning with God the Creator of all things and ending with the genealogist himself'.

Then the dinners and suppers! I think I see the first banquet the young King encountered. First there was a *bouillée*, the Scots denominate Cock-a-leekie, a mess of hot water with abundance of leeks and a fowl's head; after that came a sheep's head, with the singed wool still adhering to the skull, and more of the mess of hot water poured over it.

But, strangest of all, was a dish the host called a haggis. This is actually indescribable, but it was served in a big bladder, which, when his Majesty pierced it with his knife, shot forth a volume of strong smelling squash which besprinkled the royal vest. Had Aunt Tabitha been at table she would have gone into hysterics.

Nevertheless the King, who already had learned to conceal his thoughts by a good-tempered merriment, tasted all the dishes without making a wry face, but dined, principally, upon a hasty pudding called frumarty. On the Sabbath he had to listen gravely for hours to 'Blasts of the trumpet' and 'Sounds of the horn of God', indulging in a hearty laugh at sermon and preacher, when Giles and I attended him in his bedroom afterwards.

Within a fortnight after we landed in Scotland, Cromwell crossed the border at the head of fifteen thousand men and a large siege train. He was opposed by ministers' sons, clerks, and other such sanctified creatures, who hardly ever saw or heard of any sword but that of the Spirit. David Lesley was their commander, and they numbered seventeen thousand all told.

The King joined this strange Scottish army, on the 24th of July 1650. Lesley's lines extended from Edinburgh to Leith, and the Court and Scottish Parliament were at Perth. The King insisted upon galloping to the front, where skirmishing was going on from day to day. On one occasion he was about to charge the rebel horse, but Lesley told him that he had no right to run the risks of a private soldier, and that if he did he would lay down his commission.

The weather was most wretched, roads became impassable, and the swamps and bogs prevalent in Scotland were full to bursting. Little fighting, therefore, took place, and the King went back to Perth. Sickness set in throughout the English camp and it appeared probable that Cromwell would have to take refuge on board the fleet, when the Scottish ministers felt certain that 'God had delivered Agag into their power', and overpersuaded Lesley to leave a strong position and throw himself headlong against the most famous general of the times.

The battle of Dunbar, fought on the 3rd September 1650, resulted in the total wreck and destruction of the Scottish Kirk army. Neither did the English general spare the unhappy Kirkites. Three thousand lay dead on the field of battle, and most of the ten thousand prisoners were pitifully slashed and mangled. After the battle of Dunbar, Edinburgh surrendered to the victorious Cromwell, although the Castle held out some months under the gallant Dundas. From St Johnston's at Perth the young King wrote a letter of condolence to the Committee of Estates. "We cannot but acknowledge," he said, "that the stroke and tryall is very hard to be borne, and would be impossible for us and you in human strength, but in the Lord's we are bold and confident."[6]

We now felt the strange incongruity of the young King's Court among the Scottish Presbyterians, more than I can express. A youth, who had been revelling too much in the fashionable pastimes of the Continent, was brought suddenly face to face with a grave religious people, who thought even innocent laughter bordering upon sin. Neither did we 'malignants and profane men' enjoy the Kirk services.

Accustomed to the Church prayers offered up in grand domes such as our English cathedrals and to the solemn chaunt and rolling organ, the change to the bare walls of a Scottish meeting house and the odd nasal performance they called psalm singing, was almost startling.

Then the sermons to which we were compelled to listen! If printed they would have covered miles of paper, and they teemed with the gloomy and bewildering doctrines of predestination, terrible denunciations supposed by frail and ignorant men to emanate from a merciful Creator. Compared to the fearful threatenings of the Calvinistic preacher, the purgatory of the Papist is a blessed reformatory. So the young King often wished himself back in Paris listening to the grand music and deep toned voices of the hated Catholics.

Then the Prince gave great offence by smiling upon some of the fair Scottish lassies, and he 'was severely reprehended by a committee of Ministers, and urged to be more careful in the future in shutting the windows'.[7] Again, if his attendants showed any disposition to gaiety, and danced or played at cards, we were severely reproved and admonished against following the devil's cantrips. On Sundays we could not walk abroad without offence, and whistling was a heinous sin against the Lord's Day.

For some time the King bore the imperious treatment of the Kirk men and their committee patiently, and it was amusing to observe him listening to their long winded orations, with his large full eyes fixed upon their harsh faces, and never moving a muscle of his countenance. At last the Duke of Buckingham proposed that the Scottish ladies should go about with masks made of Scottish flannel, as long as the Cavaliers remained in Perth, which brought upon us a longer sermon than ever, the hour-glass being turned four times before it was concluded.

The King could stand it no longer, but accompanied by the Duke of Buckingham, Nanfan, and myself, he left St Johnston, and the fair maids of Perth in the middle of the night, and we rode for Lord Dedups, on the northern border of Fife.[8] Here he hoped to meet with the Earl of Athol and men who would acknowledge his authority and be loyal and true without recourse to eternal preachments, and purification of malignants.

We had not been long in Fifeshire when General Montgomery arrived with a party of horse and humbly entreated the King to return. At first Charles refused to comply, as he declared he would not submit to the indignities to which he had been subjected. Then, overcome by the importunities of the General, he was induced to return to Perth. Thus the year closed; the army of the Kirk destroyed, and yet the Kirk Commissioners dictating and sermonizing to their King.

At this time Sir Thomas Urquhart quitted his old Castle at Cromarty and joined the royal army carrying with him three huge trunks filled with manuscripts. Sir Thomas had but a poor opinion of the Presbyterians and Kirkites as Royalists. He declared them to be rebels at heart. "They make use of kings," he said, "as we do of card kings, discard them without ceremony if there be any chance of having better game without them!"[9]

This flight of the King had the effect of producing a change in the Scottish politics. It was determined to conciliate Charles by crowning him King of Scotland at Scone, and round him would rally all true Royalists like Urquhart and Lesley, while the Saints had enough to do to settle the Kirk affairs with General Cromwell. So the curtain rose on a new act to be succeeded by very different scenes.

On New Year's Day, in the year of our Lord 1651, Charles II was crowned at Scone with exceeding splendour. The Scottish army lined the road, and the King proceeded to the church with the nobility, gentry, and burgesses. He listened to a sermon full of advice to monarchs, from a preacher who declared that it was a 'damnable maxim that a king could do what he pleaseth impure and without controulment'. The King opened wide his eyes, but it did not affect his after life. Then Lord Loudon, the Chancellor, made a speech, and Charles was clothed with royal robes; the Earl of Argyle placed the

crown upon his head and the sceptre in his hand, and the people
shouted "God save the King!"

The King now set up his standard at Aberdeen, and took the com-
mand of the new army in person. The Duke of Hamilton was appointed
Lieutenant-General, Lesley Major-General, and with them were
General Middleton, and Massey, the quondam Governor of Gloucester.
Thus in the course of the spring another Scottish army was prepared to
fight for the restoration of the English monarchy.

Cromwell in the mean time was besieging Edinburgh Castle. The
King had now removed his Court to Stirling and fortified it strongly.
His birthday on the 29th of May was celebrated with great rejoicing,
and the people of Dundee presented his Majesty with a rich tent and six
cannon.

Cromwell again took the field by the middle of June. Some desultory
operations had little result on either side, when, early in August 1651
the Parliamentarians marched into Fife for the purpose of cutting our
communications with the north and intercepting the supplies. And now
there was much anxious consultation. Charles had not an army able to
fight the Ironsides of Cromwell, for his troops were raw and inexperienced. The Parliament's fleet was on the coast and would intercept
all supplies from the Continent. But the road to Carlisle and England
was open. Would the English Royalists rise in arms, if we marched into
the heart of England, and would the loyal Welsh once more flock to
their Monarch's standard? These were questions the Scottish generals
could not answer, and more than once his Majesty enquired of Nanfan
and myself, his equerries, what we thought of English loyalty?

It was not an easy question to answer. Months had passed since we
had heard from England, as our correspondence was interdicted, and
we had neither written or received letters since we left the Hague. We
could testify, and testify truly, respecting the loyalty of Worcester and
Worcestershire, of men such as Pakington, Berkeley, Berington,
Hornyold, Cocks, Dowdeswell, Cookes, Russell, Thackwell and others,
but, as regarded the sentiments of the English generally, we knew no
more than did the King.

Captain Fonwards, with his usual energy, recommended an irruption
into England, for he judged of others by himself, and he longed once
more to meet sword in hand the executioners of the King's father. For
my own part I was somewhat doubtful, more so than I cared to express,

for I knew how the spirit of the Royalists had been crushed out by a series of defeats inflicted upon gallant troops who had no generals, and whose officers, however courageous in action, never combined together for a single warlike movement, or well-planned attack.

At last it was determined to cross the border, and on the 31st of July 1651, the Scottish army, sixteen thousand strong, marched for Carlisle. With us were the Dukes of Hamilton and Buckingham, the Earls of Rothes, Lauderdale, and Cleveland, Lords Sinclair and Wilmot, Sir John Douglas, Sir Alexander Forbes, Sir Thomas Urquhart, General Massey, and the gallant Colonel Pitscottie at the head of a Highland regiment.

We marched by Annandale, stopping at Moffat for several hours for rest and supplies, and the King passed the night of the 5th of August at Girthhead, in the parish of Wamphray.[10] On the sixth day we entered England by the Carlisle road, and Nanfan and I were sent to the front with a hundred horse, and ordered to proclaim King Charles in every market town we passed through.

We soon had evidence that the English were jealous of the invasion of the Scots, looking upon them as enemies rather than allies. We had ridden into Warrington and called upon the people to declare for their King, when we were met by a mob, among whom were some soldiers of the Parliament. Conspicuous among them was a man in a fisherman's garb, who was more vociferous than the rest, and persisted in following Giles and myself as far as the bridge over the Mersey.

As he approached, I recognized my friend of Chester, the comrade of Captain Bound, and as I thought he might be useful if taken as a prisoner to head quarters, I communicated with Giles Nanfan, then rode straight at the fisherman and seized him by the collar of his garment. In a few minutes his arms were strapped behind his back, and he was placed behind a dragoon, with a promise that I would blow his brains out if he showed the slightest intention of endeavouring to escape.

The man was half stunned, and did not recognize me until we had ridden some miles. As his arms were tightly bound, he asked me to ease the bonds, which I did to a certain extent, when a light seemed to flash across him, and he said, "Did you tell 'em how to read that letter?"

It was evident that our march was unknown through all Lancashire. An attempt was made to defend the bridge at Warrington by the Parliamentarians, but the King led the attack in person, and the pass was forced with but little loss on our side. The fisherman was sent with a message to Sir Thomas Middleton to surrender Chirk Castle, but Middleton refused to listen to the summons, seized the messenger, and the unlucky man was shot as a spy. Shrewsbury was occupied by a powerful garrison and, as all our artillery consisted of but sixteen leathern guns, we had to pass on.

Here arose the question whether we should march on London, when tidings arrived that large forces of Republicans were gathering on our eastward flank. It was strongly urged that we should proceed southward to loyal Worcester and appeal to the county gentry and the bordering Welsh.

At Shrewsbury, therefore, we left the London road, but so weary were many of the Scots with their adventure, that the King had to go amongst them, cap in hand, desiring them a little longer to stick to him. Worcester being determined upon as a resting-place and rendezvous for English recruits, the King again sent Nanfan and myself ahead as knowing the country, to rally the citizens against the garrison of the Commonwealth which now occupied the town.

Just as we started, the Earl of Derby arrived from the Isle of Man, and kissed his Majesty's hand in passing. before putting himself at the head of his Lancashire levies. He declared that he would join the King at Worcester with five hundred men, and was full of enthusiasm. Little did we then think of the bloody fate which awaited this loyal nobleman, or the sad scenes he was destined to behold. As Lord Derby was leaving to rally his forces, a scout brought word that Generals Cromwell and Lambert were marching in our rear with a large army, resolved to live and die with their renowned General.

Chapter Twenty Four

THOSE WHO love the country of their birth and have been compelled to live as exiles in a foreign land, can alone enter into the sensation with which Giles and I caught sight of the Malvern Hills after our long absence. He hailed the first peep of the Midsummer Hill as it rises above Birtsmorton Court and I looked for the Worcestershire Beacon, which sometimes casts its shadow well nigh to Hanley Castle. Then there was the weird Ragged Stone. Surely its shadow had hovered above the homes of us both? Soon Worcester came in sight, the Cathedral and ruined Castle rising by Severn side and, surrounded as it was by thatched cottages, orchards laden with golden fruit, and corn-fields with ripe grain, it looked little like a city about to be desolated by civil war.

We had to be cautious so we left our weary steeds at St John's, for we knew we should find less difficulty in visiting the city as two pedestrians, than as horsemen and Cavaliers. The Commander of the Parliamentary garrison, Colonel James, had no idea of the approach of the King, and the first intimation he received was the summoning of a public meeting at the Guildhall by Mr Lysons, the loyal Mayor. Both the Mayor and the Sheriff were immediately seized and kept as hostages for the good behaviour of the citizens.

Giles and I, however, were not inactive. We took up our quarters at the Earl's Post, and, with the advantage of a moonlight night, visited the houses of several influential citizens to inform them of the approach of their Monarch, and his hope of rest and succour in a city already famous for its defence of royalty. We ascertained that the Roundheads had done little for the defence of the walls; the towers and bastions were in a state of disrepair, and but ill supplied with artillery. The next day the 22nd of August, we heard in the early morning the sound of Scottish screechers, or bagpipes, upon the Red Hill, and hurrying out of the town we found the King and the Highlanders surveying the town.

The King looked worn and anxious, and well he might, for much discordance was already rife between the Scottish and English troops. Religious dissension was sowing broadcast its hateful seed among those who should have been heartily united. The Presbyterians were almost mutinous, for they believed that the Royalists and Cavaliers yearned for that Episcopalian Church government they so hated and despised.

Aunt Tabitha's Diary contains notes of two ill omens which betokened the King's future eclipse for a season. On the same day of the year nine years before 1642, his father unfolded his standard at Nottingham. Again, at the very hour the standard of Charles II was unfurled upon Red Hill and first fluttered in the breeze above the city of Worcester, one of his father's most eloquent and zealous ministers, the Rev. Christopher Lane, suffered for the sake of his Church, his religion, and his King, upon Tower Hill. He had been condemned to death for his opinions by President Bradshawe and the Rump, and was executed notwithstanding the strenuous entreaties of General Cromwell that his life should be spared.[2]

That General had not yet reached that height of personal power, which in later times made his request a command. And yet there are thousands in England, who are ignorant of true history, who teach and believe that Cromwell was so all powerful, that he alone had the power to save King Charles I from the Army, who had determined he should die. Before mid-day on the 22nd August the whole army reached Red Hill and Perry Wood, and looked across the Severn upon the green hills of Malvern, and down upon the defences, thatched houses, and tiled roofs of the walled city.

The garrison of Roundheads, who occupied the dilapidated fortifications, defended for a short time the New Fort,[3] a defensive position outside the Walls above the Commandery, but King Charles stormed it with his Highlanders, and Colonel James, finding the Royal army so powerful, quitted Worcester at midnight and retreated to Gloucester. Early the next morning on 23rd of August, the pealing of the bells from every church tower, and the loud huzzahing of the citizens announced the evacuation of the town.

After much consultation, and no little dissension on the part of the Generals, the troops were sent to various positions, some in the city, some outside. A large force crossed the Severn to occupy St John's and Powick and, while a strong corps occupied the New Fort and Red Hill, two thousand men encamped upon Pitchcroft, the great meadow on the left bank of the Severn, where Prince Rupert had assembled his cavalry nine years before.

Preceded by the Scottish cavalry under Lesley, King Charles entered Worcester at the head of a staff of the Dukes of Buckingham and Hamilton, the Earls of Cleveland, Lauderdale, Carnworth, Rothes, with

Generals Montomery and Massey. The cortége was followed by the Highlanders under General Pitscottie, who astonished the citizens by their strange garb, bare legs, stalwart forms and squealing whistles.

The King alighted at the Guildhall, where he was received by Mr Thomas Lysons, the Mayor, and Mr James Bridges, Sheriff of Worcester.[4] In the evening he issued a manifesto, summoning 'upon their allegiance all the nobility, gentry and others, to appear in their persons, with any arms, horses, and ammunition, at Pitchcroft, near the city, on Tuesday the 26th'. Then he held a levée at the Bishop's Palace, where he was received by the Dean, Dr Crosby, as Bishop Prideaux was absent. The royal standard floated from the tower of the Cathedral and martial music was heard in the streets.

On Sunday the 24th of August, the King attended Divine service, the sermon being preached by the Dean. For a long time the service of the Church of England had not been heard within those ancient walls, and sad evidences of Puritan bigotry were all around. The organ was gone, many monuments of the illustrious dead defaced, and the painted windows shattered, but once again the well-known hymns resounded and the old familiar prayers re-echoed from the aisles and roof.

This was the Anglican Church service we Cavaliers all loved, and hoped to see restored when King Charles should reign over united England; but the performance in the Cathedral gave great offence to General Lesley and the Scottish officers, who called our devotions 'horrible Popery and the worship of the Beast'. Some were really mutinous after the Dean's sermon in defence of the Church of England. While the various sects of which our army consisted quarrelled about election and predestination, bishops and no bishops, the loyal citizens of Worcester worked like horses in repairing and strengthening the bastions.[5] On Tuesday the 26th of August, a great rendezvous took place on Pitchcroft, according to his Majesty's summons.

It was a far finer meeting of county gentlemen and Cavaliers than that which I had witnessed nine years previously, when Prince Rupert and Prince Maurice met the forces of the King. The August sun was bright and gleaming, but to a soldier there was too much of the farm element among the troopers, many of whom came fresh from the plough, or from domestic service. Lord Talbot rode on to the ground magnificently attired, with sixty horse well caparisoned; then there came Mr Charles Hornyold with forty horse and his fighting brother

John. Mr John Washburn of Witchinford, rode at the head of forty horse. Then rode down Sir Walter Blount and his four sons, Sir Ralph Clare, Mr Francis Knotsford of Holdfast, Sir Rowland Berkley riding his piebald charger, Mr William Dansey and many others.

All these 'were honoured and encouraged by his Majesty's presence, and notwithstanding which access, the number of his army was conceived not to exceed 12,000 men, that is to say 10,000 Scots, and about 2000 English, and these not excellently armed, not plentifully stored with ammunition'.[6]

After the inspection of the troops a council of war was held, and Major General Massey was detached with a strong corps to occupy Upton-on-Severn and secure the passage of the bridge. A force of Scottish Presbyterians complicated matters by their intolerance in setting fire to Spetchley, the seat of a good and honest royalist Sir R. Berkeley, because he was a Catholic.[7]

I was now ordered to accompany General Massey on his march to Upton, being well acquainted with the neighbourhood and the inhabitants. Very strange did I think this shuffle in war and politics, as I rode side by side with the quondam Puritanical Governor of Gloucester.

We halted first at Priors Court by Pixham Ferry, a moated grange where lived Mr Leach, a devoted Royalist, and from him I hoped to gain some information respecting the garrison of Roundheads who had occupied Madresfield Court since the siege of Worcester in 1646,[8] a sad change from the days of the loyal Sir William Ligon. Fortunately the garrison surrendered at the first summons, and we marched on to Severn End. Here General Massey quartered a hundred and fifty of the Scottish horse, and announced his intentions of remaining there during our occupation of Upton. Massey spoke somewhat strongly to Mr Lechmere on the subject of joining the cause of the Parliament and the Regicides, which I thought came ill from one who was once so determined an ally of the said Parliament.[9]

We now took possession of Upton, Powick, and Bransford bridges, and General Massey proceeded to throw up some entrenchments near Upton, on the right of a small farm known as Pool House, his right resting upon Pool Brook, which in happier days turned our water mill at Hanley Castle. A strange, almost bewildering sensation came over me as I found myself once more among old familiar scenes, but how changed since the days of my youth, and how changed was I.

I looked down from the lea upon the home of my youth in ruins. The mouldering towers which yet remained were ready to fall, and little was left of the well-known spots where my Father taught me the early lessons of youth, and Isabel planted her forget-me-nots, save the moats and the great fish pool. The great keep in which we lived looked like the rubbish from a quarry, but the moats were untouched, and I could see the places where Dick Bromley caught the big jack before he went off among the Genevites, and where I jumped in after little Mary Bromley.

Now, I knew not where to turn to see a face I loved, or where I should find my own relatives, or what might happen when Upton was filled by the Scottish soldiers. My anxiety about my relations was soon allayed, for I found the Waterside deserted. Kelly, fearing another outburst of war, had taken Aunt Tabitha and Isabel to a quiet nook among the Malvern woodlands known as Pickersleigh. Madam Bromley and Mary went to Gloucester, upon the report of the occupation of Worcester by the King, and many of the inhabitants of Upton who were hot for the Parliament paid visits to their relations in the villages around.

The host of the White Lion hardly recognized me with my moustache and French ringlets, but when he did it was with an air of civility. It is wonderful how quickly persons can adopt a change of manner to a change of circumstances. Sampson, faithful as ever, when he heard I was with the troops, left his young wife and appeared ready for the fray, armed with a Damascus blade he found at Kelly's, and a pair of horseman's pistols.

The 27th of August was occupied in throwing up earthworks to the westward of Pool House, placing picquets at Upton Bridge and the entrance to Upton from Gloucester and Ledbury. The archway of the bridge next the town had been destroyed, and only a single plank was available for crossing. It was necessary to guard the bridge with a company of the Scot's foot, and more of the Scot's cavalry were sent to Severn End. The lowland Scottish regiment who had ward and watch, could not resist the propinquity of the Lion tavern, and drinking sack mingled with strong waters.

Thus heavy sleep came upon the sentinels, and at day dawn on the 28th of August, a forlorn hope of Ironsides crossed the plank which connected the broken bridge with the town, and having killed the sentries took possession of the church, where they fired volleys of musketry from the windows. At the same time a powerful brigade, advancing from Pershore under General Lambert, crossed the ford at Ryall and entered the town by Dun's Lane.

The noise of the fire-arms aroused us at the Pool Hill camp, and we advanced to the town, when we found the streets of Upton blocked with our enemies. At this crisis General Massey galloped in from Severn End and, shouting to his soldiers, led the attack in his usual dashing style. But already we were outnumbered, and close to the church-yard wall Massey's horse was shot under him, and he was badly wounded in the hand and sword-arm. We had something to do to rescue him, and how we escaped with life I know not, as men were rolling over each other in the desperate hand fighting in the narrow streets, and forty carbines were fired within half pistol shot.

Our men fought hard to take the church-yard, but fresh troops of the Parliamentarians poured in down Dun's Lane, and it was evident that unless we made a rush for it, our retreat upon Worcester would be cut off. We had remounted our wounded General, so, ordering a trumpeter to sound the recall, I led Massey's horse by the bridle, and a charge of our men cleared the road to Worcester by which we retreated slowly.

Lambert thought it advisable not to pursue us, but to occupy Upton and repair the bridge. By mid-day we reached St John's, leaving the dead in Upton streets, and at night I reached Worcester with an account of our repulse and the state of Massey.

I found the King distressed by the remonstrances of the Scottish officers respecting the religious ceremonies in the Cathedral, and it was evident that a very unpleasant feeling prevailed. I was ordered to remain as an equerry in attendance on his Majesty, and the night after Lambert's occupation of Upton, spies announced the advance of General Cromwell from Pershore to Staughton, within four miles of Worcester, where he passed the night at the house of Mr Simons, of White Lady Aston. Indeed, a party of his horse faced the city that evening.[10]

In the mean time the King, with the aid of the loyal citizens, had so strengthened the defences that they were now formidable, and there is no doubt the tactics should have been to have withstood a siege until the rallying of all Royalists. On the 30th General Lambert sent a corps of Roundheads to plunder Blackmore Park and threaten our new garrison at. Madresfield, while our old soldier groom, Sampson, managed to intercept a letter which Mistress Bound had written to the regicide Colonel Harry Marten, who was now among the Council of State in London, and had brought about the appointment of the illustrious Bound as a justice of peace. The letter was as follows:

> Honred Sr, retorn you most hom bel thanks for your gret care about my hosbons commysen to be a Justice of pese for gloster sher, for the which I deszier to have it down before the essies wich ss very sodenly; and I hope then to be so hapey as to se you here which will much joye me to se you in a pore hous of mine, and good Sr let me bege that faver. And I besech you fail not to com to me when you com in to these parts, for if I should not se you when you com to Gloster it would break my hart. Sr, if you will do me the honer as to write to me and to leve it to my granmother she will send it me. Sr, my hosborn presents his hombel servet with many hombel thanks for your nobel favers to him.

This epistle was addressed:
> For the truly honred Cornell Marten thes with my servet present I pray,[11]

and sealed with the Captain's seal and device on red wax.

While General Lambert occupied Upton, General Fleetwood was at Pershore with twelve thousand men ready to cross the Severn at any time by Upton Bridge, where the gap was mended with timbers. The King was advised to withdraw his troops from Red Hill and Perry Wood on the 29th, for the principal part of the Scottish foot were encamped in the fields between St John's and Powick Bridge, while the cavalry remained in the city.

On the evening of the 29th, General Cromwell arrived at Red Hill, within a mile of the city, with a formidable force of horse and foot. Part of his army were quartered at Spetchley and part took possession of Perry Wood. A gallant attempt to surprise our enemies was now proposed by General Middleton, and a night attack was agreed upon at a council of war. In the dead of night fifteen hundred horse and foot advanced upon Cromwell's position in Perry Wood, but owing to the usual good fortune of the rebels, through their spies the attempt was frustrated.

The troops wore their shirts over their armour for distinction, and were led by General Middleton and Sir William Keyth. They would have in all probability been successful, but the design was most traitorously discovered to the rebels by one Gise, a tailor in the town, and a notorious sectary, who was hanged the day following as the just reward of his treachery; in this action Major Knox was slain, and some few prisoners taken by the enemy.[12]

On the 30th of August General Fleetwood crossed the Severn at Upton Bridge, for the purpose of attacking the Scottish posts at Powick and St John's.[13] 'He marched next day to Powick town, where they made a halt, for Powick Bridge lying upon the river Teme between Powick and Worcester was guarded by a brigade of his Majesty's horse and foot commanded by General Montgomery and Colonel Keith'.[14]

During the three next days we could see, from the tower of Powick Church, the Roundheads preparing boats and planks to form a bridge over Severn close by the mouth of the Teme. Fleetwood too was constructing a boat bridge over the Teme, in case he failed to repair the bridge at Powick.

On Sunday, the 31st, his Majesty again attended the Cathedral service, and again numbers of the Scots under Lesley took offence, and this may account somewhat for their apathy and that of their General on the following day. That afternoon the Earl of Derby reached Worcester in sad plight, for he brought with him thirty horse instead of the large reinforcements we expected.

He had been defeated in Lancashire with heavy losses and was wounded; but it was nevertheless a striking sight to see this noble Cavalier and his worn and war-stricken followers salute their King as he stood upon the steps of the Guildhall and waved his plumed hat in acknowledgment of their loyalty.

On Monday, the 1st of September, women and boys worked hard all day carrying earth and stones to the bulwarks, and some parties of soldiers were sent to destroy the bridges over the Teme at Powick and Bransford.

On Tuesday, the Parliamentarians brought up a number of boats from Gloucester, Tewkesbury, and Upton, to form bridges over the Severn and Teme. Fleetwood left Upton in the afternoon, marched over the Old Hills, and menaced our troops at Powick, but he made no attack this day.

On Wednesday, the famous 3rd of September, the King with his Generals reconnoitred the positions of the enemy from the tower of the Cathedral, but so masked were Cromwell's troops by Perry Wood, that it was impossible to learn anything of his numbers or their positions. About twelve o'clock some heavy firing was heard at Powick, and the King mounted his horse and galloped over the bridge at St John's to entreat General Montgomery to hold the position to the last. He should have taken some of Lesley's horse with him instead of leaving them idling in the streets of Worcester! After an interview with Montgomery the King returned to the city, again ascended the Cathedral tower, and there held a council of war.

The battle of Worcester did not really commence until between two and three o'clock in the afternoon, but the first onset was a determined attack by the Parliamentarians from Upton on the royalist position at Powick about one o'clock.[15]

The Royalists contested every foot of ground against overwhelming forces, and Fleetwood lost many men in the advance, for every hedge was lined with musketeers. General Cromwell, seeing the struggle, crossed the Severn below Bunshill on the bridge of boats at the head of a brigade of his own Ironsides and Hacker's horse. A sharp action was fought near the bridge at Powick, and here General Montgomery was wounded and had to be carried to Worcester.

It was while battle was raging on the green meadows by Teme side that the King and his Generals, seeing so many troops had crossed the Severn, determined to attack General Cromwell's position on the other side, at Red Hill and Perry Wood. It was now three o'clock in the afternoon, and the trumpets sounded to horse, while the Scottish bagpipes shrieked their shrill summons in every street. The King placed himself at the head of a brigade of foot, and was followed by about two hundred horsemen, most of whom were English, under the Duke of Buckingham, and Lord Grandison, Lord Talbot, Sir John Packington, Sir Waiter Blount, and other English Cavaliers, for the body of Scottish cavalry remained with Lesley, useless in the city.

The battle commenced on the slope of Red Hill, and the fighting was very desperate from the time the Royalists passed through the gate of Sidbury. The Roundheads were driven into Perry Wood, where their General had raised a breastwork at the cockshoot of the wood for the greater security of his troops. Here the slaughter was terrible, for hand-to-hand conflicts were waged within the mazes of the wood.

At one time the King was the absolute master of the rebels' great guns, but Cromwell hearing the din of war, and having succeeded in the assault at Powick, recrossed the Severn with several regiments of Lambert's troops, and everywhere the Royalists were overwhelmed by numbers. 'His Majesty gave an incomparable example of valour to the rest by charging in person, which the Highlanders especially imitated, fighting with the butt end of their muskets when their ammunition was spent; but new supplies of rebels being continually poured upon them, and the main body of Scottish horse not coming up in due time from the town to his Majesty's relief, his army was forced to retreat in at the Sidbury Gate in much disorder'.[16]

It was impossible to withstand the pressure of the masses Cromwell now brought into action. Desborough's horse and seven new regiments had crossed from Powick. The rush therefore for the gate at Sidbury, was now tremendous, and a cart laden with ammunition covered with hay was upset and lay right across the passage.

The young King, yielding to the advice of the officers around him, had consented to retreat into the city, but when he attempted to enter found the gate blocked. A rush was made by the rebels, and the King would have been cut off had they not been held in check by the bravery of the Earl of Cleveland, Mr John Hornyold, and others, who fought like tigers while the King crept underneath the ammunition cart and escaped into Worcester.

Captain Forwards was one of those who rallied a few stalwart soldiers around him and defended the entrance at Sidbury. I saw his stalwart iron-looking form amidst the thronging rebels, as Cromwell advanced in person leading his troops to storm Fort Royal. "For the King! for the King!" I shouted, and called upon some of our Worcestershire men to stand to their pikes and die rather than surrender the pass.

Giles Nanfan recognized my voice, and shouting his well-known war cry, I saw him, striking like Hercules right and left, force his way through the Ironsides who surrounded Cromwell to within a few feet of the General's horse. He was now among the most resolute veterans in the Parliamentarian army, and I saw him struck down in their very midst. I made a furious dash, followed by a dozen of our English troopers, to try and rescue my old friend, and hand-to-hand and steel-to-steel we met in the death grapple of war.

I had nearly reached the spot where Cromwell sat unmoved upon his charger, save when, with sweeping arm and eagle eye he directed some movement to his Ironsides, when an officer in the uniform of Cobbett's horse rushed upon me and we engaged in personal conflict. Our swords rang against our steel cuirasses, and more than once I staggered under the sledge hammer blows of my adversary. At last I gave him one of John Kelly's crashers over the head, and his helmet breaking revealed the features of Dick Bromley.

I lowered my sword and forthwith was struck by one of his troopers with a handspike and laid senseless and prostrate. When I came to my senses I found myself stretched on a mattress in the Commandery, which was just outside the gate at Sidbury, Dick Bromley bathing my head and a surgeon binding up my left arm, which was badly broken. Then there was a hurry and a bustle, and the Duke of Hamilton was carried past and laid in an inner room.

I lay for two long days and nights hovering between life and death, and remember little save that Dick Bromley was often by my bed-side. He sent for Aunt Tabitha, and she insisted on her arrival upon taking the surgeon's place. And verily the sight of her and Isabel was better than all the physic.

Days passed away before I learned from others the details of the battle of Worcester, after I became *hors de combat*. It seems the struggle at Sidbury Gate continued until after Cromwell had stormed Fort Royal, where he ordered no quarter to be given to the garrison, and fifteen hundred men were put to the sword by the chosen of the Lord.

At Sidbury, when the cart was cleared away, Royalists and Round-heads entered it together, and much hand-to hand fighting took place round St Peter's Church and in Friar Street. The King endeavoured to rally his forces in the city, and ran amongst them exclaiming, "I had rather you would shoot me than keep me alive to see the consequences of this fatal day!" but there was no checking the advance of Cromwell's victorious Ironsides, and the fight raged in High Street and down Lich Street, the Earl of Cleveland, Colonel Careless, Captains Hornyold, Giffard, Ashley, Thackwell, Blount and other officers rallying what men they could and charging the advancing troops of Cromwell through the streets.

They were, however overpowered by numbers and driven back, but made again a stand at the Town Hall, where another resistance took place, many citizens being killed.[17] And now Fleetwood's troops on the other side of the city, crossed the bridge at St John's, and set to work killing and plundering, 'Worcester became a scene of horrors which humanity cannot think of without a shudder'.[18]

The last stand of the Cavaliers was opposite Copenhagen Street, but the defeated Royalists fled for St Martin's Gate, as the Foregate was walled up. At last the King put off his armour in a house in Friar Street, and at the White Ladies he mounted a fresh horse and allowed himself to be conducted by a few faithful adherents on the Northern Road. How he escaped, after many strange adventures, to the Continent from Boscobel is well known and has been published.

Such was the cruel and vindictive spirit which actuated the victors, that Mr John Hornyold, having taken refuge in a barber's shop, was dragged out and shot,[19] and many innocent citizens with no arms in their hands, were put to the sword in the spirit of mere massacre. A few Royalists escaped, hidden, near the Foregate, at the Trinity.[20] The Guildhall, St Helen's Church, and the Commandery, were used as hospitals, and there died after the battle the Duke of Hamilton, Sir John Douglas, and a hundred persons of distinction.

Three days after the battle an elderly lady in deep mourning accompanied by a fair girl, apparently her daughter worked day and night attending the wounded, whether Roundhead or Royalist, and alleviating from a liberal purse to the utmost of their power the misery which filled half the houses in Worcester. The number of slain was estimated at three thousand, and the prisoners amounted to ten thousand, more than half of whom were wounded. The chirurgeons were overworked, and hundreds perished for want of attention.

As the Duke of Hamilton had been carried to the Commandery, General Cromwell's surgeon from time to time paid us a visit, while he never came without speaking of the charitable ladies and their deeds of kindness. At last Aunt Tabitha became somewhat jealous, saying that none should attempt 'Phlebotomy' but persons of experience, and young women, especially, were more in their place in the kitchen than the apothecary's shop. She then busied herself in perfuming our chamber with hot tar, and boiling the stems of *carduus benedictus*.[21]

Whether it was the tar, or the boiling of *carduus benedictus*, I know not, but my broken head became affected, and overcome with drowsiness I fell into a deep sleep. When I awoke, I beheld the deep, earnest eyes of Mary Bromley fixed upon my worn and cadaverous countenance. She looked pale and very sorrowful. She had met with Isabel, who had gone for Aunt Tabitha to an apothecary's, and Mary had come to the Commandery with fruits and flowers. Seeing her seated by the bedside, I seized her hand and kissed it again and again, until, blushing like one of her own September roses, she gently withdrew it from my grasp. Madam Bromley soon followed, attended by a serving man, bearing meats and broths, and then she engaged with Aunt Tabitha in calculating 'the effect of the harvest moon upon the reins, bowells, necks, heads, throats; knees, legs, and toes of invalids'.[21]

It was on one of her visiting excursions to the wounded that Aunt Tabitha learnt from a rebel sentry the true and faithful account of General Cromwell's compact with the Devil,[23] and her face was a sight to see as she told in measured whispers and hollow tones of the appearance of the Arch Fiend below Perry Wood on the hill slope above Worcester.

The Cathedral clock had tolled the hour of twelve, and the early morn of the 3rd of September commenced with a darkness which might be felt. A sentry who was stationed at a herd's cottage known as Woodside, saw a vivid blaze shoot up as it were from the centre of the earth, and then the darkness became denser than ever because of the blaze. Soon there followed a rushing through the air of millions of wings, and shrill voices hissing among the dense clouds which hid the stars and bright September moon in their profundity. Blackness hung like a deep pall o'er woods and hills and city.

At last a lurid glare, which appeared to rise from the earth and not from the heavens, revealed a tall horseman standing with folded arms close by the sentry's side. He was clad from head to foot in armour, but the steel was hissing hot, and his eyes glared through a closed vizor like lamps of fire. He ordered the sentry, in sepulchral tones, to summon the Lord General, and the man declared that his breath singed his beard as he spoke, and smelt like the mouth of a hot cannon.

General Cromwell was in a tent at the back of Perry Wood, and engaged with two of his officers in examining a plan of the City of Worcester by the light of rushlights. When told of the summons of the black horseman he turned deadly pale, but hastily excusing himself to his officers, went forth in the darkness to the hut at the Woodside.[24] The sentry thought it his duty to follow, and when again he reached the unearthly glare which hovered about the cottage, he saw General Cromwell and the armour-clad horseman enter the woodman's hut.

Taking up his position, as sentry, close to the door, he heard the voice of Cromwell now expostulating, now entreating, and then beseeching, in humility and anguish. At last came the voice of the stranger, if voice it could be termed, for it was a hissing not in mortal tones. And the words were, "Nine, I say Nine, No *more*! The Third of September *at this hour*!" There was a silence as of the tomb. Then the voice of the Lord General was heard in deep moans; a flash of lightning lit up the distant Malverns, and crash came a peal of thunder, which made the welkin ring and startled the way-worn soldiers from their fitful sleep.

The sentry watched and prayed until the day dawn broke, when the Lord General stole forth creeping alone from the woodman's hut, his stern frame shivering, and his head bowed. This sentry was badly wounded afterwards by the royalists on their attack at Perry Wood, and was carried into Worcester and placed in Edgar's tower. Here Aunt Tab- itha found him and heard his strange relation. He afterwards became light-headed, and died shouting, "The Third of September!"

Madam Bromley listened to this wondrous tale with proper gravity, but was inclined to believe that her cousin the General had summoned his Lieutenant, General Fleetwood, across the Severn to a midnight interview. Aunt Tabitha smiled sarcastically at this suggestion, and declared that Fleetwood's eyes were like oysters, and never could have looked like coals of fire. His voice too, was like that of the domestic hog, and not like unto the hissing of the serpent which betrayed Eve. It was the Devil himself, no other, said my aunt.

Soon after this remarkable history had been bruited abroad, John Kelly arrived and the management of the hospitals improved rapidly under his personal superintendence. General Cromwell set out for London, leaving Worcester a charnel house with the dead bodies of men and the carcases of horses. He gave orders for the walls to be pulled down, and Dick Bromley was left to superintend the dismantling of all defensive works.

From Dick Bromley I learnt what a gallant stand the Earl of Cleveland made in Sidbury Street and High Street, and how the Earl of Rothes with a party of Scots held the Castle Hill with much resolution until conditions were agreed for quarter. At first it was believed that the

King was dead, but his 'swart' body had not been recognized among the slain, and it was reported that he had escaped. Giles Nanfan had been brought into Worcester badly wounded by a pike stab, but the stern Ironsides respected the bravery of the fighting Forwards, and he was carried to the Trinity and carefully attended to by Aunt Tabitha and Madam Bromley.

It was a sad time for my gentle sister, as her Forget-me-not lay hover- ing between life and death for many days. 'It is a long lane which has no turning', and with the fall of the October leaves both Nanfan and myself were moved from Worcester; he to Birtsmorton, and I to John Kelly's house at Upton.

Resistance everywhere collapsed, and the cause of the Common-wealth was triumphant. The Duke of Hamilton died of his wounds, and the Earl of Derby, although wounded, was beheaded by those who seldom showed mercy. Lesley was shut up in the Tower with Middleton, Cleveland,[25] and Lauderdale. General Massey was reported to be dead of his wounds received at Upton, but he too was caught and imprisoned. He soon escaped and joined the King in France.

General Cromwell was elected General in Chief of the army, but more than two years elapsed after the battle of Worcester before Mr Bromley's 'pore cosen' became the Lord Protector, and High and Mighty Chief of the Commonwealth. Happy would it have been for England if the victorious Parliamentarians had showed more of the Christianity they so much preached, and more generosity towards the defeated Royalists. The deadly wounds inflicted upon society would have been more quickly healed; and there would have been less of reaction and retribution when the Restoration came.

Alas! with a few rare exceptions, such as that of the noble conduct of Sir Edward Harley to the fallen house of the Lingens,[26] any thought for the alleviation of suffering seldom entered the minds of the victors. The miseries of the clergy of the Church of England are indescribable, and very few met with the hospitable treatment shown to Mr Wood-forde, the Rector of Upton, by his successor Mr Warrenne. That kindly-hearted pastor sheltered the deprived incumbent and they shared the parsonage.[27]

Episcopal and Cathedral revenues, confiscated long before for the pay of the army, were appropriated by force, and such of the parochial clergy as were guilty of loyalty to their King, or of unpopular ceremonials, were driven from their benefices and their homes, and turned adrift, often with miserable wives and children, to live on the fifth part of their rightful income, or beg, or starve, if, as was frequently the case, that pittance was withheld from them.[28]

Now and then, when members of the same family had espoused opposite sides, as in the example of the Brothers Yates of Bromesberrow, the prosperity and influence of the one who was up, saved from spoliation the other who was down. Thus the banners of Yates the Parliamentarian, carried with the victorious troops at the battle of Worcester, served as a shield for his elder brother.[29]

With returning health came the necessity for future action. John Kelly, with the aid of Madam Bromley's peasants, had recovered a goodly sum from the ruins of Hanley Castle, but I wished to leave this intact for the benefit of Aunt Tabitha and Isabel. Kelly declared all he possessed should be mine, but I was determined to seek an independent fortune across the seas, in that western land, Virginia, where already several Royalists of broken fortune had emigrated. Hither, Colonel Washington, the brave Governor of Worcester, was now bound.

He invited me to accompany him and share his fortunes. There, at all events, we could use our Prayer Books, without being classed with murderers and adulterers, and keep Christmas time and Easter, free from the iron rule of Calvinists and Puritanism. If we succeeded, Aunt Tabitha and Isabel could join us, as there was little to keep them in England, save Isabel's attachment and betrothment to Captain Forwards. But Giles might come also. It was better than living in poverty and obscurity, under the shadow of the Ragged Stone, in the little farm which the Puritans had not yet sequestrated.

John Kelly declared that if the ladies would sail, he would sell house, and boat, and bed, and bolster, and leave Upton to Roundheads and rebels. After several interviews with Colonel Washington, it was arranged that we should sail in the month of August; survey the lands where we proposed to settle, put matters into a position of comfort, and then send for our friends.

It was now time to say farewell to Madam and Miss Bromley, who were alone at Hamme Court; Dick, now a Lieutenant-Colonel, having joined his regiment in Ireland. Isabel had spoken of our intention to emigrate, but all the details were as yet uncertain and indefinite. I dreaded that Good bye to Mary more than I can express, for I loved her heart and soul, but she was the daughter of a wealthy, fortunate family, and related to the great General of the Commonwealth, while I was a poor impoverished Cavalier, with only a few hundred gold pistoles, a broken sword, and a weary heart.

Full of the memory of old times, of happy days at Hanley Castle with my father, and of the rides and walks with Mary and Isabel among the glens of the Malverns, I started for a walk from the Waterside, in the gleaming of a June evening. Love makes a man think more of another than himself, and my thoughts were of Mary Bromley amidst all the changes to which my mind reverted, and so I walked towards Homme Court by Southend.

The road passes along a causeway raised for the benefit of passengers when a Severn flood overflows the surrounding pastures, and near it stands the stone which marked the boundary between the lands of Widow Stubbs and Captain Bound. I had heard little of this worthy since Colonel Marten had him appointed a Justice of the Peace, save that he was more covetous than ever, and since her death had annexed Widow Stubbs' allotment and right of assart to his own lands, regardless of the opinions of the neighbours. The landmark stone rises above a small but deep black pool, so deep that it is called bottomless.

Here, seated on this stone, I again beheld Captain Bound. As I drew nearer to my bitter enemy, my hand involuntarily grasped my sword. He was indeed changed; and I was startled at the unearthly expression of his countenance, its death-like hue, and the stony appearance of his eyes. He looked me full in the face, as I approached, and pointed with a thin and shadowy hand into the black and dismal pool. His lips quivered, as if he would speak but could not, and then, as the last rays of the setting sun lit up pool, and stone, and bushes, the body of Captain Bound faded away into space. Drops of perspiration rolled down my face as I felt certain that I had beheld a spirit form which had learned the secret of another existence.

And so indeed it proved. Bound had left his home at Seller's Orchard, and his body was found sodden and drowned in the black pit below the stone where I had seen his shadow. Many were the rumours respecting his fate, and it was generally believed that he had committed suicide on seeing the ghost of Widow Stubbs hovering above the landmark he had caused to be removed. Parson Woodforde was called upon to exorcise stone and pool, but even now few like to pass Bound's

Stone after nightfall, for his spirit still shimmers over Bound's Pool.

Some days elapsed after the death of the Spy, before I could make up my mind to say Farewell to Mary Bromley. I walked round by the old Saxon grange, the Eades, and wandered among the fine trees and grassy knolls of Pull Court, but could not summon courage to face the girl I loved and say Good bye, perhaps for ever. At last, in utter desperation I found myself at the door, and a greater coward than if confronted with a score of Ironsides.

I was ushered into a room where Mary was sitting alone, her father's Bible open upon a table by her side. She was engaged in sorting garments for some of the sufferers in the war, and many sadly needed them. She arose when I entered, and bid me welcome, but her pale cheeks flushed and there was a quivering of her lips, and I saw she suspected my errand. I did not beat about the bush, but told her a soldier's honest story – how England was no longer a home for men like Colonel Washington and myself; how we had determined to try our fortunes across the ocean, and that I had come to say in parting "God bless you" to Madam Bromley and the companion of my youth.

Mary listened in silence, she did not even raise her eyes, as I spoke of hopes and fears, and labour in a distant land; how, too, the time might come when bitter enmities might be calmed down, and the wanderer again look upon the dear old Malverns, and linger by the banks of Severn. Then I saw the tears falling upon the work on her lap, and at last she sobbed aloud for very sorrow. I forgot my determination not to say one word of the love which filled my heart. I knelt by her side and pressed her to my bosom and told her I was hers, heart, and soul, and body, until the grave.

Mary did not repel me, but wept as if her heart would break. I then asked if she would wait awhile for one who would be constant and true for her sake, and may be, in the land of promise, good fortune would befriend the wanderer and I might come back again to old England and claim her as my bride. Though she was educated as a Puritan and I as a Churchman, neither of us were bigots in religion, and both wished to serve God humbly and prayerfully without fussing over white surplices or Geneva gowns.

Mary now looked up, and, smiling through her tears, pointed to the Bible which lay open by her side. She then said, "Look, Richard, at the page I opened by God's mercy, just before you arrived, when after my dear Father's fashion I sought for a passage which would comfort me in much tribulation." I looked at the pages, and read:

Intreat me not to leave thee or to return from following after thee: where thou goest, I will go; and where thou lodgest I will lodge: thy people shall be my people, and thy God my God: where thou diest, will I die, and there will I be buried.

My departure from England was somewhat delayed, but Mary was steadfastly minded to go with me, and after much consideration and many consultations, Madam Bromley gave her consent, and Dick declared that as I had twice saved his life I should be trusted with that of his only sister. Thus, my dear wife, my blessing in joy and sorrow, left wealth, and home, and friends for her husband's sake, and although, as needs must be, there was sore grief at parting, she never murmured, but pressed my hand and looked up into my face in sunny confidence as we sailed over the foaming billows on board the good ship Crescent, towards the setting sun.

Not long after our departure, Giles Nanfan compounded with the Parliament on easy terms, which report said was owing to Madam Bromley's intercedence with General Cromwell. Giles then persuaded Isabel to become his wife, and Captain Forwards hung up his sword, above the great mantelpiece with the Nanfan arms at Birtsmorton Court. Aunt Tabitha was installed forthwith as mistress of the poultry yard and the confections, while in time she physicked the whole parish.

Bridget never married, but lived the life of a recluse at the farm-house below the Ragged Stone, hard by the meadow where her lover fell. She was much occupied in deeds of charity, and many a time and oft would Isabel walk with her among the Malvern glades, and converse of those deep awaitings which belong to a world to come. We heard of Lord Cockayne's marriage to a French heiress, when he left the English Church and turned Papist; a proceeding he might have carried out earlier, but that he thought it 'inexpedient'.

In the course of time Oliver Cromwell became His Highness, and the Lord Protector, in all but name a King. Then in the year of our Lord 1658, nine years after the battle of Worcester, on the 3rd of September, came a raging, roaring tempest, in the hurly-burly of which his spirit passed away, to the amazement of some, and the rejoicing of all Royalists.

At last there arrived the much longed-for and much prayed-for Restoration. But neither Colonel Washington nor ourselves returned to England. We were surrounded by farms, and children, and faithful servants. We had herds and homesteads in the sunny land we had chosen, with an English church among the forest trees; so we thought we would wait awhile, and it was well we did so.

All that was good and noble in the young King, Charles II, as I knew him, withered away under the influence of the foreign courts he frequented during the years of the Commonwealth. Thus when he became King of England, he set an example of lawless passion to his subjects which will be a byeword and a reproach through all time. As regards religion, he carried out the doctrine of 'expediency' to such an extent, that although he had long been a Catholic in heart and faith, he never avowed it until he lay gasping in death.

We shall never return to England. King James II is on the throne, and he has the honesty to avow that he is a Catholic heart and soul. But full well we know how the Jesuits have made the old faith to stink in the nostrils of the English people, and how the land will be rent by civil war, and the blood of Englishmen shed like water, before a Papist can secure the throne of Britain. We have seen strife enough, God knows!

Old John Kelly followed us to Virginia as soon as Aunt Tabitha and Isabel were settled at Birtsmorton Court. He lives in a cottage hard by, and has lately obtained some skulls from the far west which he declares belonged to a race which lived before the flood. He still manipulates, and ponders over machines which spurt and fizz, and have earned for him, even in these wilds, a somewhat uncanny reputation.

I am constantly occupied with Colonel Washington in the various occupations of an agricultural life, and leave all the letter-writing to my wife. She and Aunt Tabitha write to each other regularly twice a year epistles of grate length, and thus we learn from time to time of the welfare of our former neighbours. Many are the hospitalities in the wainscotted room at Birtsmorton Court, and Giles has furbished up the old coats of arms with bright new paint.

Old Parson Woodforde recovered his living at the Restoration and again occupied the pulpit. Honeywood Yates, the Royalist, became once more the Squire and owner of Bromesberrow, and has built a mortuary chapel in which are hung the banners which were carried at the battle of Worcester in his brother's troop. Dick Bromley settled with the Government and is now *Custos Rotulorum*. Mr Lechmere foresaw the change which was coming over the public mind, and himself applied to his Majesty, then at Brussels, for his pardon, which his Majesty most graciously granted. Mr Richard Dowdeswell still lives at Bushley Park, a Cavalier of the old school, honoured and respected by all who know him. Aunt Tabitha has sent me her Diary, all across the waters of the ocean, and in this she gives a full and particular account of Isabel's last baby, and how she wished she had Mary's to compare them side by side.

"Richard Plantagenet Forester Nanfan," she declares, "is a boy in a duzzen. God bless hitt! Amen."

Author's Notes

Chapter One

1 Allies' Folk Lore
2 Lady in time of Civil Wars. *Archeologia.*
3 Aunt Tabitha evidently consulted the Feoffee Book at Tewkesbury. For this and other notes I have to thank Mr H.P. Moore.
4 Tewkesbury Feoffee Book.
5 *ibid.*

Chapter Two

1 Now Queenhill. See *Bushley Almanack* for 1882,
2 Jardines 'Torture in England', and *Comparative History of England*, vol.ii. p. 469. The warrant still exists in the State Paper Office.
3 *Comparative History of England*, vol, ii. P. 483
4 'Notes on the dialect of South Worcestershire', by A.Porson, M.A.
5 See *Comparative History of England* and May's *History of the Long Parliament.*
6 *ibid.*

Chapter Three

1 Barber, in Lily's *Midas.*'
2 In 1644
3 A merlin.
4 Book of Days, vol.i. p.185
5 *Mercurius Rusticus.*
6 An astrological scroll of Dr. Dee's lent by Mr But was in the Worcestershire Exhibition of 1882.
7 Rain water caught on Ascension Day was bottled for eye-water as late as 1850.
8 Portraits of the Brothers Yates are in the possession of J.E. Niblett, Esq.
9 Webb's *Civil War in Herefordshire.*
10 Portraits of Sir William Russell and Mr Hornyold are in the possession of Mr J.V. Hornyold, at Blackmore Park.

Chapter Four

1 Published 1617

Chapter Five

1 Died 1640.
2 Tanner's *Notes on Monasteries*, p.616,
3 *Beauties of England and Wales*, vol.xv. p.150.
4 Took four sons to the Battle of Worcester.
5 His portrait is at Blackmore Park.
6 Now the property of Mrs Bradstreet and was in the Worcester Exhibition of 1882.

Chapter Six

1 Afterwards Sir Nicholas Lechmere. He was made a Judge of the Court of Exchequer in 1689. Portrait at the Rhydd.

2 Later on Mr Hornyold, of Blackmore Park, paid twelve pounds a month to the Commission of Parliament. Webb's *Civil War in Herefordshire*.

3 This old thorn tree was standing in the memory of some still living. It was blown down, and a young hawthorn has been planted on the same site by Mr. Hayward, who has also a sword in his possession dug up near Powick Bridge.

4 Vicars.

5 Ludlow's *Memoirs*.

6 Dugdale, *Short View*, p.357

7 Thomas's Survey

8 *Worcestershire Dialect*, by A Porson.

9 She died of smallpox when nursing him.

Chapter Seven

1 This cock eagle stone is said, in the *Mercurius Rusticus* to have been stolen from Mr Bartlett when his house was plundered in 1644.

2 The banners of Yates, the Parliamentarian, carried at the Battle of Worcester, may still be seen in Bromesberrow Church.

3 *Iter Carolinum*

4 Drayton

5 The house the King slept in is still standing. *Historic Warwickshire*, Burgess.

6 Feathers in the hat or cap were a distinguishing mark of Cavalier officers.

7 On the night of 22nd October, 1642.

8 *Historic Warwickshire*, Burgess, p.344

9 *Comparative History of England*, vol.ii. p.525

10 This was the celebrated discoverer of the circulation of the blood.

11 See *Survey* by Mr Fisher, Vicar of Kineton, and Gibson's *Additions to Camden*.

12 *Historic Warwickshire*, Burgess.

Chapter Eight

1 The earliest news-letter, *The English Post*, appeared August 1st, 1641. There is a copy in Mr Grainger's collecion at Worcester.

2 An account of these brothers may be seen, *Transactions*, Archaeol. Soc. of Gloucestershire and Bristol.

3 Corbet, Bib. Glouces.

4 Corbet.

5 *Memoirs* of Henrietta Maria, p. 34.

6 Webb's *Civil War in Herefordshire*.

7 A stone cross has been erected by W. P. Price, Esq., at Barber's Bridge, on the discovery of the skeletons at that spot.

Chapter Nine

1 Bacon's *Essay On Gardens* 1625.
2 The (then) new American tobacco plant.
3 *Tradescantia*.
4 Catalogue. Museum Tradescantium,
5 Prince Maurice was at Tewkesbury, April 9th. Speciall Passages, April 11 to 15.
6 King Henry V.
7 Mr Edward Clark, the Royalist, is mentioned frequently in Webb's *Civil War in Herefordshire*. As late as 1850 there was a blunderbuss at Oxenhall Court, said to have been used at the siege of Gloucester.
8 April 13th, 1643
9 The bridge was afterwards repaired by Mr Edward Hall. Records of Upton-on-Severn.
10 Tewkesbury Feoffee Book.

Chapter Ten

1 Bib. Glouces.
2 The desecration at Winchester Cathedral was terrible; Waller looking on.
3 *The Prayer Book* was abolished in 1644
4 See Map from Boscobel, Frontispiece
5 I have to thank the Rev. F. Hopkinson of Malvern Wells for the loan of *Mercurius Aulicus* of this date, which he exhibited with other numerous relics of olden times in the Worcester Exhibition of 1882.
6 *Perfect Diurnal*, June 7th
7 Nash's *Worcestershire*.
8 Webb's *Civil War*, vol. i p. 293
9 *Mercurius Aulicus*.
10 In some Harley MSS in possession of my brother, J. F. Symonds, there is a statement by Sir Edward Harley and Sir Robert Pye, who married Mr Hampden's daughter, that Hampden's death was caused by the bursting of one of his pistols, 'which shattered his arm in a very dismal manner'. Lord Nugent questions the truth of this statement, but without reason as it seems to us.
11 An old Worcestershire saying.
12 Wheler's *Stratford-on-Avon*. The Charnel House was destroyed in 1800.
13 Said to have been purchased by Garrick, 1769. A pair of Shakespeare's gloves (?) were at the Worcester Exhibition of 1885.
14 *The Taming of the Shrew*.

Chapter Eleven

1 Wbeler's *History of Stratford*.
2 Now Chapel Lane,
3 Strickland Portrait.
4 Judith, Shakespeare's youngest daughter.
5 The Kineton medal was struck at Oxford to commemorate this meeting.
6 Flea Flint, in *Old Troop*, act iii.; and *Hudibras*, 'Made children with their tones to run for 't, As bad as Bloody Bones or Lunsford.'

7 Noakes' *Rambles in Worcestershire*. There is a portrait of Butler at Eastnor Castle. Is it possible that his indifferent portraits may account for the want of any likeness of Sir John Pakington, Mr Charles Hornyold, Mr Cocks of Castleditch, of that period? Were they afterwards thrown aside as daubs?

8 *Hudibras* canto i,

9 Puritan Nomenclature (Bardsley).

Chapter Twelve

1 Many of the injuries to ecclesiastical buildings attributed to Oliver Cromwell were the work of Thomas Cromwell, minister of Henry III.

2 Elizabeth Harley married Giles Nanfan of Birtsmorton Court.

3 *Letters* Lady Brilliana Harley (Camden Sec.), p.xliii.

4 Speciall Passages, 120, 767.

5 *Bib. Glouc.* cxxxvii.

6 Speciall Passages.

7 The present Spa.

8 Webb's *Civil War in Herefordshire*, vol.i. p.330

9 Webb tells us that the King's Guards alone represented £100,000 a year rental.

10 A kind of teetotum made out of buttons,

11 *Bibl Glouc*, lxi,

12 There is a fine portrait of Falkland by Vandyck, at the Rhydd, Worcestershire.

13 'A True Relation', *Bib. Glouc.* 280.

14 *Bib. Glouc.*

15 *New Hue and Cry.*

Chapter Thirteen

1 *Annals of Sudeley and Winchcombe*, by Mrs Dent.

2 10 Sep. came in ye Erle of Essex from raising ye siege of Gloster." – Tewkesbury Feoffee Book.

3 *Letters of Lady Brilliana Harley*, p.198, &c.

4 *ibid.* p.33.

5 *Old Cavalier*

6 The author has seen the original compact, signed at Oxford, January 1643, in the presence of George Digbye, Robert Spotswoode (Scottish Secretary to the King, and an ancestor of the President of the Royal Society) and Daniel O'Neille. *Antrim* MSS.

7 Vebatim from *Antrim* MSS.

8 *Comparative History of England*, vol.ii. p.533

9 Whitelock.

10 Webb's *Civil War in Herefordshire*, and Dugdale's *Short View*.

11 *Oxford Mercury*, and *Mercurius Aulicus*.

12 Booker's *Almanack*, 1644

13 Mem. de Madame de la Fayett;

14 The Stewards had a 'cousinly relationship with King Charles; Carlyle's *Cromwell*, vol.i. The Rev. C.H. Steward (Ashchurch) is descended fron this family.

Chapter Fourteen

1 Hallam, and *Comparative History of England*, vol, ii.
2 As an example of the King's cipher—'d 5. 81. 38. 44. 48. 50. 1. 57. 78.' expressed the words *his honesty*. 'n 1. g 5. 83. 58. 3. 64. reads *to my service* – Ormonde, ii.
3 *Epistolary Curiosities*.
4 Professor Rogers in *Notes and Queries*.
5 A tune of the date of the Wars of the Roses.
6 The mistletoe thrush
7 Destroyed by Waller, 1644. A description is given in Symonds' *Diary*.
8 Hearne's *Notes to Leland*.
9 *Book of Days*, Vol. ii. p. 12. 'The Parliament of London will put the King to death.'

Chapter Fifteen

1 Symonds' *Diary*
2 Webb's *Civil War in Herefordshire*, vol.ii. p.10
3 Mynne was lodged at Captain Stephen Skinner's house.
4 Webb's *Civil War in Herefordshire*, vol.ii p.10
5 Charles II gave wood from the Forest of Dean towards the repair of Newent Church.
6 I learn from the Rev. Joseph White that cannon balls have been dug up at Woeful   Hill,
7 *True Informer*, Dec., 1643
8 Symonds' *Diary* (Camden Soc.). Mrs Tennant, the Eades, Upton–on–Severn, possesses an interesting relic of the Cavalier Antiquary and author of the Diary. It is a silver heart inscribed on one side, 'Prepared bee to follow mee. C.R.' On the other, 'I live and dy in loyaltie', and a heart pierced with arrows. Inside is a medallion of the head of Charles I and *Martyr Populy*.
9 *Mercurius Aulicus* and *The Spie*.
10 Webb's *Civil War in Herefordshire*.
11 *Mercurius Rusticus*.
12 'Two thousand lay scattered about the streets and suburbs, bighways and fields.' Webb's *Civil War in Herefordshire*.
13 May's *History of Evesham*.
14 Symonds' *Diary*, p.27
15 'On his back he lay, his eyes half open on me,
      His forehead pale, and with a frown still on it,
      His breast thick choked with gore, the clustered locks
      Matted upon his neck, his fingers clenched
      Tight on his sword, as he yet dared the foe.'
      Plays from English History – Grindrod.
16 Twenty–six soldiers and 80 countrymen perished. Luke's MS Letter–book and Symonds' *Diary*.
17 Clarendon.
18 May's *History of Evesham*.
19 *Iter Carolinum*, and Beesley's *History of Banbury*.
20 Symonds' *Diary*.
21 *ibid.* p.28.
22 Memoirs in Strickland's *Queens of England*.

Chapter Sixteen

1 Symonds' *Diary*, p.155
2 This was Marten the regicide, who died in Chepstow Castle. His name was Uarry not Henry, as he pleaded when indicted.
3 Recipe in an Almanack of the period among the Marten papers at Hinton Manor.
4 A table which King Charles used is still shown at Buckland Rectory.
5 Symonds' *Diary* – Poetry of the Period
6 Queens ofEngland.
7 *Squire Papers* – Carlyle
8 Symonds' *Diary*, p. 39
9 *ibid* p.40
10 *Civil War in Herefordshire*
11 Corbet.
12 Clarendon,
13 Introduction to Lady Brilliana's *Letters*.
14 Corbet.
15 *Bib. Glouces.*, p.112
16 Seventeen according to the Register.
17 Afterwards Governor of the Isle ofWight, when the King fled there for refuge.
18 At this period of the war there were numerous spies, and some when caught were cruelly tortured.
19 Symonds' *Diary*, p.146
20 *ibid*. p148.
21 The grandfather of Earl Somers remembered the old doorway of Castleditch studded with slugs and bullets.

Chapter Seventeen

1 Hall's *Satires* 1538.
2 Masque of Christmas
3 *Perfect Passages* and *Moderate Intelligencer*, April, 1645
4 Webb's *Civil War in Herefordshire*.
5 See *Comparative History of England*, vol.ii. p.552, and compare with Webb's *Civil War in Herefordshire*, vol.ii. p.165 for this history.
6 'The Bishops of Hereford had a fayre palace (at Bosbury) in the time of King Offa.'–Harlian MSS. 672
7 Now the residence of Michael Biddulph, Esq., M.P.
8 *Mercurius Aulicus*.
9 The old Church doors showed relics of the Ledbury fight. Mr Piper, of Ledbury, lent me slugs and bullets which he extracted from the timbers.
10 'Why is there not some page to tell
      The secrets of that narrow cell
      Tradition, history, all are dumb,
      There rests but the decaying tomb.'
      From an old poem in the possession of Miss Biddulph.
11 Massey's despatch to the House of Commons.
12 Letter dated April 24, 1645 Strickland's *Queens of England*.
13 *Comparative History of England*, vol.ii. p.716. Nearly 4000 persons were executed for witchcraft during the Long Parliament.

14 *Glanville on Witches* 1672

15 Mr Lees, the Worcestershire botanist, gives much information on the ancient lore of plants in his well-known works. See also Noakes' 'Notes and Queries for Worcestershire', on the executions for witchcraft at Worcester in 1643, &c. Mr Lygon, of Madresfield, rescued a poor woman from the water ordeal at the close of the last century.

Chapter Eighteen

1 Webb's *Civil War in Herefordshire*.

2 Clarendon.

3 Symonds' *Diary*, 192

4 This cabinet is now in the possession of Mr Dent at Sudeley Castle.

5 Sprigge's Map in *England's Recovery*, published two years after the battle.

6 Grandfather of Dean Swift.

7 Grandfather of the 'Man of Ross'.

8 Wilton Castle was afterwards burnt by Lingen and Scudamore.

9 See *Muniment antiqua* King, and *Castles of Herefordshire* Robinson.

10 Now at the Upper Hall, Ledbury.

11 Pengethly Papers and MSS. See Webb's Appendix in his *Civil War in Herefordshire*.

12 Dancumb's *Collections*.

13 Webb's *Civil War in Herefordshire*

14 Symonds' *Diary*, p.205,

15 Churchyard.

16 Symonds' *Diary*, p.212.

17 *ibid*.

18 Webb's *Civil War in Herefordshire*

19 Warburton.

Chapter Nineteen

1 *Iter Carolinum*.

2 Lake of Llangorse.

3 Slingsby's *Diary*.Sir Henry Slingsby was executed in 1658 for the conspiracy of the Sealed Knot. Cromwell's wife and daughter interceded for his reprieve in vain.

4 Harley MSS.

5 *Cotswold Muse* 1651

6 Symonds' *Diary*, p. 196,

7 Date of letter 8th Feb, 8 1642, the letter is at Oulton Park.

8 Taken down 1768

Chapter Twenty

1 Symonds' *Diary*, p.240

2 Comp. Hist. Eng., vol. ii. p. 550, and Rushworth.

3 Symonds' *Diary*, p.269.

4 *ibid*. p.269

5 Slingsby's *Diary*

Chapter Twenty One

1 Ashbunham,
2 See and compare *Comparative History of England*, vol.ii. p.552; Macaulay's *History*, vol,i. p.126.; and Webb's *Civil War*, vol.ii. p. 180.
3 Strickland's *Queens of England*, vol. v.
4 *Memoirs* of Mlle. de Mottville.
5 Waller.
6 *Memoires* of Mlle de Montpensier, tome I, p. 143.
7 Clarendon's *History of Rebellion*.
8 *Court and Times of Charles I* and *Queens of England*.
9 Waller's *Poems*.
9 Records of Upton-on-Sevem.
10 *Newcastle Chronicle*, Feb. 25, 1882 Annals of Northern Counties.

Chapter Twenty Two

1 *Memoires* of Mlle. Montpensier.
2 *Comparative History of England*, vol.ii. p.560.
3 *Memoires* of Mlle. Montpensier.
4 Almanack of the time at Hinton Manor, Berkshire.
5 Bridget Nanfan never married. There is a charge upon the Bloody Meadow for a sum of money she left to the poor of Berrow and the preaching of a sermon, annually, against duelling.
6 *Comparative History of England*,
7 An account of this transaction was published by Colonel Cooke, and I have to thank Sir W. Guise for the perusal.
8 This paper is still in the British Museum, Personal Memorabilia of Charles II.
9 Maidstone's letter to Winthrop (Thurloe, i. 766.)
10 *Comparative History of England*, vol,ii. p.552
11 *Memoirs* of Cardinal de Retz.

Chapter Twenty Three

1 Diary of the Pére Gamache.
2 Symonds' 'Collections of Anecdotes and Memoranda', Introduction to *Diary*, p viii.
3 *Memoires* of Madame de Motteville.
4 *Monarchy Revived*, and *Augustus Anglicus*.
5 *Scenes and Legends of Scotland*, Hugh Miller.
6 Thurloe Papers.
7 Burnet's *History*, vol. i. p. 53.
8 Personal Mems., Charles II.
9 *Scenes and Legends of Scotland*.
10 Personal Mems., Charles II.

Chapter Twenty Four

1 See *Malvern Chase.*

2 Carlyle.

3 See Map.

4 Expenses of Charles II at Worcester. Woof.

5 'In a few daies fortified it beyond imagination'. *Diary* of Judge Lechmere, in
    'Personal Expenses of Charles II in the City of Worcester', 1651 Woof

6 *Boscobel* by Blount of Orleton, 1st ed.

7 Nash's *Worcestershire*. Many very interesting Royalist relics, among them a
    magnificent Bible and Prayer Book of Charles I, were lent by Mr. Berkeley
    to the Worcester Ehibition of 1882.

8 Some furniture of the period from Priors Court appeared at the Worcester
    Exhibition.

9 'Hee treated my people civilly, but threatened extirpation to mee and my
    posterity, by cause I was joined to the army of the p'liant.' *Lechmere Diary*,
    Woof

10 *Boscobel.*

11 Verbatim from the Marten MSS. in the possession of Captain Loder Symonds at
    Hinton Manor, Berks.

12 *Boscobel.*

13 Carlyle says Fleetwood crossed to Upton on September 2nd; a mistake. *ibid.*

14 *ibid.*

15 Sept. 3. 1651 'The battell began in those very fields where my brother-in-law,
    Colonell Edwyn Sandys, the 23 of Sepr. 1642, fought with Prince Rupert, and
    receaved the wounds whereof afterwards (I Dec. 1642) he died.' *Lechmere Diary.*

16 *Boscobel.*

17 Woot's Expenses of Charles II.

18 Mems. of Charles II.

19 Catalogue of Worcester Exhibition.

20 This specimen of Old Worcester should be seen by all who enjoy such relics.

21 The recipe is in an Almanack of the period at Hinton Manor,

22 *ibid.*

23 Earchard's *History of England*, I i

24 The tradition of the country people assign Woodside as the locale of the
    Diabolical Conference. Old maps indicate the spot

25 The warrant for the arrest of the Earl of Cleveland, signed by Bradshaw, is
    among   the Marten papers at Hinton Manor, Berks,

26 Sir Edward Harley presented to Lady Lingen the sequestrated Lingen property
    which the Parliament gave to him.

27 Records of Upton-on-Severn.

28 Waker's *Sufferingss of the Clergy.*

29 These banners are still in Bromesberrow Church.

Bibliography

W.S. Symonds

Personal Notebook of Natural History with illustrations. Malvern Library Local
Collection.

Old Stones: 'Notes of Lectures on the Plutonic, Silurian, and Devonian rocks in the
Neighbourhood of Malvern'. Malvern, 1855.

—New Edition: Simpkin, Marshal & Co., London, Malvern, 1880.

'Geology as it affects a Plurality of Worlds'. pp.94. An Essay reprinted from the
Edinburgh New Philosophical Journal for 1855–6. London and Worcester,1856.

Stones of the Valley: pp.xii. 270. 8 plates.Bentley, London, 1857.

'On the Passage Beds from the Upper Silurian Rocks into the Lower Old Red
Sandstone at Ledbury, Herefordshire'. *Quarterly Journal of the Geological Society*,
vol.xvi. pt2.no..2 May 1860.

Old Bones: or 'Notes for Young Naturalists', pp.viii 127. 10 plates. Worcester, 1860.
London, 1861. 16mo.

—Second Edition: 'thoroughly revised', London, 1864.

—Third Edition: London, 1884.

'On the Sections of the Malvern and Ledbury tunnels and intervening line of
Railroad'.illus. *Proceedings Geological Association*, 1861.

'On the Geology of the Railway from Worcester to Hereford', pp.34. Reprinted
from the *Edinburgh New Philosophical Journal* for 1862. Harwick, London.

'Notes on the Geology of the Ross district'. 1863.

'Address on the enjoyment to be derived from the study of Natural Sciences'.
London, 1863.

'Notes on a Ramble through Wales'. A Lecture delivered to the Worcester Natural
History Society, etc.Worcester, Cheltenham, 1864.

'A Lecture of Progress and Development.' London, Gloucester, 1869.

Records of the Rocks: or 'Notes on the Geology, Natural History, and Antiquities of
north and south Wales, Devon, and Cornwall.' pp.xx. 433. illus. London, 1872.

'The Geology and Archaeology of the South Malvern District'. pp.10. A paper read
to the Cotswold Field Club, July 1875,

Malvern Chase: 'An Episode in the Wars of the Roses and the Battle of Tewkesbury.'
pp.viii. 336. 8 illus. W. North, Tewkesbury, 1880.

—Second Edition: pp.viii. 336 8 illus. W. North, Tewkesbury, 1881.

—Third Edition: pp.viii. 336 frontis. W. North, Tewkesbury, 1883.

—Fourth Edition: pp.viii. 336 frontis. W. North, Tewkesbury, 1885.

—Fifth Edition: pp.viii. 336 frontis. W. North, Tewkesbury, 1887.

—Sixth Edition: pp.viii. 336 frontis. W. North, Tewkesbury, 1901.

—Seventh Edition: pp.viii. 336 frontis. W. North, Tewkesbury, ? 1907.

—Eighth Edition: pp.viii. 336 frontis. W. North, Tewkesbury, 1913.

—Reprinted Edition: Malvern Bookshop, 1974.

Hanley Castle: an Episode of the Civil Wars and Battle of Worcester, pp.xi. 347
W. North, Tewkesbury, 1883.

The Severn Straits: or 'Notes on Glacial Drifts, bone caverns, and old glaciers, etc.,
pp.65 W. North, Tewkesbury, 1883.

Biography

William Samuel Symonds was the son of William Symonds and Mary Anne Beale and was born at Elsdon in Herefordshire in December 1818. He graduated from Christ's College, Cambridge, in 1842, and in the following year was appointed as a curate at Offenham near Evesham.

He became Rector of Pendock in Worcestershire in 1845 and a few years later inherited Pendock Court from his mother. He devoted a great deal of energy to researches in archaeology, geology, and natural history, and made several visits to the Auvergne in a search for ancient glaciers. He was a member of the Worcester Natural History Society, the Woolhope and Cotteswold Field Clubs, and for eighteen years President of the Malvern Field Club.

William Symonds wrote forty-three papers on scientific subjects; edited two books by Hugh Miller; compiled pamphlets on geology and natural history for younger readers; and wrote *Malvern Chase* and *Hanley Castle*, the two historical romances for which he is best known.

He and his wife Hyacinth had three sons and a daughter, also called Hyacinth, who married Sir Joseph Hooker, the explorer, President of the Royal Society and supporter of Charles Darwin.

From 1877 onwards William Symonds' health declined and he lived with his daughter and son-in-law at Sunningdale. He died in Cheltenham on the 15th of September 1887 and is buried at Pendock.

An Exact Ground=Plot of ẙ Cit[y]
WORCESTER,
As it ſtood fortify'd 3 Sept. 16